Ex Libris

HOW WE GOT
OUR FLOWERS

HOW WE GOT OUR FLOWERS

by

A. W. ANDERSON

Curator of the Botanical Gardens
Timaru, New Zealand

DOVER PUBLICATIONS, INC.
NEW YORK

Published in Canada by General Publishing Company, Ltd., 30 Lesmill Road, Don Mills, Toronto, Ontario.
Published in the United Kingdom by Constable and Company, Ltd., 10 Orange Street, London W. C. 2.

This Dover edition, first published in 1966, is an unabridged and unaltered republication of the work published by Ernest Benn Limited in 1951, and originally published by Williams and Norgate Limited in 1950 under the title *The Coming of the Flowers*. It is published under special arrangement with Ernest Benn Limited, Bouverie House, Fleet Street, London EC4, England. This Dover edition contains a new index by the author.

Library of Congress Catalog Card Number: 66-21180

Manufactured in the United States of America
Dover Publications, Inc.
180 Varick Street
New York, N. Y. 10014

SOME OF THEM WILL SAYE, seeing that I graunte that I have gathered this booke of so many writers, that I offer unto you an heape of other mennis laboures, and nothing of mine owne. . . . To whom I answere that if the honye that the bees gather out of so many floure of herbes, shrubbes and trees, that are growing in other mennis meadowes, feldes, and closes may justelye be called the bee's honye . . . so maye I call that I have learned and gathered of so many good autoures . . . my booke.

WILLIAM TURNER 1551

ACKNOWLEDGMENT

The author wishes to acknowledge permission from the Editors of *The Gardeners' Chronicle* and *The Gardeners' Chronicle of America* to reproduce certain material which first appeared in their pages.

FOREWORD

THE twentieth century has given us access to far more technical information about gardening than has ever been available before. Books, periodicals, lectures, films and broadcasts offer us a greater mass of horticultural instruction than even the most voracious learner could assimilate in a lifetime. But in the pursuit of technical knowledge and skill we have tended to lose sight of the gentler and more romantic aspects of gardening and the plants we grow. With the increasing tempo of modern life this is scarcely to be wondered at, for in spite of all the labour-saving devices that science has given us, we seem to have less leisure time than ever. We sometimes promise ourselves that one day, when we have retired from business maybe, we shall pursue a point that has aroused our interest—some obscurity, perhaps, in the origin of a plant or the life of a famous botanist or plantsman —and seek out the truth among the musty tomes of a library, reaching back into the dim, forgotten past. But for most of us the opportunity never comes and we go on, perhaps to the end of our days, wondering how Marguerites acquired such a delightful name; why there should be such confusion between Syringa and Philadelphus; who Forsyth, Dampier, Tradescant or a hundred other people were, men and women whose names are immortalized in the botanical nomenclature of our garden flowers. For botanists and gardeners have adopted a delightful system of keeping fresh the memory of those whom they have been proud to honour and naming a plant in the memory of a famous man or woman provides a beautiful and living memorial.

Our gardens teem with history, but in our ignorance it passes us by. Therefore we must be grateful to Mr. Anderson for *How We Got Our Flowers*. He has done what many of us long to do, taken time to burrow among the ancient records and extract for our delight a thousand facts about the plants we grow and the

men and women who gave them to us. Some of the stories he
tells will be familiar, but, like the nursery rhymes of our childhood, they gain in richness with each retelling; others we learn
for the first time, and no one who reads this book can fail to
extract a deeper enjoyment from his garden, for an acquaintance
with the lore and legends of our plants adds immeasurably to
the pleasure they give to us.

ROY HAY

Haslemere, Surrey

CONTENTS

	PAGE
IN THE FAR PAST	11
DIVINE FLOWER	16
SAFFRON	20
FLEUR-DE-LYS	23
MEDIEVAL FAVOURITE	27
"THE HONORE OF OUR SCEPTER"	30
"BROWN'S SUPERB BLUSH"	35
JOHN GERARD AND HIS "HERBALL"	41
THE TRADESCANTS	45
MARGUERITES	49
PLANTS OF THE HUGUENOTS	53
THE STORY OF THE TULIP	57
LILAC TIME	63
LILIES FROM THE SEA	66
A PIRATE'S NAMESAKE	70
LINNAEUS	74
"KING'S BOTANIST"	80
A SAILOR'S GIFT	85
GAY BOUGAINVILLEAS	90
CITIZEN LABILLARDIERE	95
THE COVETOUS BURGOMASTER	100
THE GARDEN OF AN EMPRESS	103
A MYSTERIOUS ROOT	109
TWO TREES FROM CHINA	113
ROMANCE OF THE TREES	117
CEDAR OF LEBANON	121

PAGE

SIR JOSEPH BANKS 124

PIONEER PLANT-HUNTER 130

GOLDEN FLOWER FROM CHINA 134

THE TWO FORSTERS 138

DAVID NELSON 143

THE STORY OF THE FRANGIPANI 150

VICE-REGAL NUTS 154

GEORGE CALEY 160

THE CAPE PRIMROSE 164

ALAN CUNNINGHAM 167

"FORSYTH'S PLAISTER" 173

THE BITTER ROOT 177

DAVID DOUGLAS 179

THE OCONEE BELLS 183

THE STORY OF THE POPPIES 186

PANSIES AND VIOLAS 191

SWEET VIOLETS 195

BENEDICT ROEZL 199

A FAMILY OF ARISTOCRATS 203

ROBERT FORTUNE 212

THE STORY OF THE DAFFODIL 217

"SWEET-SCENTED PEAS" 224

THE NEW ZEALAND TEA PLANT 227

THE STORY OF THE LILY 232

GEORGE FORREST 241

"OF GARDEN ORIGIN" 249

PATIENCE AND PERSEVERANCE 257

OUR DEBT TO THE MISSIONARIES 260

INDEX 269

Illustrated by

ALEX JARDINE & E. SEARS

In the Far Past

OUR gardens are gay with flowers: from mats of fragrant Thyme to bands of lordly Lilies they charm us with their colour, scent and beauty, and thrill us with their infinite variety. But we seldom pause to wonder how it is that they have been brought to us from their wild homes all over the world, or to imagine why it is they came to be grown in our gardens.

The story of how all the different varieties found their way into our gardens is as diversified as the flowers themselves. A few are simply European wildflowers that have been grown and loved for many hundreds of years, wildflowers whose every slight variation has been cherished and encouraged until with the passing centuries they have gradually developed into present-day favourites that we all love so well. Some are the results of strange and perilous journeys to the remotest corners of the earth, having been gathered by all sorts and conditions of travellers in their wanderings down the ages. Some come from careful breeding under watchful eyes, while others are but chance seedlings that were first noticed in a cottage garden, a large commercial nursery, or perhaps on a wild hillside, and might never have reached our gardens had not some flower-lover been attracted by their singular beauty.

Brightly coloured flowers must have greatly helped primitive man to discover that our world is beautiful. The old-time Maoris loved their Red Kowhai, *Clianthus puniceus*, and planted it near their homes long before the coming of the white man. When the Rev. William Colenso reached New Zealand in 1834 he found this handsome scarlet-flowered shrub growing apparently wild on a few rocky islets off the north coast. He travelled as a missionary over the length and breadth of the country for upwards of sixty years, but never again did he see it growing wild.

Although now quite common in our gardens it has never again been seen as a wilding, but may occasionally be found marking the site of some old deserted Maori settlement. There is little doubt that the primitive Maori, captivated by the masses of scarlet flowers, saved this species from extinction. When Sir Joseph Banks explored New Zealand in the course of Captain Cook's voyage of 1769 he found the Maori people still living in the Stone Age, and practising cannibalism, and was very surprised to find the "Glory Pea," as he called it, growing around their homes—a genuine example of primitive man's love of beauty for its own sake. The appreciation of gaily coloured wildflowers in a primitive community may seem a far cry from the expensive plant-hunting expeditions undertaken in our own time, but the underlying principles are the same.

Our successful plant-hunters are honoured members of society nowadays, and our ways of showing this are very different from those meted out to their predecessors in the days of long ago. In one of his books Johannes Andersen tells how the primitive Maori treated one of the successful plant-hunters away back about the end of the fourteenth century. In the old days the chief crop grown by the Maoris was the Sweet Potato, *Ipomoea Batatas*, which they knew as the Kumara. On account of the cool New Zealand winters they had to take desperate measures to prevent the active life-principle of this tropical plant from returning to the warm islands of the Pacific from which it had been brought by a man named Taukata. The Tohungas came to the decision that Taukata was the only person who could prevent such a calamity and when the first crop had been gathered he was invited into the store-house and slain. His blood was sprinkled over the door frame and the skull preserved. Every year at planting time it was dressed with feathers, small tubers were placed in the eye-sockets, and it was conveyed with due ceremony to the kumara gardens and left to guard the young crop. After harvest it was taken back to watch over the store-house throughout the winter.

We are apt to think that the love of new and rare plants is a thing of modern growth, and it comes as something of a shock to find that the first recorded plant-hunting expedition was organized more than 3,000 years ago. It was inspired by Queen Hatshepset of Egypt when she built a fine new temple at Luxor about 1570 B.C. A fleet of ships and a company of gardeners went to the Land of Punt, now known as British Somaliland, and brought back plants, seeds, and living trees. The main purpose of the expedition was to find incense-bearing trees for the temple gardens and in due course the Queen's sculptors recorded that thirty-one living trees had been established there. Those trees have been identified with the Boswellia, that still grows in the Land of Punt, whose characteristic brittle resin is still put to the same old uses as in the days when the Pharaohs ruled supreme. In the dry state it is known as "frankincense" and is used in religious ceremonies, and when softened by boiling in oil is used as a pitch for caulking ships.

About one hundred and fifty years later another Egyptian monarch left a record that among the treasures of ebony and ivory, gold and precious stones, brought back from a successful foray against the Assyrians, were many new and rare plants, including a variety of Vine, a Pomegranate, and a Water-lily. Among the flowers that were grown in the Egyptian gardens of thousands of years ago were the Southernwood, Rue, Chicory, Oleander, Gentian, Poppy, Thyme, Lavender, and fragrant white Jasmine that are known and loved in gardens to-day. They spread along the Mediterranean coast in the days of Greece and Rome and the hardiest sorts penetrated into the colder parts of the world where they appear again and again to gladden the hearts of us all, a living contact with the men and the centuries that have gone.

Foreign wars have done something to enrich our gardens. There is an old tradition that the Double Yellow Persian Rose and the tree we know as the Lombardy Poplar were brought back by the soldiers of Alexander the Great on their return from the Persian wars. Even in the days of chivalry, when culture was at its lowest ebb, knights returning from the Crusades did not forget their ladies who tended tiny gardens within the walls of lonely castles. Many of the gaily coloured wildflowers of southern Europe and the Levant came to us about that time. One of the first is the great scarlet Ranunculus of Palestine, the familiar *R. asiaticus*, of our spring gardens, said to have been brought back by Louis IX of France to his mother Blanche of Castile, who had a famous garden about the middle of the thirteenth century. About the same time we got the old red Peony and perhaps the white Jessamine. Another old favourite that may date back to the crusading days is *Lychnis chalcedonica*, which has been grown for so long in gardens that its clusters of brick-red flowers, borne proudly aloft throughout the summer, are affectionately known as "Jerusalem Cross" in almost every country in Europe.

As the Church developed and its influence increased throughout Europe flowers began to be grown for decorating the altars on feast days, although the first monastery gardens were devoted to plants of medicinal value only. Although many of those medicinal herbs were plants that we would now look upon as weeds, the Physic Gardens of the Infirmaries were quite gay with their clusters of Foxgloves, Fleur-de-lys, Madonna Lilies, Paeonias, Opium Poppies, Celandine, Mallows and Roses. As with the gardeners of to-day the medieval monks were always willing to pass on seedlings, slips, grafts or pungent roots to friends and to fellow enthusiasts. Varieties of special virtue or of religious significance such as Madonna Lilies, the gaily coloured Anemones from the Land of the Holy Cross, or Snowdrops—the Fair Maids of February that were sacred to the Purification when the image of the Virgin Mary was taken from its place of honour so that they could be scattered there—were all carried far and wide over the whole of Christendom in the wallets of palmers and wandering friars, to be given as an appreciation of the hospitality that was always so freely given.

With the fall of the monasteries horticulture suffered a serious decline when, as some authorities assert, the garnered wisdom of a thousand years was lost in a single generation. The ultimate result was to spread the knowledge of plants and how they should be grown. The discovery of printing made possible the early herbals, and if their bias was towards medicine and medicinal plants the persecution of the Huguenots of France and the Low Countries scattered those who knew something of market gardening to all parts of Protestant Europe.

So it has been down through the changing centuries, our gardens have been enriched by men of every walk of life, wanderers and stay-at-homes, parsons and pirates, all have worked together to increase the variety of our cultivated plants and the beauty of our gardens.

Divine Flower

CENTURIES of care and devotion have gone to develop our modern carnation from the insignificant little Clove Pink, *Dianthus Caryophyllus*, that grows all over southern Europe from the sunny limestone cliffs of the Pyrenees to the great plains of the Ukraine. Grown by the Greeks long before the beginning of the Christian Era, it became known as Dianthus, the Divine Flower, a name that was later adopted for the whole clan. The flowers have long been valued for their scent and beauty and it was from their use in garlands, Coronae, that the common name "Carnation" is derived. The specific name, *Caryophyllus* or nut-leaved, seems to refer to the resemblance between the scent of the old Clove Carnation and the leaves of the tree from which the cloves of commerce are obtained.

Although it is often met with on the chalky downs of southern England there seem to be some doubts as to the Clove Pink being a true native of the British Isles; some authorities believe that it became naturalized from specimens brought from Europe as garden plants by knights returning from the crusades. There is a tradition that it was brought over from the sunny gardens of Normandy about the time of William the Conqueror, but whether as a reminder of the homes they had left behind or accidentally with the stone used in some of their castles, is unknown. In this respect it is of interest to know that it may still be gathered from the rocky prominence on which stand the walls of the ancient fortress of Falaise in Normandy, where William was born.

By the middle of the sixteenth century garden varieties were already showing so much improvement on the wild type that William Turner noted, "they have been made pleasant and sweet by the wit of Man and not by Nature." Fifty years later Gerard recorded, "A great and large volume would not suffice to write of every one at large in particular, considering how infinite they are, and how every yeare, every clymate and countrey bringeth forth new sorts, and such as have not heretofore bin written of." He calls them Clove Gillofloures and goes on to tell of one "with yellow flours: the which a worshipful Merchant of London Mr. Nicholas Lete procured from Poland, and gave me thereof for my garden, which before that time was never seen nor heard of in these countries."

In another old book we are told something of a "Flower Christening," getting an interesting sidelight on the doings of flower-lovers in the olden days. They met in a London tavern and while the owners discussed serious matters in an upper chamber their assistants held a more convivial gathering down-stairs. Later all foregathered and drank toasts to their respective flowers, naming each one as they did so, according to their opinion of its merits. Perhaps it was at such gatherings that the Gillyflower growers of Queen Elizabeth's day met to name and admire their "latest novelties" such as "Ruffling Robin," "Master Bradshawe his Daintie Ladie," or the "Lustie Gallant." In some parts of the country they were known as "Sops-in-wine" from the old custom of casting the petals into flagons of wine or beer so that the beverage might be flavoured with that peculiar aromatic tang so characteristic of the old Clove Carnation.

Apparently the art of dressing flowers for exhibition was unknown until the beginning of the nineteenth century when carnations were enjoying a period of public favour such as they had not experienced since the days of Queen Elizabeth. One of the first to practise this art was Kit Nunn, a barber of Enfield, who turned from the task of arranging the elaborate coiffures of the Georgian ladies to that of adjusting the petals of his show carnations. An enthusiastic admirer tells us that "he was the Father of the Art. Upon such occasions he had as many applications to dress flowers as to dress wigs. The novices of the day who did not know his secrets, and trusted to Nature, were no match for him. He began where Nature left off and perfected what she left imperfect."

The spicy fragrance and attractive colouring of these flowers have a perennial appeal, and the slow but steady improvement in colour and shape has kept them among the indispensables of the garden. The high centre and perfect form of our modern varieties is the most recent development of the race, and this continuous improvement and selection brings ever newer and better varieties on the market. Some, such as "Anne Boleyn," that originated in 1836 and is still grown, are an instant success and for many years are held up as a standard of their type; others on account of some flaw in their makeup are soon lost and forgotten although they may have been hailed as one of the greatest developments of their time.

Until comparatively recent times Carnations were not differentiated into the many groups we are so familiar with to-day, although at the beginning of the seventeenth century Parkinson knew both Gillyflowers and Carnations. The French were the first to find a type that flowered outside the normal season, midsummer, and the Americans were quick to see the possibilities of such an advance. As a result the American race of Perpetual-flowering Carnations soon came into being, but their

serrated petals gave the blooms such a rough, unkempt appearance
that they made no appeal to the conservative English growers.
Little notice seems to have been taken of them in Europe until
in 1897 Messrs. Hugh Low & Co. secured an Award of Merit
from the Royal Horticultural Society of England for the variety
"Mrs. W. T. Lawson." This lovely pink bloom, said by some
growers to be the "most wonderful pink flower ever raised,"
had originally changed hands for $30,000, and came as a great
surprise to the English growers. Its advent shook them out of
their complacency and they had to recognize the existence of
the American Perpetual-Flowering Carnation.

Probably one of the greatest sensations experienced by flower
lovers was the arrival of the variety "Fiancée." Distributed by
a Chicago firm that was fully alive to the value of advertisement,
Fiancée was introduced to the floral world by means of a booklet
of glowing scarlet. Her virtues were praised so enthusiastically
that the variety had to be withdrawn from the market for a year
until sufficient stock had been raised to meet the extraordinary
demand. That year went by, and then another, and still Fiancée
lingered coyly in the background, although tales of her charm
and beauty were allowed to leak out to an expectant world.
When she finally made her début, with all the ceremony of a
royal princess, her admirers were sadly disappointed. Unfortunately, although not without a certain charm, she was found
to have inherited most of the vices and few of the virtues of the
family. Too temperamental for this world, she soon faded away
and was seen no more.

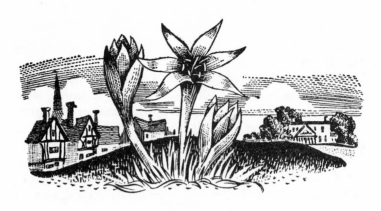

Saffron

ALTHOUGH not one of the most conspicuous of our autumn flowers, the Autumn Crocus is one of the most interesting, having been known for hundreds of years as the source of Saffron. It has given its name, one of the oldest still in common use, to the whole Crocus tribe. In the ancient languages of the East, when the consonant sounds were given more attention than the vowels, it was written K.r.k.m., and the various renderings, karkum, kurkum, and so on became the Krokos of the Greeks, which was latinized as Crocus by the Romans.

Saffron yellow, the colour of light, has long been considered of sacred and of royal importance, and so far back as human history goes the soft yellow of saffron-dyed garments has been a familiar sight in the Orient. As a dye-stuff saffron fell from its high estate with the development of synthetic dyes during the early part of the last century, but the pretty lilac-coloured flowers, with their characteristic orange stigmas, are always an attraction during the dull days of autumn. Gerard gives a very pleasant description of the "True Saffron." "The floure of Saffron doth first rise out of the ground nakedly in September, and his long smal grassie leaves shortly after, never bearing floure and leaf at once. The floure consisteth of six small blew leaves tending to purple, having in the middle small yellow strings or threds; among which are two, three, or more thicke fat chives of a fierie colour somewhat reddish, of a strong smell when they are dried, which doth stuffe and trouble the head."

Like many plants *Crocus sativus* is something of a mystery. At present nothing is known of its original home, and even although it has been matched with every known wild type of Crocus it does not appear to correspond exactly with any of them. All trace of its origin has been lost in antiquity and we have only some old traditions to account for it. Some writers think it may have been brought over by the Romans, while an old story says that it was introduced into England by Sir Thomas Smith of Saffron Walden about 1330. Hakluyt writing his *Remembrances for Master S.* in 1582 tells the traveller who is on his way to Turkey that, "Saffron, the best of the universall world, groweth in this realm. . . . It is a spice that is cordiall, and may be used in meats, and that is excellent in dying of yellow silks. This commodity of Saffron groweth fifty miles from Tripoli, in Syria, on a high hyll, called in those parts Gasian, so as there you may learn in that part of Tripoli the value of the pound, the goodnesse of it, and the places of the vent. But it is said that from that hyll there passeth yerely of that commodity fifteen moiles laden, and that those regions notwithstanding lacke sufficiency of that commodity. . . . It is reported at Saffron Walden that a pilgrim, proposing to do good to his countrey, stole a head of Saffron, and hid the same in his Palmer's staffe, which he had made hollow before of purpose, and so he brought the root into this realme with venture of his life, for if he had been taken, by the law of the countrey from whence it came, he had died for the fact." Such is believed to have been the foundation of the Saffron industry in England, an industry that survived for over five hundred years.

One of the most remarkable aspects of this industry was the fact that a sufficiency of the thread-like stigmas could be produced to satisfy even a comparatively modest demand, no fewer than 4,300 being required for each ounce of the dry, raw material. The vast numbers required, the uncertainty of the crop because of its peculiar nature, and the fact of the flowers maturing in the autumn, all combined to keep up prices and provided unscrupulous persons with plenty of opportunity to experiment in the art of adulteration. One old writer says, "Nothing is so subject to sophistication as Saffron, and therefore the only trial of true Saffron is this; if a man layeth his hands upon it he shall heare it cracke as if it were brittle and ready to burst; but that which is moiste,—a quality coming by some indirect and cunning cast,—yieldeth to his hands and maketh no noise."

In Richard Banckes's *Herbal*, the first to be published in the English language, and generally believed to be a compilation from an old medieval manuscript, we are told that, "the virtue of the herb is thus. It will destroy all manner of abominations of man's stomack, and will make a man to sleep. It is good for many medicines, and namely for cooks to colour their meat therewith. It groweth in gardens, and it is hot and dry."

During the reign of Henry VIII a law was passed prohibiting the dyeing of Irish linen with Saffron, because the dyed sheets were not washed often enough! The material was credited with many remarkable properties and apparently the populace was of the opinion that the dyed linen retained certain antiseptic qualities. In his book written towards the end of the seventeenth century, Hertott tells us of some of those beliefs. He advises his readers to mix the precious stuff with dragon's blood, dried Camomile flowers, swallows' nests, the worm-eaten heartwood of an old Oak, and the fat of a mountain mouse. From the text it is obvious that the Saffron was the all-important ingredient and the other items were merely expected to render its qualities more potent.

Such are the changes that take place in public taste, that Saffron is no longer a commodity of any commercial value. At one time grown by the acre in the south of England, it is now only to be met with as an ornamental garden plant. In the olden days it was supposed to keep up the spirits of the populace during the six long weeks of Lent. This may have been because in earlier times it always held a very prominent place in banquets and other ceremonial feasts, being considered of great importance as a preventive of drunkenness. "Our wine-knights when they propose to set square at the tavern and carouse lustily, if they drink saffron never fear surfeit nor for the overwhelming of the braine; and they are verily persuaded that this keepeth them from drunkenness and maketh them carry their drink well."

Fleur-de-lys

THE Fleur-de-lys of France is generally assumed to be derived from a conventionalized form of the Iris and there are several old legends telling of its origin. Most of them show that the original Fleur-de-lys was the golden Water Iris, *I. Pseudacorus*, that "prospereth well in moiste meadows and in the borders and brinks of rivers, ponds, and standing lakes," throughout western Europe. According to one version of the tale, early in the sixth century Clovis, king of the Franks, was hemmed in by a superior number of Goths in a bend of the Rhine near Cologne and was saved from annihilation by observing some yellow Irises growing far out into the river bed. This lead him to realize that the river was shallow enough to be used as a ford, and he was able to escape. Another account states that it was the Goths who were encamped by the river and the Franks by finding a ford were able to attack them in the rear and gain a victory. In either case the grateful king is said to have adopted the Iris as his device and it was for long the badge of the royal family.

Five hundred years later, when Louis VII of France had been excommunicated by the Pope, he resolved to take up the Cross and join the Crusaders who were fighting to free the Holy Land from the infidel. No doubt some old tradition of King Clovis induced him to choose the Iris, which thus became known as Fleur-de-Louis, and this later became Fleur-de-luce, which was gradually corrupted to the familiar Fleur-de-lys or Fleur-de-lis.

For centuries this, in one or other of its forms, remained the accepted name for the plants, the various species being differentiated as the Venetian Floure-de-luce, or the Flower-de-luce of Dalmatia and so on. When Linnaeus came to take up the task of simplifying plant names he discarded the old form and named the clan "Iris" from the Greek personification of the rainbow, and within a few generation Fleur-de-lys had been almost forgotten.

The best-known members of the family are the Bearded Irises frequently listed as *Iris germanica*, although this old favourite has had little or no influence in the development of our modern hybrids and very few of them bear any of its blood. The German Iris has been in cultivation for more than eleven hundred years, as Walaford Strabo records that it grew in his monastery garden in the ninth century. Throughout medieval times Irises were always sure of a welcome in the monastery garden because the rhizomes were used for many medicinal purposes. Orris root was used, not only to cure ulcers and induce sleep, but was regarded as the sovereign remedy for a "pimpled or saucie face." In more modern days it has achieved great popularity on account of the pleasant violet-like perfume which makes it a valuable ingredient in toothpaste and cosmetics generally.

Its origin and early history are lost in the distant past, but modern research has shown that *Iris germanica* is not a true species because it appears to be incapable of producing fertile pollen and rarely sets viable seeds. Some authorites believe it to be a natural hybrid between *I. aphylla* and *I. pallida*, while others are of the opinion that *I. Kochii* from the woods of northern Italy is its nearest approach to a wild form, but the many species and varieties that grow in central and south-eastern Europe are so difficult to differentiate that its affinities have not yet been ascertained. The hybrid origin of this, the best known of all the Bearded group, does much to explain how it is that the cultivated forms took so long to show any marked improvement under garden conditions.

One of the earliest Iris fanciers was a French nurserymen, M. Lemon, who in 1840 offered the first named collection for sale. During the next half century he raised a number of varieties of which his "Madame Cherau" and "Jacquesiana" were still in cultivation within the past twenty years. About 1880 Sir Michael Foster began growing Irises at Shelford, in Cambridgeshire, and he became so interested in the genus that he persuaded friends and acquaintances, traders and missionaries, and indeed all whose business or pleasure took them to the lands where the wild Irises grow, to send home seeds, bulbs or roots. He grew them all side by side and not only did the garden at Shelford demonstrate something of the possibilities of the family, but

Sir Michael Foster became a leading authority on their cultivation and classification.

By the close of the century many hybridizers were at work, but at first progress was slow as it takes six or eight years for a new variety to reach the market in quantity, and in those days the market was very limited. In 1910 the French nurserymen, Messieurs Andrieux-Vilmorin et Cie, sent out the well-known "Alcazar" which was one of the first to take the world by storm, and did much to create the modern demand for Irises. "Ambassadeur" was raised about the same time, but the First World War intervened and it did not reach the market until 1922. The next great step forward was the introduction of "Dominion" in 1917 at the then remarkable price of five guineas per root. It is said that Dominion flowered for the first time in 1910, but Mr. Bliss was then so obsessed with his efforts to get a crimson variety that he thought nothing of it until his young niece, commemorated in the rose-pink "Susan Bliss," rescued it from the rubbish heap in 1915 by saying it was the finest Iris in the garden.

About this time Mr. W. R. Dykes of the Royal Horticultural Society was working on Irises. For long he was interested only in the wild forms and it was he who discovered the true history of the handsome *Iris albicans*, which had always been regarded as the best form of the old Florentine Iris. There was another white form of *I. florentina*, but this one, with its aristocratic bearing and flowers of a purer white, always bloomed in advance of the others. Mr. Dykes discovered that although *I. albicans* is to be found all through the Mediterranean region from the Levant to Spain and Morocco, its true home is among the dry mountains of the Yemen district of Arabia. For centuries it seems to have been associated with Mohammedan graveyards, much as the Yew was with the churchyards of northern Europe, and that explains how it came to be naturalized in all the lands to which the Saracens penetrated.

About 1920 Mr. Dykes raised a yellow variety that he named "Amber" which is believed to have originated from a capsule of seeds sent from southern Europe by a friend. This is said to have sent him off on the quest for a fine golden-yellow variety. He achieved success with a seedling that flowered a few months after his death in 1925 and was afterwards sold for £20. With the soft crinkly texture of its golden flowers, whose falls are sometimes flecked with purple, this variety, which became known as "W. R. Dykes," set a new standard among Bearded Irises and became the ancestor of most of the yellows now in cultivation. During the past thirty years the Bearded Irises have risen from one triumph to another, and their popularity can be gauged by the fact that their varieties may now be numbered by the thousand, and that the rarest novelties of even ten years ago are now among the commonest of the rank and file.

Medieval Favourite

THE fragrant Wallflower, *Cheiranthus Cheiri*, has been so long in cultivation that no one knows when it first began to be grown in gardens. Away back in the immemorial past it was found only on the limestone cliffs of southern Europe and nothing seems to be known of how and when it was first brought under cultivation. The first plants to reach the gardens of the north may have been brought by the wife of some Roman centurion stationed in that outpost of civilization, Britain, or may have been grown from a capsule of seeds picked by some wandering pilgrim who thought the fragrant yellow flowers would be a pleasant souvenir of his travels when he returned to the monastery at home. The old herbalists of the sixteenth century tell us that by that time it had many common names, a sure sign that it had already established itself in the affections of the people. It was familiar to many as Sweet William or Herte's Ease long before these names were usurped by the flowers that own them to-day. Other names were Bloody Warrior, Beeflower, Yealowe Violet, and Cherisaunce, while William Turner, the Father of British botany, says, "Cheiry, Herte's ease, or wall Geleflower, it hath yealowe floure."

Cherisaunce, of which the diminutive may be Cheiry, is an old term for comfort and links the traditional name of the flower with the old legend of the Maid of Neidpath whose broken-hearted lover is said to have got some measure of "heart's ease" or "cherisaunce" from wearing her favourite flower in his cap.

The old ruined keep of Neidpath, standing on a grassy knoll above the rushing waters of the Tweed, belonged to the powerful Earl of March away back at the end of the fourteenth century when Robert III sat on the throne of Scotland. Robert was what we used to know in our school days as "a weak King" and the Earl in his quest for supreme power contrived to have his only daughter, Elizabeth, betrothed to the heir to the throne. The betrothal aroused so much powerful opposition that the Earl, fearing for the girl's safety, sent her to Neidpath Castle. There she seems to have fallen in love with the son of a Border Chieftain, Scott of Tushielaw. The young man, although of an

ancient family, was no match for the heiress of March, and when
the Earl heard what was going on he was furious to think that
she, who might yet be Queen of Scotland, was prepared to throw
away everything for the sake of a nobody.

The Maid of Neidpath was kept in close confinement and the
young man gave out that he was off to the foreign wars, but in
the guise of a wandering minstrel he visited the castle and, seated
under her window, began to sing. He sang of enduring love
that overcame all obstacles and how a maiden had escaped from
her father's castle one moonlight night when, at the call of a
moor-cock, her lover threw a rope over the ramparts. Elizabeth
understood his message and dropped a sprig of Wallflower at his
feet, but when the call came she was so flurried that she did not
fasten the rope securely and fell to her death on the courtyard
below.

Wandering far over Europe young Scott of Tushielaw gained
great fame as a minstrel, and in course of time other strolling
players followed his example of wearing a sprig of Wallflower
in their caps, and so the flower came to be accepted as the
emblem of comfort and constancy to the girl-friend at home.

Growing as wildflower on limestone cliffs or on ancient walls
the sweetly scented flowers are usually bright yellow in colour,
although dark velvety-brown forms are sometimes found. It
would appear that these are the original colours because varie-
gated petals do not receive any attention before the beginning of
the seventeenth century. Nowadays many beautiful varieties
are cultivated in gardens ranging from pale primrose-yellow
through tones of orange and gold to the gorgeous fiery reds and
the deepest shades of maroon and ruby. Nevertheless the outstanding characteristic of the Wallflowers is their fragrance, that
same sweet fragrance that Francis Bacon had in mind when
writing his essay "On Gardens" in 1625. When discussing the
advantages of planting scented plants in the garden he says

"The breath of flowers is far sweeter in the air (where it comes and goes like the warbling of music), than in the hand, therefore nothing is more fit for that delight, than to know what be the flowers and plants that do best perfume the air," and then goes on to enumerate some of them including "wallflowers which are very delightful to be set under a parlour or lower chamber window."

"The Honore of Our Scepter"

"The rose doth deserve the cheefest and most principal place among all flowers whatsoever, being not only esteemed for his beauty, vertues, and his fragrant and odoriferous smell, but also because it is the honore and ornament of our English Scepter."

JOHN GERARD 1596.

ACCIDENT rather than design lead to the adoption of the Rose as the national flower of England. The White Rose of York is generally believed to have been a form of *Rosa alba* which grows wild all over the great Eur-Asian continent from the hedgerows of England to the roadsides of far Cathay. This old favourite can always be recognized by its pale glossy-green leafage and fragrant flowers. When Henry III of England married Eleanor of Provence in 1236 she had already adopted the white Rose as her emblem. In due course it was inherited by her son, who became Edward I, and he had it incorporated in the Great Seal of State.

The Red Rose of Lancaster was the device of Edward's younger brother, Edmund, who became first Earl of Lancaster. Sometime about 1277 Edmund was sent by his father, who had acquired Champagne as a dowry, to quell a riot and avenge the death of the Mayor of Provins. Edmund spent three or four years in France and on his return to England brought home a new red Rose. This plant had been brought from Damascus by the Comte de Brie on his return from the Crusades. Edmund was so proud of this red Rose, which he thought so much better than his brother's white one, that he adopted it as his emblem, and thus it came about that the two sons of Henry III had Roses as their devices and, as was the fashion of the day, they and their retainers had them enamelled on their arms and embroidered on their clothes.

When their descendants became rivals for the Crown of England during the latter part of the fifteenth century they carried out a long, futile conflict that became known as the Wars of the Roses. Little seems to have been recorded as to how the trouble began, and no one knows how much truth there is in Shakespeare's story that it was caused by a quarrel between the Dukes of York and of Somerset which took place in the Temple Gardens in London in 1455. Richard, Duke of York, evidently picked a white Rose and called on those who supported him to do like-wise, thereby causing Somerset, who was one of the King's strongest supporters, to pluck a red Rose and urge his followers to do likewise. Such may have been the beginning of a civil war that rent the country for nearly a generation and is said to have cost the lives of nearly one hundred thousand Englishmen.

A compromise was finally reached by the marriage of Elizabeth, Duchess of York, to Henry Tudor, and about that time we are told that a new Rose appeared in a monastery garden in Wiltshire, bearing both red and white blooms. This was regarded as a portent of the times and became popular as the "York and Lancaster Rose," and was described as such by Monardez in 1551. According to his description it had "irregularly shaped flowers, that may be pure red or pure white, or part red and part white. Flowers of these different colourings may, and often do, appear on the bush at the same time."

The rise of the Tudor Dynasty brought the Tudor Rose as the badge of the new Royal House and ultimately of England. This Rose was first depicted as a sort of double Rose with a red inner row and a white outer row of petals, signifying a conventional union of the devices of York and Lancaster. Since then there have been some slight modifications, but the national flower has long been accepted as a red Rose.

The true York and Lancaster Rose is considered a variety of the old Damask and has the characteristic scent of the tribe. It should not be confused with the older and perhaps better known *Rosa mundi*, which is one of the Gallica clan. This variety is probably one of the very first of the "old-fashioned Roses," having been grown in English gardens long before the days of Shakespeare, long before the brawl in the Temple Gardens, and even before the fourteenth century when Chaucer knew it and wrote of its "floures partie white and red."

Rosa mundi differs from the York and Lancaster in having two colours present in the individual petals which may be pale pink with irregularly striped and blotched markings that flush the purest white background to pink or deep red and give the blooms their peculiarly mottled appearance. There is little

doubt that this form did not originate in England, and it may
have died out in English gardens for a time, but there is an
excellent drawing of it in the library of the Jardin des Plantes,
Paris, dated 1640, and although Parkinson does not mention it in
his *Paradisus* his description of the York and Lancaster obviously
includes *Rosa mundi*, and it would appear that he lumped them
both together. He says, "the one half of it is sometimes of a pale
whitish colour, and the other of a paler damask colour than the
ordinary; this happeneth so many times and sometimes also
the flower has divers stripes and marks on it, as one half white
or striped with white, the other half blush or striped with blush,
sometimes also all striped with blush, sometimes also all striped
or spotted over, and at other times no stripes or marks at all as
nature listeth to play with varieties in this as in other flowers.
Yet I have observed that the longer it abideth blowen open in
the sun, the paler and fewer stripes, markes, and spots will be
seene in it; and the smell thereof is of a weak damask rose scent."
Although it was described by L'Obel in 1581 as *Rose gallica
versicolor* and is still known by that name, it has been grown
in English gardens since the twelfth century as *Rosa mundi*
because of its association with Fair Rosamund, who was the
mistress of Henry II of England.

Henry Plantagenet fell in love with Rosamund Clifford,
daughter of Sir Walter de Clifford, several years before the
fateful battle of Wallingford, in 1154, brought him to the throne
at the age of twenty-one. When he had made sure of his affairs
at home he consolidated his position by a State marriage with
Eleanor of Aquitaine, the greatest heiress of Europe, who had
sovereignty over all of south-western France from the River
Loire to the Pyrenees. This did not interrupt his devotion to
Rosamund, a state of affairs that stung the Queen to a fury so
that she determined to get rid of her rival. As with most of these
old legends it is difficult to arrive at the truth, but it appears

that the Queen bribed one of the servants at Woodstock Castle to show her into Rosamund's bower where the girl awaited the King. Fair Rosamund saw her coming while engaged at her embroidery and ran to hide in the maze. Apparently she thrust her ball of silk into a pocket but left the end attached to the needle, and as she ran the thread unwound and led the Queen to her hiding place. The angry Queen forced Rosamund to drink poison and when Henry found her body he was prostrated with grief. He ordered the body to be taken to the Godstow Nunnery near Oxford, where the coffin was heaped high with her favourite Roses before burial. The tradition goes on to say that the King left instructions that each year, on the anniversary of Rosamund's death, the grave was to be covered with Roses. While it is now impossible to declare with certainty that the Rose we grow as *Rosa mundi* is identical with the historical variety, it is pleasant to think that it may be that same old flower, a Rose that has remained unchanged all through the eventful years since it used to bloom by Fair Rosamund's bower, in the tiny garden she tended inside the walls of Woodstock Castle.

The White Rose of the Jacobites has never been satisfactorily explained and still remains something of a mystery. A few writers believe that it may have been any white Rose that happened to be growing in the garden, but most authorities think that it may have been the old *Rosa alba* which has for many centuries been associated with the Royal House of France. When Mary, Queen of Scots, married the Dauphin of France she acquired the right to wear the royal Rose and she presented a silver replica to the poet who produced the best festal poem on that occasion. So far as we know this is the first time the white Rose was associated with the House of Stuart, and when the family went into exile three or four generations later it became one of the signs used as a means of identification among those who gave their allegiance to the "King over the water."

On the other hand the Rose has been the emblem of silence ever since the Greeks defeated the Persian king, Xerxes, in 479 B.C. The Greeks are believed to have planned the battle in the greatest secrecy, in a bower of Roses near the Temple of Minerva. As a result the Rose became one of the chief motifs in the carvings above confessionals and apartments where influential people met to transact matters of importance, as a reminder that the confidences received there should not be repeated elsewhere, but were in fact *sub rosa.* Thus it may be that the White Rose of the Jacobites was merely a symbol to remind the initiates that only "under the rose" could the work of the cause be brought to fruition.

"Brown's Superb Blush"

WHEN Eve was about to be banished from the Garden of Eden she begged to be allowed to take away one flower, and when permission was granted she walked round the garden trying to decide which she loved best. At last she chose a dainty white Rosebud and it is said to have blushed to be paid such a compliment, and that is the reason why pink Roses are still acclaimed the Queen of Flowers.

Roses have been grown and loved since before gardens were thought of, tens of centuries having passed since Roses were first admired in China and in the Near East. Some of the old favourites have survived unchanged since the very dawn of history, but many have been lost as the tide of popular fancy has swept on, taking first one sort and then another as its ideal of floral beauty, carelessly leaving behind the favourites of yester-year. Probably no other flower has made such a place for itself in song and story as has the Rose. "Among all floures of the worlde the floure of the rose is cheyf and beeryth ye pryse. And by cause of vertues and sweete smelle and savour. For by fayrenesse they fede the syghte; and playseth the smelle by odour, the touche by soft handlynge." This tribute was recorded by a scribe in the middle of the thirteenth century and he is believed to have been thinking of the common Cabbage Rose, that same old Rose that has remained unchanged since before the time of Christ.

Pliny, who perished in the Pompeii disaster in A.D. 67, noted that "The essential points of difference in the rose are the number of petals, the comparative number of thorns on the stem, the colour and the smell. The number of petals, which is never less than five, goes on increasing in amount till we find one variety with as many as a hundred, thence known as centifolia." Botanists still refer to the Cabbage Rose as *R. centifolia.*

Its origin is lost in the dim ages of the past but modern belief is that it may be a native of the Caucasus Mountains or one of the many species from the Near East that have played their part in the development of our modern Roses. Descriptions are both scarce and vague, but it would appear that since the Huns sacked Rome the Cabbage Rose, in common with many other flowers, has no recorded history in Europe for more than twelve hundred years. It was still grown in the countries under Moslem rule, being one of the chief varieties used in the manufacture of the far-famed Attar of Roses. It is still grown for this purpose in the Balkans and the perfume is still produced by much the same methods as were used by Dr. Avicenna, discoverer of the process of distillation, early in the tenth century.

The scent of the Rose has always been one of its great attractions, but such a transient character is rather difficult to define and it is not easy to decide just which is the "true old rose scent," as so much seems to depend upon individual opinion and climatic conditions. The old Damask Rose, for example—one of the sources of Attar of Roses, and generally accepted as being deliciously fragrant—is dismissed by Bacon in his discussion on scented flowers, "Roses damask and red are fast flowers of their smells; so that you may walk by a whole row of them and find nothing of their sweetness; yea, though it be in the morning's dew."

Despite its name the Austrian Briar is not of European origin, but hails from the sunlit hillsides of Asia Minor. The capture of Constantinople about the middle of the fifteenth century brought a change to the whole of south-eastern Europe, and many plants that were hitherto unknown gradually spread along the Mediterranean coast and among them was this delightful old Rose. The flowers of soft aureolin yellow were something that had never been seen before, and it was not long before the Austrian Briar was being grown all over southern Europe. It received the common name because it was introduced into Holland by a wandering botanist who first saw it growing in the garden of an Austrian monastery. The gay vermilion-coloured variety known as the Austrian Copper appears to have originated in the Low Countries, but nothing very definite is known at present.

Strangely enough the fine old "Persian Yellow," that is valued so highly for its semi-double flowers of golden yellow, also reached us via Austria. When Clusius, the famous French botanist, was picking up a precarious living at the court of the

Emperor Maximilian about the middle of the sixteenth century, he saw a paper model of a Turkish palace that had recently been sent from Constantinople. His experienced eye noticed that in the garden was a model of a yellow Rose that differed considerably from any of the species that he knew. Through the services of one of his many correspondents he was able to acquire a living plant, and in this way another variety came to enhance the beauty of our gardens.

Standard Roses are so common nowadays that it is a little difficult to realize that they are a comparatively modern development in the long history of this favourite flower. The first standards were grown in England in 1818 by the famous nursery firm of Lee and Kennedy, of Hammersmith, that did so much to foster an interest in new plants during the latter part of the eighteenth century. Lewis Kennedy had seen them for the first time when he went to give the Empress Josephine advice about laying out her new garden at Malmaison, in the middle of the Napoleonic wars. Careful advertising is worth while, and Messrs. Lee and Kennedy had more business than they could cope with when it was noised abroad that a Royal Duke had bought one thousand of the new French Rose-trees at the cost of a guinea apiece.

The first British Rose catalogue was issued by Thomas Rivers of Sawbridgeworth, in 1833, and listed nearly five hundred varieties. Mr. Rivers invited his London customers to inspect the nursery and advised them that they would have to take the coach leaving the Flower Pot Inn at Bishopsgate every morning at six, seven, or eight o'clock. No doubt those Rose lovers of a century ago had a very pleasant journey through the dewy lanes while they discussed the virtues and weaknesses of "Aimable Beauté," "Royal Virgin," "Blush Royal," and "Brown's Superb Blush." As they inspected the nursery the gentlemen were no doubt delighted with "Moraga la Favorite" and "Infidelities de

Lisette," while their wives and daughters tried to assess the charms of "Assemblage des Beautés," "Oracle du Siècle" and "Desespoir des Amateurs," but we cannot help wondering what those Victorian dames thought of the "Spineless Virgin." Apparently not all Rose growers of the day were so particular about the names of their Roses as William Paul, who is immortalized in the superb "Paul's Scarlet Climber." We have read somewhere that when a visitor suggested one of his new Roses should be called "Queen Mab"—the Queen of the Fairies—Mr. Paul solemnly considered the problem and asked with all the severity of the upright Victorian, "Was she a good woman?"

Perhaps the most charming of all the Roses that ruled the gardens of great-grandmother's day were the Lawrenceanas, or Fairy Roses, a race of pygmies that came as part of the booty when the island of Mauritius was taken from the French, in 1810. Obviously of Chinese origin, their early history has been lost, but no doubt they arrived by sailing ship in the days when Pierre Poivre was Intendant, when Mauritius had one of the best botanic gardens in the tropics. At his own expense M. Poivre built up the "Jardin de Naturalization," which was of great value in the development of French possessions in the tropics. On its arrival in England the first of the Fairy Roses was named *R. Lawranceana* as a compliment to Miss Mary Lawrance, whose *Collection of Roses from Nature*, consisting of ninety paintings, had been published a few years earlier. The dainty little flowers were in great demand during the early years of the century, but unfortunately very few of them have survived into our own days. Most of the varieties did not exceed twelve inches in height, and there are rumours that one of the most bewitching of them all was so tiny that dressed in all the glory of its miniature blossoms it could be hidden under half an eggshell.

The best known member of the family—if it is a member:

both its origin and its antecedents have been lost in the silence of the past—is *Rosa Roulettii*. It was first heard of as a window plant in the Swiss village of Mauborget, and no one seems to know whence it came. Grown there for generations, it may have been brought home by some wandering soldier or sailor about the time when France was making a bid for the control of the East. Many years ago the tiny village of Mauborget was destroyed by fire with the exception of one outlying chalet. Fortunately the tiny Rose was grown there and survived the disaster, and when the village had been rebuilt the fortunate neighbour gladly supplied young plants to the small community. The first outsider to take any interest in the Rose was Major Roulett of the Swiss Army, who visited the lonely village during the First World War and was charmed by the dainty little flower.

When the war was over Major Roulett visited his friends in Mauborget and secured a few plants. One of them he gave to Henri Correvon, the well-known alpine specialist of Geneva, and when sufficient stocks had been raised it was listed in his catalogue as *Rosa Roulettii*. Within ten years Major Roulett's Rose was being grown wherever alpine plants are cultivated. Grown as a pot plant in the Swiss village *R. Roulettii* is said to flower all the year round and not to reach more than three or four inches in height. Being perfectly hardy in the open ground in all but the coldest climates, it has proved eminently satisfactory in the rock garden where its simple beauty is quite in keeping with the surroundings. Under such conditions it usually towers away up to a height of nine or ten inches and is content to produce its erect little clusters of dainty pink flowers during the summer months only.

John Gerard and his *Herball*

"I HAVE never, either in gardens or in wild land or in the Alpine Mountains, where the beauty of plant life is at its highest, seen anything that struck me more than a *Gerardia*. I once met with some on the roadside in New Jersey, growing here and there like a little tree in habit, fifteen to eighteen inches high, bearing most graceful Pentstemon-like flowers, but far more refined in colour and more distinct than any Pentstemon. Naturally I asked why such a plant was not in cultivation and learnt that the Gerardias are mostly parasitic on the roots of other plants." The plant to which this charming tribute was paid by William Robinson in his *English Flower Garden* is evidently a New Jersey form of *Gerardia purpurea*, one of the most attractive members of a very delightful race of plants that is all too rarely to be seen in our herbaceous borders. There may be some truth in the story of its parasitical tendencies, but our experience has been that Gerardias flourish in the open border with a minimum of trouble if they are treated in exactly the same way as the ordinary hybrid Penstemons, cut down in the spring and renewed by means of cuttings every second or third year.

These attractive little plants keep green the memory of John Gerard, who is one of the best known of the old English herbalists, and one whose name was almost a household word at the close of Queen Elizabeth's reign. A "Master of Chirurgerie," he sometimes acted as examiner to the candidates seeking admission to the Barber-Surgeons Company, the corporation that controlled all the physicians in the London area. For about twenty years he controlled the gardens belonging to Lord Burleigh, the great Elizabethan statesman, in the Strand and also at Theobalds. The latter was one of the show places of Tudor England, and according to some authorities was the garden Francis Bacon had in mind when he wrote his immortal essay "On Gardens."

Although Gerard has left little or no information about the famous gardens that he administered for so long he had a well-stocked garden of his own at the little village of Holborn, at that time a fashionable residential suburb. In 1596 he published a catalogue of the plants growing there, and this is his greatest claim to fame because it was the first list ever published of plants growing in a garden. In all he mentions over one thousand species and although many were herbs and wildflowers of the countryside some were "but newly come to England and yet I have them in my garden."

John Gerard is most widely known as the author of the *Herball, or Generall Historie of Plantes*, published in 1597. For more than a generation it remained the textbook of the British gardener and, although it was an improvement on all existing works it would appear that, like the wild Gerardias of New Jersey, the Elizabethan herbalist had parasitical tendencies. There is plenty of evidence that the book was not an original work, being mainly the translation of a book that had been published in Antwerp several years before, and that much of the actual translating was the work of another man. It appears that John Norton, the printer, had commissioned a Dr. Priest to do the work, but that he died before it was completed. Gerard was given the job of preparing it for publication and he seems to have adopted Dr. Priest's translation, remarking that "Dr. Priest, one of our London Colledge hath, (as I heard) translated the last edition of Dodonaeus which meant to publish same, but being prevented by death, his translation likewise perisheth."

In those days the art of healing was closely linked with the study of herbs, and Gerard persuaded the Barber-Surgeons Company to establish a Physic Garden of its own. Land was actually bought for the purpose, but unfortunately he died before the project could be carried into effect and no one else seems to have been sufficiently interested to do anything about it.

The seventeenth-century herbalists knew that while many plants were of direct benefit to man some were of evil repute, although there were some with magical properties which could be used to counteract witchcraft and other malignant influences. Gerard seems to have accepted all of this contemporary folklore, which he combined with his extensive knowledge of the plants in cultivation to produce a very charming volume. We cannot give him any credit for a modern scientific outlook, however, when we find him deliberately going out of his way to confirm the existence of the "Goose or Barnacle-Tree" from his own observations.

This curious tree is a fable of great antiquity and even by the preceding century was beginning to be discredited. When Aeneas Silvius Piccolimini, who later became Pope Pius II, visited the King of Scotland in 1436 he was most anxious to see a specimen of this tree, and when he was informed that it was only to be seen in the far away Orkney Islands, he expressed some doubt as to its existence, complaining that throughout his travels he had always been fobbed off with the story that it grew only "away in the far north." Gerard was more credulous, however, and besides giving an illustration of the fabulous tree goes on to give testimony, "What our eies have seene, and our hands touched we shall declare. There is a small Ilande in Lancashire called the Pile of Foulders, wherein are found the broken pieces of old and brused ships, some whereof have been cast thither by shipwracke, and also the trunks or bodies with branches of old and rotten branches, cast up there likewise; where is found a certaine spume of froth that in time breedeth into certaine shels, in shape like those of muskle, but sharper pointed, . . ." These growths are described at considerable length and full details are given of the development of a birdlike creature within the shell, and of its emergence, concluding "in short space after it cometh to full maturitie, and falleth into the sea, where it gathereth feathers, and groweth to a foule, bigger than a Mallard and lesser than a Goose."

John Gerard has summarized for us the outlook and the knowledge of the Elizabethan herbalist, and perhaps we should not judge him too harshly in the light of the knowledge that has been gathered in the past three-and-a-half centuries. We can enjoy the *Herball* and his delightful descriptions of the plants he loved, bearing in mind, "How hard and uncertaine it is to describe in wordes the true proportions of plants . . . they best knowe who have the deepliest waded into this sea of simples."

The Tradescants

EVER since the foundation of the Colony of Virginia at the very beginning of the seventeenth century there has been a great period of industrial expansion in Europe and of colonization in the lands beyond the seas. This has been reflected in a continuous flow of wildflowers from all parts of the world into the gardens of the homeland. In the early stages of colonization everywhere the pioneers had but little time to admire wildflowers; they were too busy carving new homes out of the wilderness. In the early days of the settlement of the New England States, for example, the multitudes of wildflowers growing by riverbank and lakeside were almost entirely overlooked. This was chiefly because the colonists wanted English wildflowers, and the medicinal plants they knew, growing about their homes—the old familiar favourites that would remind them of the happy days of childhood and those they had left in the homeland beyond the seas.

In England, however, strange new flowers were always

welcome, and one of the earliest plant-hunters to leave her shores was John Tradescant, who sailed to the Americas in 1637 for the express purpose of exploring the floral wonders of the New World. He introduced many new plants, such as the Coneflower, Virginia Creeper, Swamp Cypress, the Red Maple, and the Canadian Columbine, with its flowers of scarlet and gold. One of his greatest favourites was *Lobelia cardinalis*, which became an instant success on account of "its handsome appearance which should not be wanting in curious gardens as it excels all others in the richness of its scarlet flowers."

Among the very first of the American wildflowers to find a welcome in the old colonial gardens was the Oswega Tea, sometimes known as Bee Balm or Bergamot. With its gay vermilion-coloured flowers terminating every branchlet, this attractive plant lights up the dark places of the woods all through the Eastern States from the margin of the Great Lakes to the upland meadows of the Appalachian Mountains. There is no doubt, however, that the colonial housewife grew it in her garden because she had learnt from the Indians how to brew a substitute for tea from the aromatic leaves, rather than on account of its handsome appearance. Tradescant introduced some specimens into England, but they were soon lost and it was not grown here for more than a hundred years.

Many of the plants that are the backbone of the modern herbaceous border—Phloxes, Lupins, Cornflowers, and Michaelmas Daisies—are derived from some of the American wildflowers gathered by John Tradescant more than three hundred years ago. The quaint old-fashioned Spiderwort, beloved for its daily procession of deep violet-purple flowers which appear all through the summer, was named *Tradescantia virginiana* in honour of the traveller and now serves to commemorate the whole family.

Parkinson tells us, "Upon this plant I confesse that I first imposed the name, by considering duly the parts thereof, which until some can find a more proper, I desire may still continue. The soon-fading Spiderwort of Virginia, or Tradescant his Spiderwort, is of late knowledge and for it the Christian world is indebted to that painful and industrious lover of all Nature's varieties, John Tradescant, who first received it of a friend, that brought it out of Virginia thinking it to bee the Silke Grasse that groweth there, and hath imparted herof, as of many other things both to me and to others."

Little has survived of the early history of John Tradescant the Elder, who is believed to have been a native of the Low Countries, and may have been the child of Huguenot refugees who sought sanctuary in England. He is first heard of in London during the last years of the sixteenth century, and there is a possibility that he may have been one of Queen Elizabeth's gardeners. There is some evidence that he was sent to search through Europe, about 1611, for new and rare plants for Lord Salisbury's garden at Hatfield. This lends colour to some connection with the Huguenots, who included in their ranks some of the most famous gardeners of the day. He bought thirteen thousand Tulip bulbs in Holland, and at Leyden acquired two pots of Gilliflowers, for which he paid twenty-six shillings—a high price in the days when an artisan was paid a shilling or so for his week's work. This extravagance was compensated for in Paris where he picked up "one pot of Gilliflowers that cost nothing." Another souvenir of this journey was "an exceedingly great cherye called Boore's Cherye" which is still in cultivation under the name of Tradescant's Heart, or sometimes Oxheart.

About nine years later he published his *Voiag of Ambassad by Sir Dudlie Digges in the yeare 1618*, in which he mentions seeing Russian wildflowers including "Helebros albus, enough to load a ship," at the Monastery of St. Nicholas near Archangel. Within a year or so he was off to Africa as a gentleman volunteer

against the corsairs of Algeria. Among his trophies was the old
"Algiers Apricocke" that for more than two centuries was the
most popular apricot grown in British and American gardens.
Through the influence of the Duke of Buckingham he was
appointed gardener to Charles I, although the post had been
promised to someone else. About 1629 he began his Museum and
Physic Garden at Lambeth, which in years to come became
famous throughout the land as "Tradescant's Ark." He was
supplied by "noblemen, gentlemen, and sea commaunders with
such toyes as they could bring from other parts," and it was his
collecting instinct that led him to become a member of the
Virginia Company, and to send his son to the New World in
search of plants and curios for the "Ark."

It was he who discovered the quaint Plymouth strawberry,
one of those remarkable plants surviving in the "gardens of the
curious" but never finding its way into the commercial lists.
Fragaria vesca var. *hispida*, is a plant in which all parts of the
flower have developed into leafy structures, both petals and
stamens being tiny green leaves while the odd-looking fruits
have the red flesh garnished with minute leaves instead of pips,
and have Elizabethan ruffs made from the petals and sepals.
It is recorded that "Mr. John Tradescant was the first to take
notice of this strawberry, and that in a woman's garden at
Plimouth, whose daughter had gathered and set the roots in
her garden instead of the Common Strawberry; but she finding
the fruit not to answer her expectation, intended to throw it
away; which labour he spared her, in taking and bestowing it
among lovers of such varieties."

John Tradescant the Elder died while the son was in America,
and with the fall of King Charles the family had to depend on
the Ark as the main source of income. Loyalty does not always
bring its own reward, and after the Restoration Tradescant was
prosecuted for running his Museum without a Royal Licence.

He made himself known to the King, however, and the charge was withdrawn. He seems to have died a few months later and to have left all his curiosities to an old friend, Elias Ashmole. According to some versions of the tale Mrs. Tradescant contested the will and, on losing the action, drowned herself. The case certainly was dealt with in the Court of Chancery in 1664, but the truth appears to be that matters were settled out of court and that the parties lived amicably until Mrs. Tradescant died sixteen years later. The "rare and ingenious collection of Art and Nature" passed to the Oxford University and is now known as the Ashmolean Museum.

Marguerites

THE autumn-flowering Chrysanthemums of China and Japan have so completely overshadowed the European sorts that we are apt to overlook the fact that Ox-eye Daisy of the northern pastures, the Moon Daisies from the upland meadows of the Pyrenees and the variously coloured Paris Daisies from the Canary Islands are members of the same family, with a long and interesting history that goes back to the years when the Far East was little more than a legend. At one time or another each of these Daisies has been referred to as a Marguerite, and even at the present time are still grown under that name in various parts of the world. The pretty Ox-eye Daisy, *Chrysanthemum Leucanthemum*, is the Marguerite of North America, while the big Moon Daisy, *C. maximum*, is the Marguerite of Scotland, but the flower that is most generally accepted under that name is the Paris Daisy, *C. frutescens*.

Long ago, when it was the fashion for the aristocracy to wear some badge that could be readily recognized, more than one royal princess adopted the Marguerite as her own. One of the foremost of them was Marguerite of Anjou who, at the age of fifteen, was married to Henry VI of England in 1445. She wore three Marguerites, which were in all probability the common Ox-eye Daisy, and had the device embroidered on the robes and cloaks of her courtiers and attendants. The King was weak and incompetent, and when the Wars of the Roses broke out she became the leader of the Lancastrians. Queen Margaret was a lady of considerable resource, as her encounter with the Hexham robber proves. She was hiding in a wood after the defeat of the King's men at Hexham and was discovered by a robber chief. She appealed for help in securing the "safety of the King's son," and so eloquently did she plead her cause that she was given food and shelter and escorted across the Scottish border. The Ox-eye Daisy is seldom seen in gardens, but there is a handsome variety known as the White Swan or Memorial Daisy. It has dainty ivory-white double flowers which are somewhat larger than those of the Pyrethrum, and is a valuable contribution to the herbaceous border.

During the latter part of the sixteenth century Marguerite de Valois, Queen of Navarre, was taking some interest in Marguerites, but the authorities differ as to whether her favourites

were the Moon Daisy that adorns the subalpine meadows in the
old Kingdom of Navarre or whether they were the first of the
Paris Daisies that had arrived about that time from the Canary
Islands. This princess was famed for her beauty and charm, but
was forced by the political circumstances of the time to wed
Henry of Navarre, chief of the Huguenots, and the wedding was
the signal for the massacre of the Huguenots in August 1572.
The years that followed were filled with many troubles, but in
September 1578 she paid her first visit to Navarre and was given
a great reception at Bordeaux. On arrival she was presented with
a bouquet of the "Marguerite of Marguerites," and is reported
to have assured her people that henceforth she would adopt the
flowers as her own. She settled down at the Court of Nerac and
planned a vast new garden, a garden that became so famous
as to be used by Shakespeare as a setting in *Love's Labour's Lost.*
In one of her letters the Queen tells of how she went to Mass in
the chapel in the Park while the King attended a Protestant
service. "Then when we came forth, we would meet and walk
together in the fine garden among the laurel and cypress, or in
the park I had had made, down the long alleys by the river's
bank."

This period of reconciliation did not last, however, and a few
years later they agreed upon a divorce on the grounds that the
marriage had taken place by compulsion. The Queen went to
live at the ancient Castle of Usson, where she made a garden
which has been described as "between the shining turrets one
sees sweet smelling shrubs which winter and summer are covered
with fine flowers and ripe fruit." There she may have grown the
Moon Daisy, whose cultural requirements are of the simplest.
Nowadays we have such a variety that the blooms may be seen
from early summer to the frosts that come after the Michaelmas
Daisies have faded and gone. The season begins with "Early
Giant," and in a week or two "Shasta" makes its appearance, to be

followed by the pretty "G. H. Sage," whose florets are serrated so as to give the blooms a pleasantly fringed appearance. With flowers up to six inches in diameter "Mrs. C. Lothian Bell" is the largest flowered form in the group. The double "Esther Read" is no doubt well worth growing, but its stiff habit lacks the grace that is so essential for the really popular flowers.

About the year 1600 Marguerite de Valois went to live in Paris, and her residence at Issy soon became famous for the garden on which she lavished so much time and trouble. It was there that the Paris Daisies were grown, but they were long in reaching the general public because on her death the estate was bequeathed to the Church and became a nunnery. The Paris Daisy did not reach England until the end of the century and by that time it was quite a favourite among the florists of France and the Low Countries. The Chrysanthemums grouped under this type of Marguerite are many and various and include the very old variety "Comte de Chambord," a small yellow form with a clear centre, and the white form known as "Brown Eyes" because of the rich maroon colour of the disc florets in the bud stage. Most widely grown of all are the semi-double anemone-flowered variety that has long been known as "Mother's Favourite," and the soft canary-coloured "Étoile d'Or," a sport from the old "Comte de Chambord," that appeared in a Parisian nursery about 1880. Of late years the Pink Marguerites have become better known than they used to be. These are probably all forms of *Chrysanthemum erubescens*, and the best, most desirable, is probably "Anna Hay," whose blossoms of soft amaranth-rose are set off by a fine golden yellow centre.

Plants of the Huguenots

ALL through the Middle Ages the monasteries were the only places where peaceful men could enjoy a quiet life spent happily among books, trees, and flowers. Conditions in the outside world were so rough and turbulent that the gentle art of husbandry was scarcely known and the result was that when the monasteries were overthrown early in the sixteenth century the cultivation of vegetables and medicinal herbs was almost unknown to the people of the countryside. In Britain, for example, it took two or three generations to revive horticulture, and Samuel Hartlib, writing in 1651, records something of the conditions existing "in the Old Queen's time." "Gardening," he says, "was first brought to England for profit about seventy years ago, before which we fetched most of our cherries from Flanders, apples from France, and hardly a mess of rathe-ripe pease but from Holland, which were dainties for ladies, they came so far and cost so dear. Since, gardening hath crept out of Holland to Sandwich, Kent, and thence to this county (Surrey), where they have given six pounds an aker and upwards, they have made their rent, lived comfortably, and set many people on work."

Something of this change may be traced back to the Huguenot refugees who sought sanctuary in England from the religious intolerance that reigned in France and the Low Countries. Although a few were members of the French aristocracy, the majority of these Protestant refugees were middle-class merchants and professional men, while many were gardeners, embroiderers, lacemakers or weavers in silk and wool. A quiet and industrious people, they soon began to establish their own ways of life in the new land, and brought a skill on gardening and a love for individual flowers that was hitherto unknown outside their own country.

In those days there was a thriving trade in both fruit and vegetables across the English Channel, and many of the refugees took advantage of this to smuggle out their valuables and even their children. Several stories are recorded of the French aristocrats disguising themselves as orange sellers or green-grocers and travelling through the country with all their worldly wealth hidden in the panniers of a mule, under a layer or two of Oranges or salad plants. One well-known family bought a freight of vegetables, and posing as poor gardeners travelled to England with the youngest member hidden in a hamper among the roots of Rhubarb, Saffron and Savory.

Very few records were kept, and it is now almost impossible to tell of all the garden plants that came to us through the agency of those who fled from their homes for conscience sake. Although some of the names have come down to us it is not always a simple task to fit them to the plants we grow to-day. Many, such as the *Outlandish Rose, Rosa ultramarina,* are well known to us,

however, because they have remained unchanged during the
centuries, and this one is familiar to every school-child as the
Hollyhock. Another of those old favourites is the Fair Maids
of France, the double form of *Ranunculus aconitifolius*, whose
clouds of dainty white rosettes are one of the most charming
sights of early summer. It is pleasant to think that the Double
Sweet Rocket and the fragrant Honesty have remained essentially the same as in the days when they were smuggled across
the English Chanel.

Parkinson, writing in 1629, tells of Wilmer's Double Daffodil,
"one great faire double flower" that may have been brought
to England by the Huguenots, as it seems to have arrived about
that time. "Wee first had it," he says, "from Vincent Sion,
borne in Flanders, dwelling on the Bankside in his lefe's time,
but now dead, an industrious and worthy lover of all fair
flowers, who cherished it in his garden for many yeares without
bearing any flowers until the yeare 1620, that having flowered
with him, (and he not knowing of whom he received it, nor
having ever seene the like flower before,) he sheweth it to Mr.
John d' Franqueville of whom he supposed he had received it
(for beyond the sea he never received any) who findeth it to be
a kinde never seene or knowne to us before, caused him to
respect it the more, as it is well worthy. And Mr. George Wilmer
of Stratford Bowe, Esquire, in his life's time having likewise
received it of him (as myselfe did likewise) would nedes appropriate it to himselfe as if he were the first founder thereof, and
call it by his owne name Wilmers double daffodil which since
hath so continued."

John Tradescant, Parkinson's "goodlie friend," is believed
by some writers to have been the child of Huguenot parents,
but little of his early life seems to have come down to us. He
and his son played a prominent part in the development of
gardening in England and are commemorated in several fruits

and flowers, including the white flowered *Aster Tradescantii* brought from America by the son in 1637. Another Huguenot gardener was Nicholas Cotterau, who had charge of the Royal Gardens during the reign of William and Mary. After living many years in England he longed to grow some of the flowers he had known in his youth in the south of France. He returned in search of them, was recognized by an old enemy, denounced, and thrown into the Bastille, where he died seven years later. The fine old Nectarine we know variously as "Elruge" or sometimes "Elrouge" is believed to be another link with the Huguenots. It was first mentioned in 1670, but is thought to be very much older—the pale green fruits with their dark red flush on the sunny side were a time honoured link in the evolution of the modern Nectarine—and it is still listed among the dozen best varieties. The name is said to be an anagram of that of Gourle, a French Huguenot, who, as a nurseryman at Hoxton in England, was the first to distribute it.

Another of the Huguenot plants that has remained unchanged is the Sweet Maudlin, *Achillea Ageratum*, a sturdy little bush with bright green leaves above which rise myriads of erect flower-stems bearing the typical flattened heads of blossom of the family, which cover the whole plant with a dress of faded gold brocade all through the summer. Better known than Sweet Maudlin are the Auriculas, which arrived about the same time and soon became great favourites. By the beginning of the eighteenth century they had developed a great diversity of colour and form, and are believed to be the first flowers to have the honour of having a society to look after their welfare and development. The Sweet William, with its chintz-like flower-heads of velvety crimson and white, was a great novelty in those days, and Gerard, with all the frankness of the Tudor days, tells his readers that the flowers were "kept and sustained in gardens more for to please the eye than either the nose or belly. They are not used either in meat or medicine, but esteemed for their beauty, to deck up gardens, the bosoms of the beautiful, and garlands and crowns for pleasure."

The Story of the Tulip

THE aristocrat of the spring garden is the Tulip. Tall and stately in the sunshine, a company of these lovely flowers with their fresh clear colour can now be the delight of anyone's garden. Nevertheless their quiet dignity reminds us that there was a time when they moved in the most exclusive society.

No one seems to know when the Tulip was first grown in gardens, but this wildflower from the Levant had already achieved great popularity and developed into many varieties, one of the sure signs of many years of domestication, when it was first seen by a European growing in a garden near Constantinople in 1554. The lucky finder was O. G. de Busbecq, who was on his way to take up the appointment as Ambassador of the Emperor Ferdinand I of Austria to Solyman the Magnificent, who was Sultan of the vast Turkish empire. "Having delayed at Adrianople one day," he says, "we were going on towards Constantinople, now near, for we were almost accomplishing the end of our journey, and as we were passing through the district an abundance of flowers was everywhere offered us, —Narcissus, Hyacinths, and those which the Turks call Tulipan, much to our wonderment, because of the time of the year, it being almost the middle of winter, so unfriendly to flowers. Greece abounds in Narcissus and Hyacinths remarkable for their fragrance. Scent in the Tulipan is either lacking or very slight, they are admired for the beauty and variety of their colours. The Turks cultivate flowers with extreme zeal and though they are a careful people do not hesitate to pay a considerable sum for an exceptional flower." He goes on to tell how he acquired a few bulbs "at great price" which later flowered in his Vienna garden.

About that time the Swabian family of Fugger reigned as the most important merchant princes in Europe, and it was in their garden at Augsberg that Conrad Gesner, the famous botanist, first saw Tulips growing. There they kindled a blaze of enthusiasm that swept through Central Europe until it reached a strange climax in Holland three-quarters of a century later. Following the lead of the Fugger family the wealthy merchants and landowners of Holland and Germany began to vie with each other in an effort to obtain all the latest varieties from Turkey and the Levant. At first these were so expensive that only the very rich could afford to invest in Tulips, but some of the big importers began to include Tulip bulbs in their consignments of goods from the Near East, and the results were so satisfactory that they decided to cater for a wider market. Some of the commoner sorts were imported in bulk and found a ready sale among people of quite modest means.

Sir Thomas Hanmer, writing in 1659, says "Wee had it first out of Turkey about fifty yeares since, where it grows wild in some parts, particularly about Jerusalem as they write, and is thought to be that flower, translated ill a Lily, that was sayed to be more gloriously arrayed than Solomon." It was when the sedate beauty of the self-coloured flowers gave way to the flames of purple, rose, crimson, and gold of the Bizarre varieties, that the popularity of the Tulip reached its highest levels. Many thought that the flowers must be "moon-struck" to produce such extraordinary combinations of colour, but others believed that they could be induced by careful cultivation, and one old English gardener tells us how it was done, "Take the plaister of old walls and powder it very fine; mix this with drift sand, or such sand as is sharp and found by the sea-shore; to this add the water that runs from dunghills or lakes, and mix these as well as possible, and put it over the surface of the bed a little before you plant your Breeding or Plain Tulips; and it will bring them into stripes to a wonder, as related to me by a gentleman of great honour."

By and by the production of new varieties became the fashion, and wherever they were grown their colour and elegance caught the public fancy so that Parkinson did no more than voice the sentiments of the day when he remarked that "Tulips do carry so delightful a form and abide so long in their bravery that there is no lady or gentleman of any worth that is not caught with their delight." The popularity of the flowers grew and grew until it reached a climax when the "Tulipomania" swept through the Netherlands in 1634. The craze gained such impetus that merchants, landowners, farmers, seamen, citizens, maidservants, and even chimney-sweeps and old-clothes women were tempted into an orgy of speculation along with the "ladies and gentlemen of worth." As one writer puts it, "The gaudy Tulip was an object which at one time drove the grave, the prudent and the ambitious Dutchman as wild as ever did the South Sea Bubble the gullible John Bull."

Matters reached such a state that it became necessary for the Government to step in and regulate what had become little more than a species of reckless gambling. In the early stages forty bulbs were sold for 10,000 guilders (a guilder is about 1s. 8d.), and in the city of Alkmaar one hundred and twenty bulbs were sold, for the benefit of the local orphanage, for 9,000 guilders. Presently there came a time when even greater sums were paid for single bulbs, and when we consider the value of money in those days, the sums were truly enormous.

"Semper Augustus" was one of the favourite varieties and we are told of one enthusiast who actually paid 13,000 guilders for a single bulb of it. In many cases, however, the actual bulbs did not appear in the transactions, being in fact merely a medium for gambling. A tourist in Holland at that time says, "Before the tulip season was over, more roots were sold and purchased, bespoke and promised to be delivered, than in all probability were to be found in the gardens of Holland; and when Semper Augustus was not to be had anywhere, which happened twice, no species perhaps, was oftener purchased and sold."

At one time there were only two bulbs of this variety in Holland; one belonged to a dealer in Amsterdam, the other to a collector in Haarlem. The latter was offered twelve acres of good building land—and refused it. The Amsterdam bulb brought its fortunate owner 4,600 guilders, a new carriage and two grey horses with harness complete. About the same time a bulb of the variety "Viceroy" figured in an even more curious transaction, changing hands for:

2 lasts of wheat	4 fat oxen
4 lasts of rye	8 fat swine
12 fat sheep	4 tuns of beer
2 hogsheads of wine	2 tuns of butter
1 complete bed	1 silver drinking horn
1 suit of clothes	1,000 lbs. of cheese

The whole being valued at 3,500 guilders.

This traffic in expensive bulbs was not without its own peculiar hazards, as one Dutch importer proved to his cost. A sailor called at his warehouse to announce that a shipment of goods from the Levant had arrived in record time. The merchant was so delighted that he presented the sailor with a red herring for his supper. On leaving the warehouse the messenger spied what he took to be an onion lying among the costly silks and velvets, and thinking that it would be a decided improvement to his supper, slipped it into his pocket. Some little time afterwards the bulb was missed and the merchant, calling out "Where is my Semper Augustus?" began a frantic search. Hunt where they would the precious bulb was nowhere to be seen, and then suddenly someone remembered having seen it just before the departure of the sailor. Alas! by the time the sailor had been located, supper was over and the Semper Augustus had gone the way of all good onions. The indignant merchant promptly hauled the unfortunate sailor before the magistrate and charged him with stealing a tulip bulb worth 2,800 guilders. As a result the unfortunate fellow had to spend several months in prison as a punishment for his mistake.

In 1636 Tulips were offered in the London Exchange, but although the dealers did their utmost to reach the fabulous prices ruling in the Netherlands, they met with little success. As might be expected, a visit to Scotland was even less profitable, and they were unable to persuade any Scotsman to pay as much as 100 guilders for the root of a flower. Towards the end of the following year the bottom fell out of the market with the most disastrous results for all concerned. It appears that some of the shrewder of the dealers, realizing that the boom prices could not possibly last for ever, had quietly sold out, and when this became known there was a panic, followed by a slump.

Many persons who had believed themselves to be in easy circumstances woke up to find that their only possessions were a handful of bulbs that nobody wanted. The whole country was involved in the catastrophe, and it was only after a period of prolonged recriminations, threats of legal action for broken contracts and so on, that the people began to settle down and build up some form of livelihood from the wreckage. By and by it was found that the country was endowed with a soil that enabled it to become the bulb nursery of the world. A great bulb industry was built up with Haarlem as its centre; an industry with world-wide ramifications that sent out millions of bulbs to all parts of the world. When Holland was overwhelmed by the Germans in 1940 she was sending roughly one hundred million tulip bulbs to the United States of America annually. Thus out of the misery and delusion following the collapse of the "Tulipomania" of three centuries ago the Dutch people built up an industry that brought more money into the country than was ever dreamed of during that time of crazy speculation.

ALEX JARDINE

Lilac Time

FOR more than three hundred years the fragrant plumes of the Common Lilac have been familiar in our gardens, and their quiet charm has come to be considered the very essence of that delightful season when spring is giving way to summer. Lilac time brings the golden rain of Laburnums, the scarlet and gold of Azaleas, and all that happy atmosphere of singing birds and butterflies that are woven into our memory of the garden at its best. Known only as a garden plant the Lilac, *Syringa vulgaris*, was brought from Constantinople in the days of Queen Elizabeth, but in its native land remained unknown until about a century ago, when wild specimens were found growing in mountain thickets in the Bulgarian hinterland.

Towards the middle of the seventeenth century the Persian Lilac, *S. persica*, made its appearance in the gardens of England, although it had been known from time immemorial in the gardens of western Asia. When the wild type was discovered in Afghanistan some sixty years ago, it was found that during centuries of domestication some minor alterations had taken place in the cultivated variety. The first hybrid of which we have any record is the Rouen Lilac, a cross between the Common and Persian forms, which appeared in the Rouen Botanic Garden during the latter part of the eighteenth century. Grown under a variety of names, it is best known as *S. chinensis*, a name drawing attention to the fact that it has been known in the Far East for about one hundred years and is still grown in the gardens around Pekin. No one seems to know how it got there, whether it originated independently in China and in France or, as is much more probable, was sent from Europe in the early days of trading with the Orient.

A shrub of singular beauty, with long arching sprays of blossom, it is not so robust as the Common Lilac, and for this reason is very useful in town gardens. By the beginning of last century a number of varieties had already made their appearance, and in consequence the French growers saw the possibilities of careful hybridization. So successful were they that for more than a century varieties such as the lovely old Charles X have been grown for the cut-flower trade throughout the year, with the exception of a few months in summer.

About fifty years ago the famous nurserymen, Messrs. Lemoine of Nancy, began to experiment with Lilacs, and the results of their work are all the lovely single, double, and semi-double varieties that are grown so much to-day. They are of almost every shade, from the peculiar light blue of "Mrs. August Belmont," through various tonings of violet, purple, and soft magenta to the lovely pink of "Lucie Baltet," which is one of the most attractive members of the family.

A new page in the history of these old favourites was begun in 1920 when Miss Isabella Preston, of the Ottawa Experimental Farm, began crossing the species lately introduced from China. Blooming later than the old types these new hybrids, known as *S. Prestoniae*, are already of great value in carrying the season

of Lilac blossom a few more weeks into the summer. There
has always been some confusion because *Syringa*, the botanical
name of the Lilacs, is often confused with Syringa, the common
name of the Philadelphus or Mock Orange. This confusion can
be traced back to the herbalists of the sixteenth century. Syringa
is derived from *syrinx*, the old Greek term for the pipes of Pan,
and refers to the young growths of these and other shrubs
having been hollowed out and used as stems for the long pipes
used in Turkey and the Near East.

Both the Common Lilac and the Mock Orange were brought
from Turkish gardens about the same time, and their use as
pipe-stems struck the popular imaginations, causing them to
be known everywhere as the Blue and White Pipe Trees. In
Gerard's day three Pipe-Trees were known and, until Linnaeus
brought order out of chaos some hundred and fifty years later,
there appears to have been little or no discrimination between
them. Linnaeus gave the name *Syringa vulgaris* to Gerard's
Blew Pipe, and while his White Pipe, now known as the Mock
Orange, became *Philadelphus coronarius*, his Arabian Pipe
became *Jasminum Sambac*.

Although this ruling was accepted by most botanists, the
older usages lived on in common speech in various parts of the
world. In British and American gardens the Mock Orange is
often referred to as Syringa, in France it is Seringat, while in
Germany and some of the Scandinavian countries both this
and the Jasmine are known as the Pipe Shrubs.

When a sixteenth-century writer tells of his experiences with
the White Pipe there is little doubt that he was dealing with
the fragrant Mock Orange. In those days the shrub was one of
the latest novelties, and in describing the flowers he says,
"They have a pleasant sweete smell, but in my judgement
troubling and molesting the head in a very strange manner. I
once gathered the flowers and laid them in my chamber windowe,

which smelled more strongly after they had lain together a few
houres, but with such a pontick and unacquainted savour that
they wakened me from sleepe, so that I could not take rest till
I had cast them out of my chamber."

Lilies from the Sea

THE dawn of the seventeenth century saw the beginnings of
the great European struggle for the dominance of the Orient
and the capture of its wealth, and it was not long before the
hospitable shores of the Cape of Good Hope presented themselves as a convenient half-way house forming the natural
resting place where ships could be watered and careened in
the course of their long voyage. At first the merchantmen of all
nations made use of this haven and, such was the comradeship
of the seas, those which were outward bound left letters
and messages to be picked up and delivered by ships on the
homeward run.

We can scarcely expect to find any record of how and when the first of the South African wildflowers arrived in Europe, but we can imagine that their gay colours and strange shapes would soon attract some attention. As a matter of course a race of flower-lovers such as the Dutch would soon take home bulbs and roots, and as the years went by an ever-varying procession of South African flowers arrived in Europe, until the Cape flora, now known to be one of the richest in the whole world, became almost legendary. Our earliest knowledge of these flowers is preserved in a book published in Amsterdam in 1644, which describes a number of them, including the well-known Red Hot Poker, *Kniphofia aloides*.

The friendly relations between the mariners of different countries began to change as the long struggle between Britain and Holland for the mastery of the seas began to take shape. It was probably the wreck of the *Haarlem* in 1648 that first showed the Dutch the importance of the Cape, and the possibility of founding a colony there. The shipwrecked crew camped on what is now the site of Cape Town for about five months, and not only lived amicably among the natives but were able to grow crops. In due course they were rescued and taken home by some of their countrymen homeward bound from the Spice Islands of the East. The story of their adventure and the demonstration that Europeans could live in peace and plenty in that little-known land induced the Directors of the Dutch East India Company to plant a settlement there. In the leisurely manner of the age this took about four years to accomplish, and it was not until 1652 that the first five hundred colonists arrived at Table Bay. Included among them were two gardeners whose business it was to grow fruit and vegetables for the infant colony, and to collect such of the South African wildflowers as might be of value to the gardens of the homeland.

Thus it came about that many of the ships engaged in the East India trade brought home bulbs and plants that had been collected and acclimatized by the first colonists of South Africa. In 1659 one of those Dutch ships was wrecked in the English Channel, and among the debris washed ashore were a number of bulbs of a flower that came to be known as the Guernsey Lily. No notice seems to have been taken of them at the time, and they were buried in the sandy shore by the action of the wind and the waves, but with the autumn, "to the great delight and surprise of the inhabitants, the scarlet flowers appeared in all their pomp and glory." In the genial climate of the Island of Guernsey they flourished and increased to such an extent that it was thought worth while to send a consignment of them as cut-flowers to the London market. The venture was a great success. The graceful flowers and their attractive colouring, ranging from glowing scarlet to charming tints of crimson and rose-pink, had an instant appeal, and ever since the demand has been greater than the supply. Not until many years afterwards when Francis Masson found it decorating the rocky slopes of Table Mountain was the true home of this plant, now known as *Nerine sarniensis*, discovered. It was distributed throughout the world as the Guernsey Lily, and had always been assumed to be a native of Japan because the ship from whence it came had been homeward bound from the Far East.

About one hundred and twenty years later another Dutch vessel on the homeward run from South Africa was driven ashore on the rocky shore of eastern England. In this case the lovely *Vallota speciosa* was washed ashore among the remains of the wreck. The citizens of Scarborough were not long in recognizing its worth as a garden plant, and it has long been known the world over as the Scarborough Lily. Although the blooms are not quite so elegant as those of the Guernsey Lily, their chalice-like form and attractive cardinal-red colouring, set off by a large white eye, are always worthy of the most sheltered place in the garden.

Between eighty and ninety years ago a small storm-tossed vessel limped into the sheltered harbour of St. Georges in Bermuda in great distress after having been blown far out of her course by contrary winds. On board was a missionary on his way home from the mission fields of the China coast, and he carried a few bulbs of a lovely Lily he had found growing wild on some of the small islands that lie off the southern shores of Japan. In appreciation of the ready hospitality extended by the Rev. Mr. Roberts, Rector of Radnor, the missionary gave him a few bulbs, which were planted in the Rectory garden. The Lilies grew and flourished in the shallow limestone soil and maritime climate of Bermuda until within a generation they had become one of the features of the island.

About 1876 an American nurseryman, Mr. W. K. Harris of Philadelphia, went to Bermuda to recover from an illness, and was charmed by the lovely funnel-shaped blooms of the purest white and their delightful fragrance so reminiscent of orange blossoms. He soon realized the importance of such a find and could see the advantage of getting the bulbs from Bermuda forced in time to flower for Easter. He launched his find under the name of *Lilium Harrisii*, the name by which is is still commonly known, though now classified as *L. longiflorum eximium*. It became a great favourite as the Easter Lily, or sometimes St. Joseph's Lily, and by the end of the last century the export of bulbs from Bermuda exceeded three million per annum. The tale of the Bermuda Lily and how disease almost wrecked it and the island, and how the menace was conquered is another story, but here we are content to show how even the vagaries of the wind and the sea have contributed something to the beauty of our gardens.

A Pirate's Namesake

PROBABLY one of the most romantic characters that ever took more than a passing interest in wildflowers was Captain William Dampier, pirate, navigator, and naturalist, the first Englishman to reach the shores of Australia. There are few stranger figures in history than this wanderer who turned pirate in order to see the world, who could stop to admire a drift of wildflowers while on his way to fire a village or rob a church. He has been described as "a man of great ability and no small scientific attainments, united to a persevering and inquiring mind, which, considering him for so many years the associate of some of the most desperate and abandoned buccaneers and rovers that infested the seas of both hemispheres, is much in his honour." He kept a record of all his wanderings and adventures, including sketches of many of the strange birds, beasts and flowers he came across, and this alone made him something of a curiosity in that age of rough illiterate seamen. Evelyn, writing in his Diary under the date of August 6th, 1699, says, "I dined with Mr. Pepys, where was Captain Dampier who has been a famous buccaneer . . . he seemed a more modest man than one could imagine by the relation of those he had associated with."

Born in 1652, William Dampier lost his parents in early youth and had little difficulty in persuading his guardian to allow him to go to sea. At the age of fifteen he sailed as a cabin boy to Newfoundland, and as the years passed by had many adventures as he roved the seven seas in search of fame and fortune. He reached the West Indies at about the age of thirty and, falling in with a band of "gentlemen of fortune," crossed the Isthmus of Panama, attacked the city, and stealing four ships set off to prey on the rich Spanish galleons bringing home the treasures of Chile and Peru. In 1686 he accompanied the notorius Captain Swan of the *Cygnet*, in one of his forays against the Spanish settlers of the west coast of the Americas. The *Cygnet* came off second best and was forced to seek sanctuary on the little-known coast of California. There the pirates had hoped to trade with the natives, but on account of the barren nature of the country this was quite impossible and they were compelled to live off the land as best they could. A tribe of friendly Indians showed them how to prepare the fleshy roots of a Yucca by cooking them in an earthen oven, but the dish was far from popular with the "gentlemen of fortune." It reminded some of them too vividly of the boiled burdock served in the prisons of England.

Crossing the Pacific to the Solomon Islands the pirates marooned their tyrannous captain and continued on their way until the west coast of Australia was reached in 1688, and while the ship was being careened Dampier was in his element exploring the countryside. There was still much discontent among the pirate crew, and when the Nicobar Islands were reached some of the more unpopular members, including our friend Dampier, were given their share of the spoils and left to fend for themselves. In due course he reached London and published his

Voyage Round the World, which told of some of the wonders he had seen. Among the plants mentioned is the "Physic Nut," seeds of the Castor Oil Plant that were used as medicine in the Amazon country. He also mentioned visiting the island of Guam, where he had seen "The Bread-fruit tree, high as our apple trees; it hath a spreading head full of branches and dark leaves. The fruit grows on the boughs like apples; it is as big as a penny loaf, when wheat is at five shillings a bushel; it is of a round shape and hath a thick rind; when the fruit is ripe it is yellow and soft and the taste is sweet and pleasant. The natives of Guam use it for bread. . . . This fruit lasts in season eight months of the year, during which the natives have no other food of the bread kind." No wonder the West Indian planters of a later generation were impressed by this description and were successful in interesting the Government sufficiently to make an effort to transport the tree as a source of cheap food for their Negro slaves.

Dampier's book was a great success, and it was not long before two gentlemen from the Admiralty were waiting on the author with the suggestion that he go out and explore the possibilities of planting a settlement on the west coast of Australia. In 1699 Dampier put in at Shark's Bay in search of water, and being unable to locate a creek, an effort was made to find some by digging on the sands of that inhospitable shore. Coasting along in a northerly direction he came on a group of islands now known as the Dampier Archipelago, but was not at all favourably impressed by the new land he was seeing for the first time. As he reported later, "If it was not for that kind of pleasure that results from the discovery of even the barrenest spot on the globe, this coast of New Holland would not have charmed me much."

One of the islands of the group appeared to be rather more fertile than the others, and a party was sent ashore in the hope of finding water. While his men were digging a well in what proved to be another vain quest the ex-pirate, who was now exploring on behalf of His Britannic Majesty, went off in search of wildflowers. His is the first description of the plants that grow in that remote place. "There grow here two or three sorts of shrubs, one just like Rosemary; and therefore I call'd this Rosemary Island. It grew in great plenty here but had no smell. Some of the other shrubs had blue and yellow flowers and we found two sorts of grain, like beans. The one grew in bushes, the other sort on a sort of creeping vine that runs along the ground, having thick leaves and blossoms like bean blossoms but much larger, of a deep red colour looking very beautiful."

The ship foundered in the harbour of Ascension Island, on the homeward voyage, and many of Dampier's notes and sketches were lost, but some forty herbarium specimens were saved and are now preserved in the Herbarium of Oxford University. The leopard does not change its spots, and before many years had passed William Dampier was back again practising the doubtful art of piracy on the treasure ships of Spain. His was the ship that marooned Alexander Selkirk, prototype of Robinson Crusoe, and later rescued him from a life of loneliness.

Over a century was to pass before Dampier's creeping vine received any attention, but early in the nineteenth century Alan Cunningham gave it the name *Clianthus Dampieri* in honour of its finder, who is believed to be the only pirate ever commemorated in this way.

As becomes a pirate's favourite *Clianthus Dampieri* is not at all amenable to domestication, and does its best to test the skill of all who attempt to grow it. The best method seems to be to catch your seedlings while still in the baby stage and to graft them on the roots of the Bladder Senna, *Colutea arborescens.* Treated in this way the pirate's foundling will prove to be a very decorative plant whether grown in a basket or trained as a climber in the conservatory. In due season the silvery leaves will be decorated by multitudes of orange-scarlet flowers whose glowing colour is accentuated by a blotch of intense purple-black in the centre.

Linnaeus

WHEN Linnaeus was invited to select the plant that should bear his name he chose the little Twin-flower because it is a native of the north, "lowly insignificant and dis-regarded, flowering for a brief space,—like Linnaeus who resembles it." Closely related to the Honeysuckles, the Elderberries, and the Abelias, *Linnaea borealis* is well worth a place in the rock garden because of the fragrant pinkish-white blossoms that nod so daintily above the dense carpets of small round leaves. *Linnaea* is not one of those flaunting beauties that paint whole hillsides with their myriads of blossoms, but is a shy woodlander that prefers to scent the lonely forests of the north with its delicious fragrance.

Many of those who traverse the northern wastes must pass it by unheeding, but as Dr. Stoker says even the most indifferent traveller would probably look twice at the dainty little twin flowers if he knew it to be the favourite of the great Linnaeus and if he guessed "that the same plant was at that very moment sparkling on the Siberian wastes, gallantly holding up its colours amid the bleakness of north-eastern Asia, all a-glitter in the mountains of Japan, sniffed by the migrating caribou in Arctic America and actually competing with the glories of California."

Carl von Linne was born in 1707, the son of a country parson, and when he achieved international fame as a naturalist his name was latinized, according to the fashion of the eighteenth century, to the familiar Linnaeus. At the age of twenty-two he entered the University of Upsala to study medicine, just after the botany department and the botanic garden had been destroyed by fire. Discovered taking notes in the dilapidated garden by Celsius, he was befriended by that famous botanist who allowed the young man the use of his extensive library. This kindness had an amusing aftermath many years later. At that time Olaus Rudbeck, whose name is commemorated in the Coneflowers from North America, the Rudbeckias, was Professor of Botany at Upsala, and it was not long before the young Linne was an inmate of his home, and was ekeing out his slender resources by acting as tutor to some of the Professor's twenty-four children.

On leaving university Linnaeus spent a few years travelling in Lappland and other parts of Europe. While in Germany he gained considerable unpopularity on account of his quest for truth. The city of Hamburg was the proud possessor of a "Seven-headed Hydra" that was believed to be part of the loot brought back by the Crusaders. Linnaeus secured permission to give the specimen a critical examination, as he is said to have objected to the idea that the Creator would have endowed such a lowly creature with seven separate brains. When he discovered that the "Hydra" consisted of seven heads of weasels, which, with two clawed feet, had been skilfully fastened together and covered with snake-skin! The Mayor and Corporation had been dallying with the idea of turning the curiosity into hard cash, and this untimely revelation was not received in the spirit in which it had been made. Linnaeus thought it advisable to leave the city without undue delay.

He spent the next two years in Holland as Curator of the famous Hatrecamp Botanic Garden which, owned by George Clifford, a wealthy Englishman and one of the Directors of the Dutch East India Company, was one of the most important establishments in the Netherlands. It was for the purpose of obtaining plants for this garden, as well as to meet prominent British botanists, that he decided to visit England in 1736. He received a warm welcome from Peter Collinson, a devout Quaker, who took him to see Gorse in all the glory of its golden blossoms in Putney Heath. Hardy as it is, the Common Gorse cannot stand the rigorous winters of Scandinavia, but this was not the first time Linnaeus had seen Gorse blossom, although his experience at Lubeck had not prepared him for the beauty of an English common.

While barely thirty years of age Linnaeus had perfected his new method of classifying plants, and in consequence he got a somewhat cool reception from Dillenius, Professor of Botany at Oxford. After introducing him to a friend, Dillenius whispered "This is the young man who would confound the whole science of botany," and although the visitor did not understand the remark he sensed the antagonism.

One of the problems of the day was where to place the Ivy-leaved Toadflax, *Linaria Cymbalaria*. This wildflower, which is commonly grown as a window plant under the old name Mother

of Thousands, has roundish heart-shaped leaves cut into five
lobes that give them something of the appearance of tiny ivy-
leaves, and are responsible for another common name, Kenilworth Ivy. The pretty little flowers of lavender-violet resemble
a miniature Snapdragon and are always turned towards the
light, but as soon as the seeds are set the pods turn away so that
the seeds may be deposited in the crevices of the rocky walls
on which it loves to cling.

While the party inspected the Oxford Botanic Garden
Linnaeus was carefully steered towards a wall over which the
problem plant was growing. When asked to give an opinion,
far from being disconcerted by the enquiry Linnaeus seemed to
welcome it and gave such a convincing explanation of the
structure and affinities of the flower that he completely won the
heart of Dillenius. The old botanist was so anxious to keep
him in England that he offered to share his house and salary
if only the young man would remain as his assistant. Within a
few years Linnaeus was back in Sweden, and eventually he
became Professor of Botany at Upsala, where he reigned for
nearly forty years as one of the leading naturalists in Europe.
His greatest contribution to the study of plants was his simplified
method of naming them. Among other things he swept away
many of the superstitious ideas that lingered on from the Middle
Ages, which were "for the most part a mere chaos of confusion,
whose mother was barbarity, whose father dogmatism, and
whose nurse prejudice." He used many names with classical
association such as Adonis, Andromeda, Euphorbia, Daphne,
Narcissus, Nepenthes and Musa. While many of his names go
back to the very earliest times we cannot now be certain that
the plants that now bear them are the same species as were known
in ancient times.

The Nepenthes, the extraordinary Pitcher plants of the
tropical forests, were unknown to the Greeks and Romans, but

Linnaeus used the name from Helen of Troy's wine which freed mankind from all ills because "If it is not Helen's Nepenthes it certainly will be for all botanists. Who would not be filled with admiration if, after a long and tedious journey he should find this wonderful plant. In his astonishment past ills would be forgotten on seeing this strange work of the Creator." Andromeda is another of the classical names he adopted. In this case the plant "is always fixed on some little turfy hillock in the midst of the swamp, just as Andromeda herself was chained to a rock in the sea, which bathed her feet as the fresh water does the roots of this plant."

Euphorbia, the name he gave to that vast family of strange plants that try to deceive the unwary by pretending to be Cacti, takes us back to the days of ancient Rome when Augustus Caesar was Master of the World. About 12 B.C. he suffered from some internal complaint that would not yield to the usual treatment. He was cured by a physician, Antonius Musa, who used hot fomentations and some sort of curried food alternating with salads and cloths dipped in icy cold water, and Caesar showed his gratitude by dedicating a statue to Musa. The physician's brother Euphorbus was court doctor to the King of Numidia, who, spurred by Caesar's action, dedicated a plant to his doctor and wrote a treatise on its virtues. *Euphorbia* was accepted as a plant name by Linnaeus, who remarked, "Where now is Musa's statue? It has perished and disappeared!! But the Memoriae of Euphorbus endures perennially and can never be thrown down." He did his best to rectify matters by dedicating the Banana plant to Musa.

Having thus shown that the practice of naming plants was a method of honouring men among the Ancients, he proceeded to assign many species to botanists and other notables, and quaint are the clues provided to show the connection. *Magnolia*, for example, is a "tree with very handsome leaves and

flowers, recalling the splendid botanist Pierre Magnol, Professor
of Botany and Director of the Montpellier Botanic Garden."
The lovely Persian-blue Spiderwort, whose flowers are such an
attraction in the herbaceous border, was named *Commelina* on
account of its "flowers with three petals, two of which are
showy while the third is not conspicuous, from the two brothers
Commelin, for the third died before accomplishing anything."

All his commemorative names were not exactly complimentary, however. *Millera*, for example, referred to "an American
plant whose calyx is close, short, and completely enclosing the
seeds, being called after a man who spent much labour over
acquiring rare American seeds and preserving them carefully."
He evidently remembered that Philip Miller of the Chelsea
Physic Garden was not among those who adopted the Linnaean
system of plant classification. Miller was notoriously close-
fisted and liked to keep his new plants and all information about
them to himself.

The Browallias from Peru are among some of our most
valuable flowers for the cool greenhouse, where their neat habit
and attractive blue flowers are always welcome. The history
of the well-known *B. demissa* gives an amusing sidelight on
the scientific outlook of the eighteenth century. It arrived in
Europe while Linnaeus was in charge of the Hatrecamp Botanic
Garden in Holland, and he named it *Browallia elata* in honour
of John Browall, Bishop of Åbo, in Finland, who had published
a paper "of more spirit than solid learning" in support of the
Linnaean system. Within a year or two His Lordship the Bishop
published another treatise, this time dealing with the evaporation
of water, and his purpose was to confute a theory put forward
by Celsius, that the level of the sea is constantly receding.
Linnaeus sprang to the defence of his old friend and renamed the
plant *Browallia demissa*, the low Browallia. According to tradition this marked the rupture in his friendship with the Bishop,

and their permanent estrangement was commemorated in *Browallia alienata*, but we have not been able to verify this, so there may be something in what another writer, B. D. Jackson, says, "the species has never been seen since, and is thought to be an invention."

"King's Botanist"

ONE of the rarest trees in all the world is *Franklinia Altamaha*, which has not been seen in its native haunts, along the banks of the Altamaha River in Georgia, U.S.A., for over one hundred and fifty years. An elegant tree, with its slender trunk clothed with a peculiar kind of bark that has been likened to the tan-coloured skin of a greyhound, the Franklinia reaches a height of twenty-five to thirty feet. From the end of summer to the first hard frosts of winter it keeps up a long procession of exquisite chalice-like flowers, each of the purest white and between two and three inches in diameter. They are produced long after the scarlet glory of its autumn tints has faded and gone, so that even during the first sunny days of winter we may admire the tracery of its bare branches starred with the scented white blooms that glisten like the Magnolias of springtime.

This remarkable tree takes us back to the old colonial days of the eighteenth century when George III was king and America little more than a vast unexplored continent; back to the days when John Bartram, the first American to receive international fame as a botanist, was exploring the flora of the New World. John Bartram was a farmer born of English parents at the end of the seventeenth century, and at the age of twenty-five he braved his wife's displeasure and the censure of the neighbourhood by hiring a man to manage his farm while he studied botany in Philadelphia. He is said to have done this after discovering a flourishing colony of *Viola pedata*, the Birds'-foot Violet, by the edge of one of his fields. Struck by their beauty—this is one of the most attractive members of a delightful family, with the two upper petals of dark purple and the lower three of lavender—he dreamed of them in the night and next day made the decision to know something of the scientific study of plant life. Finding that he could accomplish little without a knowledge of Latin, he mastered that language within three months and so became fully qualified to study the American wildflowers as they grew. In contact with all the leading botanists and gardeners of the day, he is credited with sending more than two hundred species of American plants to the gardens of England. These included the Sugar Maple, the Tulip Tree, some of the best-known Magnolias, Dog's-Tooth Violets, Gentians, and Michaelmas Daisies. *Lilium superbum* flowered for the first time in Europe in Peter Collinson's garden in 1738, and the well-known *L. philadelphicum* received its name from Linnaeus because he had received his specimens from John Bartram of Philadelphia.

By this time Bartram had bought some land at Kingsessing on the banks of the Schuylkill River, at that time about three miles from the city, but now in the heart of it. There about 1731 he built his own homestead and laid out what became the first botanical garden in America. After his death in 1777 the garden became a nursery, and after passing through many vicissitudes, was incorporated into the Parks Department of Philadelphia in 1891. Its historical interest was fully appreciated under the management of the Fairmount Park Commissioners, and as much as possible of the atmosphere of the old Colonial days has been restored by growing many of the plants known at that time.

One of Bartram's most enthusiastic correspondents was Peter Collinson, a London textile dealer, who had one of the finest collections of American plants in England. Collinson was so delighted with the many new plants coming from America that he persuaded a group of friends to contribute £10 a year towards the cost of Bartram's botanical explorations and the despatch of plants to England. John Bartram was a great reader, and as books were scarce in the young colony he was constantly asking for the latest London publications. At last even Peter Collinson thought he was overdoing things, and remarked that even Solomon did not get all his wisdom from books, but Bartram took the chiding in good part and replied, "I take thy advice about my books kindly enough, although I love reading dearly; and I believe, if Solomon had loved women less and books more, he would have been a wiser and happier man."

Through the goodwill of his influential friends Collinson managed to obtain the appointment of "King's Botanist" for his friend in America, and it must have been a red-letter day for this modest man when he received the great news. "My repeated solicitations have not been in vain, for this day I received certain intelligence from Our Gracious King that he had appointed you his botanist, with a salary of £50 a year. . . . Now, My Dear John, thy wishes are in some degree accomplished to range over Georgia and the Florida. As this is a great work and must be

accomplished by degrees, it must be left to thy own judgement
how to proceed."

Thus it came about that in 1765, accompanied by his son
William, the old plant-hunter, now nearly seventy years of age,
set out on his travels again, this time to make the long journey
to the south that he had set his heart on many years before.
It was in the course of this, his last expedition, that he found the
strange new tree which he named *Franklinia Altamaha* in honour
of his old friend Benjamin Franklin and the river on whose banks
it grew.

The name was not published for several years, and by that
time plants raised from seeds sent to England in 1773 had
flowered and become known as *Gordonia pubescens*, as it was
seen to be closely allied to the Loblolly Bay that had been named
in honour of James Gordon, the Mile End nurseryman, some
forty years before. As a result of this hasty diagnosis Bartram's
tree has been known as Gordonia ever since. Within recent
years, however, it has been subjected to a critical examination,
and although the flowers were found to be very similar to those
of Gordonia the fruits of the two trees were quite distinct.
This means that the original name *Franklinia Altamaha* must
stand.

When William Bartram revisited the location of this tree in
1773 he found that it was still occupying its few acres of rich
bottom land near Fort Barrington. In 1790 his cousin, Dr. M.
Marshall, visited the spot and found the tree plentiful in its
limited area, but he was the last scientist to see it growing wild.
There seems to be no record of the time when this valley was
cleared and no one knows when this tree became extinct in the
wild state, and in consequence the specimen planted in the
Kingsessing Garden by William Bartram was for long the only
specimen of its kind in America, and all those in American
gardens are believed to have been derived from it.

Towards the end of last century this historic specimen died to the ground and was thought to have been lost, but presently it sent up a strong young shoot that has since developed into a handsome tree. Although still rather rare the *Franklinia* is gradually becoming better known, and fortunately the growing demand may be satisfied fairly rapidly as the tree lends itself to modern methods of propagation. As may be expected from the conditions under which it grew in the wild state *Franklinia* grows best in a moist, well-drained soil by a river-bank or lakeside where it may be depended upon to develop into one of the most attractive of flowering trees. It is rather surprising that although a native of the warm south-east of the United States this tree is very much hardier than we should expect. Under the rigorous climatic conditions of the Arnold Arboretum in Massachusetts, records show that *Franklinia Altamaha* has proved itself capable of enduring so much as fifty degrees of frost.

A Sailor's Gift

THE Fuchsia has had a strange and eventful history since the first of its kind was found by Father Charles Plumier, a distinguished French traveller and botanist, who made three voyages of discovery to the West Indies and the tropical parts of South America about the end of the seventeenth century. In 1703 he published a book dealing with the new plants he had discovered, and mentioned therein a pretty red-flowered shrub from San Domingo. He named it *Fuchsia triphylla coccinea*, and half a century later when Linnaeus published his new method of recognizing plants by the use of only two names, this species was listed as *F. triphylla*.

As the years rolled silently by, more and more new plants were discovered and classified by botanists under the name of Fuchsia, but nothing whatever was seen or heard of Father Plumier's original plant. By the time a century and a half had passed its very existence began to be doubted. Plumier's description was somehat vague and the portrait rather crude, no other Fuchsia had been found bearing only four stamens—

the usual number is eight—and no plant had been collected from any of the West Indies that could be referred to the genus *Fuchsia*. As a result Plumier's plant became something of a mystery, and in 1877 Hemsley of Kew recorded the impression that "the figure is so rude that nobody, I believe, has been able to identify it with any living or dried plant. Possibly it is not a Fuchsia at all in the sense of the present application of the name, for it is represented as having only four stamens."

In the meantime Thomas Hogg of New York had received some seeds from the West Indies in 1873, but it was not until nine years later that one of the resultant plants turned up at Kew. This was a new sort of Fuchsia, and when it came into the hands of the London Fuchsia specialists, Messrs. Henderson & Sons, they sent it along to Kew to be identified. Hemsley was delighted to find that he had been wrong, and that it corresponded exactly with Plumier's drawing made so long ago and that it could be none other than the long-lost *Fuchsia triphylla*, which had been lost to science for nearly two hundred years.

The story of how *Fuchsia coccinea* first arrived in the gardens of England is one of the most romantic tales of plant introduction. This is generally believed to be the first of its family to be grown in Europe, but there has been so much confusion of names that it is extremely difficult to ascertain which species is being discussed under any given name.

A sailor boy wandering along the shores of South America—accounts vary as to whether in Chile or Brazil—saw a handsome flowering shrub which he felt sure his mother would love to see, so he carefully lifted a young one and nursed it on the long voyage home across the Atlantic. By-and-by it grew in the window of his mother's cottage in Wapping, by the side of the River Thames, and it was there that James Lee, the nurseryman of Hammersmith, saw it in 1788. He was so impressed by the grace and beauty of the strange new flower that he determined to buy it. The old lady, whose love of flowers had induced her son to dig up this lovely thing far beyond the seas, declined to sell, saying that her son, a sailor "had brought it from foreign parts and she could not bear to part with it, no not for all the gold of the Indies."

Mr. Lee had to depart empty-handed, but he did not give up the quest, and on a later visit his persuasiveness, combined with the sight of eighty golden guineas, proved too much for the old lady. One of the conditions of the sale was that the original owner was to get the first two rooted cuttings of the plant, and we are told that after completing his part of the bargain James Lee was successful in raising about three hundred cuttings, which he had no difficulty in disposing of at one guinea each.

On account of the confusion of names there is some doubt as to which Fuchsia the young sailor brought home for his mother. Some authorities are of the opinion that it is the plant we know as *F. coccinea*, while others think that it may have been *F. triphylla*, but by the information available it would appear that Mr. Lee took his specimen along to Kew, where William Aiton diagnosed it as *F. caccinea*. Apparently the species was lost to cultivation within a comparatively short time, probably because it was not able to stand up to the rigours of an English winter. Matters are further complicated by the appearance about the same time of the well-known hardy species *F. macrostemma*, which according to some authorities was introduced during that same year from southern Chile by a Captain Firth. This would account for its being confused with Lee's plant, and as one writer puts it rather bitterly, "it usurped the name of *Fuchsia coccinea* and spread it into every garden in the kingdom." The true *F. coccinea* disappeared from circulation and remained unknown until it was discovered in a local garden by Mr. W. Baxter, curator of the Oxford Botanic Garden, in 1867.

James Lee was then at the height of his career, having become one of the leading nurserymen in England when he entered into partnership with Lewis Kennedy in 1760. From then on the Vineyard Nursery in Hammersmith became famous all over Europe as a source of new and uncommon plants. His name is commemorated in *Cereus Leeanus*, a Mexican plant that he raised from seeds received from the Empress Josephine's garden at Malmaison. It is a very striking species of stiff, erect habit, reaching about twelve inches in height and deeply furrowed with sharp angles; at or near the summit it produces a number of large, brick-red inclining to scarlet, flowers which have a tube of some three inches in length, and the open blooms measure about the same in diameter. It is a handsome species well worth growing, apart from its historical associations.

James Lee was the true plantsman, always prepared to hand on information about the latest novelties, a complete contrast to Philip Miller, curator of the Chelsea Physic Garden, who preferred to conceal the names and origin of his greatest treasures. This contributed in no small degree to Lee's reputation. Evidently all the wrappings of the foreign seeds that arrived at Chelsea were dropped into the Thames, and Lee is said to have kept a boy for the express purpose of retrieving them, even if he had to swim. By this means all particulars about Miller's new arrivals were always available at the Vineyard Nursery, greatly to the surprise of the establishment up the river.

With Mr. Lee's discovery the gardening public took the Fuchsia to its heart, and for more than a century its graceful blooms had a vogue such as few garden flowers have ever enjoyed. Fashions in flowers change just as they do in clothes, houses, and gardens, and so the Fuchsia suffered an eclipse when public taste veered round to ribbon borders and carpet beds, and the great influx of hardy annuals that reached Europe towards the end of last century. Many of the favourites of eighty years ago are forgotten, and it is only in the pages of old gardening periodicals that we find some memory of their charm and beauty.

Of the fifteen hundred or so named varieties known in those days, scarcely one-third survive, and this has brought home to us that something precious has been lost with so many of those old-world favourites. The desire to revive an interest in them is world-wide and has lead to the formation of the American and British Fuchsia Societies, which have already been responsible for bringing back some of the old varieties from the window ledges, cemeteries, and old-fashioned gardens where they sought sanctuary in days gone by. Passed as cuttings from friend to friend, many of the old names have been forgotten and replaced by local ones, but these old favourites are still being found and can be matched with the exquisite illustrations made when they were young. When their old names have been restored and their histories made known it is very pleasant to welcome them back to our garden to take their place as old friends.

Gay Bougainvilleas

THE warm sheltered valleys of southern Brazil have given us many garden plants, the Verbenas and Petunias of the flower garden, the Jerusalem Cherry whose fruits of orange and gold are so valuable for winter decoration, and the gay Bougainvilleas that are so indispensable for draping walls and pillars of greenhouse and conservatory in cool climates and for porches and pergolas in tropical lands. There are about a dozen recognized species of Bougainvillea, but only two of them, *B. glabra* and *B. spectabilis*, are of any garden value, although a hundred years of cultivation combined with bud variation and hybridization have developed many forms that rival and even surpass their parents. The riot of colour, ranging from a deep magenta-purple through crimson and soft-pink to brick red and an attractive bronzy-gold, by which the Bougainvilleas are so well known, is not provided by the flowers as is generally supposed, but by three large bracts. The true flowers are inconspicuous, green or pale yellow organs completely encircled by the showy bracts.

Bougainvillea glabra reaches ten feet or so in height and has bracts of a clear phlox-purple that are in evidence through most of the year. Of a spreading habit with few spines, it is rather more compact than *B. spectabilis* that tends to grow into a rampant climber. All forms, however, can be kept under control by judicious pruning. One of the best-known varieties of *B. glabra* is *Sanderiana*, which is also one of the hardiest and can be depended upon to withstand a few degrees of frost. *B. spectabilis* and its varieties are all of a softer colour and is the source of newer varieties which have lost the traditional purple of the family. One of the most beautiful of all is the lovely "Mrs. Butt," which was originally found in Colombia about forty years ago. It reached England a few years later via the Botanic Garden at Trinidad, and for many years the only specimen in Europe was a plant growing in the Succulent House at Kew.

The Bougainvilleas commemorate Louis Antoine de Bougainville, the first Frenchman to cross the Pacific Ocean. He had been so depressed by the decline in French prestige with the loss of Canada to the British that in 1768 he obtained the royal permission to provide and lead an expedition to the South Seas in search for new colonies for France. In those days no explorer would have dreamed of setting sail without a naturalist, and Bougainville's choice was Philibert de Commerson, a studious old gentleman from Caen. Before leaving France Commerson founded a prize of two hundred francs to the University of Paris to be awarded to the person who did the most disinterested act to his fellow men during the year.

He took as his assistant Jean Baret, who has been described as a vivacious young man of about twenty-six years of age, not particularly good-looking, but quiet and industrious. When the expedition reached Rio de Janiero the botanist took the opportunity to go plant-hunting while Bougainville made final arrangements about stores for the long voyage, and it was here that Commerson named the gaily-coloured *Bougainvillea mirabilis* in honour of the commander. One of the best known of his plants is the charming Water Poppy, *Hydrocleis Commersonii*, which is sometimes referred to as *H. nymphoides*. He found it among the quiet waterways of Brazil and the south-eastern coast of South America. It is well worth growing for its flowers of a bright and cheerful yellow that stand well above the bright glossy floating leaves. Each bloom lasts but a single day, but they are produced continuously over a long period. A short stop was made at Montevideo, and there Commerson found several new plants, including the dainty pink *Zephyranthes Commersonii*. He was enchanted by the beauty of the countryside, arriving as he did when the whole landscape was lighted up by untold millions of Zephyr Lilies, *Zephyranthes candida*, whose white chalices were growing in such profusion as to make the plains gleam like silver. It is believed that the Rio de la Plata, the River of Silver, was so named by the Spanish explorers of 1513 on account of silvery plains of Zephyranthus.

Wherever a stop was made Commerson and his assistant seized the chance of botanizing, and Bougainville noted in his "Journal" that young Baret faithfully accompanied his master on all these expeditions, even amidst the snows of the frozen peaks of the Straits of Magellan. No matter how difficult the country they traversed Baret carried all the provisions, arms, and bulky portfolios of botanical specimens with a cheerful perseverance that earned for him, from the naturalist, the title of his "beast of burden."

Among the plants they discovered were *Ourisia antarctica*, an exquisite blue-eyed beauty that is rarely even heard of in gardens, the lovely *Viola Commersonii*, *Berberis empetrifolia*, a distinct low-growing species that is rarely seen and is famous only as one of the parents of the incomparable *B. stenophylla*. They also found *Myrtus nummularia*, an evergreen that spreads itself over the ground and produces an embroidery of white flowers followed in due season by pink berries. From the same place came *Philesia buxifolia*, a magnificent semi-procumbent shrub with stiff evergreen foliage and an array of charming delicate crimson bells throughout summer and autumn.

Soon after their arrival in Tahiti their botanizing was cut short by a painful incident. A young chief who had attached himself to the expedition was noticed to be taking a great interest in young Baret and to be murmuring something in his own tongue. One day when the botanist and his assistant were studying the wildflowers around the shore a hefty young savage seized Baret and made off at great speed. Fortunately an officer and some soldiers happened to be handy and the abductor was forced to relinquish his victim, whose dishevelled appearance revealed him as a young woman.

Needless to say the incident caused a great sensation, and the kindly old botanist had to put up with much playful good humour on the part of his companions, while the crews of both ships of the expedition became very solicitous for the welfare of Jeanne Baret, as she was now called. A confession had to be made to the commander, and it came to light that Commerson had given in to her pleadings and, out of the goodness of his heart, had taken her on as his assistant because of her consuming desire to go round the world. Bougainville was perfectly satisfied that there were no underhand motives, and recorded the opinion that "she knew from the outset the goal that was in prospect, and the idea of partaking in such a voyage had excited her curiosity. She would be the first woman to accomplish it and I must do her the justice to acknowledge that at all times while she was on board ship she was the model of propriety. It must be admitted however, that had the two vessels been shipwrecked in this vast ocean on some desert island Fate would have played some strange tricks on Baret."

The sensitive old botanist was greatly distressed by the disclosure, and when the Island of Mauritius was reached decided to postpone his return to France in the meantime. He undertook the study of the natural history of the French possessions in the Indian Ocean, and appears to have suffered considerably from ill-health until his death in 1773. Mlle. Baret remained with him and spared no effort in her attentions to him. After his death she married a soldier and later returned to France, but the subsequent history of this, the first white woman to go round the world, is unknown.

When we see the gay colours of the Bougainvilleas we are reminded of Louis Antoine de Bougainville and the kindly old botanist Philibert de Commerson who accompanied him in that long-past expedition across the vast Pacific. Unfortunately, so far as we know, there is no commemoration of Jeanne Baret, that brave young woman who had the courage and determination to be Commerson's "beast of burden" so that she might work her way round the world.

Citizen Labillardiere

THE searchers had been looking for their companion for nearly two days and were weary with thirst and fatigue when a joyful shout intimated that a spring of fresh water had been found. As the men crowded round awaiting their turn to drink, their leader, Citizen Labillardiere, noticed a pretty little shrub with orange-red pea-flowers. He collected specimens and long afterwards named them *Chorizema ilicifolia*, from the Greek words *choros* (a dance), and *zema* (a medicinal draught), because he and his companions had been ready to dance with joy at having found water. *Chorizema ilicifolia* with its prickly evergreen leaves and dainty flowers represents a group of Australian plants that are all very desirable for the cool greenhouse where they may be depended upon to provide masses of blossom during the short cold days before winter gives way to spring.

To understand how this party of Frenchmen came to be wandering along the shores of Australia on that broiling day in 1792 we have to know something of the story of French exploration in the Pacific. In 1785 Comte de la Perouse had sailed from France to continue the exploration begun by Bougainville twenty years earlier. For more than two years he had sailed all over the Pacific, but after that he and his two ships disappeared, and the details of their fate are still among the unsolved mysteries of the sea, though their wreckage was found. As year after year passed by and nothing was heard of the explorer, his name and possible fate were in the thoughts of all who were interested in science and exploration. When some South African bulbs produced their flat clusters of handsome blue flowers during the summer of 1790 in the garden of the lady who was to become the Empress of the French, they were named *Lapeyrousia corymbosa* in honour of the missing explorer.

France was already deep in the throes of the Revolution, but La Perouse had powerful friends at Court and in 1791 Louis XVI despatched a relief expedition under the command of a naval officer, Bruni D'Entrecasteaux. The commander and most of his officers were royalists while the scientists attached to the expedition seem to have been republicans, and were very indignant because D'Entrecasteaux ignored the Tricolour and used the Royal Fleur-de-lys exclusively as his flag. These political differences soon led to open enmity and Labillardiere, the botanist, lost no opportunity in airing his views and criticizing the actions of the royalists.

Co-operation and friendship between naturalists and their commanding officers seem to have been the exception rather than the rule. There were few friendships such as existed between Bougainville and Commerson, or Bligh and Nelson, but there were many cases of bickering and strife, although few commanders went so far as Vancouver, who had to put Menzies under arrest in order to extract an apology. Their methods of exploration and the very nature of their work were diametrically opposed. The botanist wanted to be put ashore and be allowed to

penetrate far inland in order to acquire a comprehensive survey
of the flora of the country, whereas the seaman was content to
sail slowly along off shore, noting the physical features of the
coast-line as they made their appearance.

The incident that led to the finding of the Chorizema is only
one of many instances in which naturalists wandered away.
In this case C. A. Riche, who was Labillardiere's chief assistant,
went ashore among some sand-dunes and, although the crew of
his boat waited until nightfall, he did not return. They reported
to the commander, who arranged to send a search-party with
Citizen Labillardiere in charge. Riche's tracks were found early
next morning, but it soon became obvious that he had lost his
bearings. He eventually found his way back to the landing place
after an absence of fifty hours, having lost all the plants he had
collected. During this time his only food had been the tasteless
white berries of the Pigeon Bush, that was later named *Leucopogon Richei* in memory of the incident. Riche had seen a number
of natives and had approached them in the hope of getting some
food, but they had been so scared of the strange apparition that
they disappeared.

The expedition went on its way, but the incident did nothing
to improve relations between the two political factions, and
Labillardiere's entry in his diary speaks for itself. They had
arrived at the Dutch settlement of Amboyna. "All of us had the
greatest need of remaining on shore in order to recover our
strength, and the Governor gave us leave to take lodgings in
the town as we intended to remain at Amboyna for at least a
month. . . . The other naturalists and I had agreed to live in
the same house. It was prepared for our reception and our baggage had been carried into it when to our great astonishment
we found it occupied by some officers of the two ships who
knew very well that we had hired the house, but the man who
had the key, when he gave it to them, thought he was forwarding

it to us. This malicious trick, of which we did not think them capable, amused them vastly, but it was easy to find other lodgings."

The expedition continued in its search for La Perouse and in the meantime shattering events were taking place at home: the King had been guillotined and France was again at war with Britain and Holland. Next time the ships sought to refit at a Dutch port they were interned, and the scientific members of the expedition had to find their way home as best they could. Labillardiere reached France in 1796, only to find that his collections were held as prizes by the British. He was able to get them back through the efforts of Sir Joseph Banks, who said that they had not been examined lest he might "deprive the man who, at the risk of his life, had gone forth to win them, of a single botanical idea."

Among those specimens were many species of Australian and Tasmanian plants that are now familiar in our gardens and greenhouses. They include the Blue Gum, *Eucalpytus Globulus*, the best-known member of the family both as forest tree and as a garden plant. Young specimens of the Blue Gum are of great value for sub-tropical bedding schemes by reason of their elegant habit and symmetrical growth combined with the beauty of their unusual glaucous-green foliage. While discussing the Tasmanian forests in which they grow, Labillardiere says, "We were filled with admiration at the sight of those ancient forests in which the sound of an axe had never been heard. The eye was astonished in contemplating the tremendous size of the trees, amongst which were some more than 150 feet in height."

He also found the handsome *Lobelia gibbosa*, which in its best forms reaches some eighteen inches in height with flowers of a delightful shade of blue rather larger than those of the well-known bedding forms; the quaint Flannel Flower, *Actinotus Helianthi*, a herbaceous perennial with its flower-heads surrounded by star-like clusters of woolly grey-green bracts which give it the appearance of being a giant Eidelweiss, although it is really a member of the carrot family. His assistant is commemorated in the shaggy *Craspedia Richei*, whose golden globes of blossom have earned for it the name of Australian Bachelor's Buttons, a nine-inch perennial that would be an ornament to any garden.

Labillardiere's name is written large among the wildflowers and ferns of Australia and New Zealand, but most attractive of all are the *Billardiera*, a genus named in his honour. All are climbers of a refined habit of growth, with pleasing flowers during the summer followed by crops of handsome berries in the autumn. Probably the best-known species is *B. longiflora*, whose dainty pendulous bells are usually cream or yellowish-green, although purple and even good blue forms may be obtained by raising young plants from seeds. The dark violet-blue fruits, more rarely pure white, are about an inch long and are the real glory of the plants as they remain in evidence for months on end.

The Covetous Burgomaster

SPRING comes with gladness and beauty, with the purple and gold of the early Crocuses, the tender green of fresh young leaves, and as the days grow longer and warmer the French Anemones quietly don their brocaded gowns and come out to take the air. At one time they were a gay company bearing the names of kings and princelings, but nowadays we prefer the nameless crowds and grow our anemones in poses of orient red and crimson, intermixed with orchis-purple, violet, and white. Great drifts of these gay colours are spread over the barren hills of Palestine and the Levant at the end of each rainy season when *Anemone coronaria* comes into bloom. This may account for the widespread belief that this is the plant referred to in the Bible, "Consider the lilies of the field, how they grow; they toil not, neither do they spin: And yet I say unto you, That even Solomon in all his glory was not arrayed like one of these."

The story of how the first of these flowers found its way to Italy seems to bear out the old tradition that this Anemone has not always been so plentiful in the Mediterranean region as it is to-day. Umberto, Bishop of Pisa, in the days of the Second Crusade, was a thrifty soul who pointed out that ships returning from taking soldiers to the Holy Land could be more usefully employed if they brought back, as ballast, good soil instead of barren gravel. He made arrangements that this soil be taken to the Campo Sancta at Pisa so that the honoured dead, including, no doubt, the worthy Bishop himself, could be buried in doubly consecrated ground.

It appears that our Anemone was a stowaway in one of those cargoes of soil, and when it made its appearance, like many another stowaway, it created something of a sensation. The superstitious clergy, astonished to find the strange blood-red flowers gracing their sacred Campo, proclaimed that it must be a miracle, and attributed its presence to the blood of martyrs shed in the defence of the Holy Land. We are told that along the Dalmatian coast and other parts of southern Europe this Anemone is known as "Blood Drops of Christ."

Because of its supernatural origin the French Anemone came to be one of the first plants to be grown in the old monastery gardens, although it does not appear to have been credited with any medicinal properties. It gradually spread over the greater part of Europe, as no wandering pilgrim could give his temporary hosts a more acceptable gift than a dry root of this lovely flower from the Land of the Holy Cross. Long before the Reformation new varieties had appeared, and by the end of the sixteenth century Gerard records that he grew twelve different kinds, adding "and yet I do heare of divers more differing very notably from any of these; every new yeare bringing with it newe and strange kinds; and every country his peculiar plants of this sort which are sent to us from far countries, in hope to receive from us such as our country yeeldeth."

These flowers are said to have become known as French Anemones because of a particularly fine strain, notable for its rich and brilliantly coloured blooms borne on long stalks, grown by a Maître Bachelieu, one of the most important florists of Paris, in the seventeenth century. It appears that Maître Bachelieu, like many another keen gardener who has been fortunate to come across something out of the ordinary, instead of gardening with "patience and generosity" as Canon Ellacomb advises us, liked to keep his good things to himself. We are told that "for ten long years he grew these plants without giving so much as a fibre of his double anemones, or one seed of his single ones to any person." During all that time the Burgomaster of Antwerp had cast a covetous eye on the handsome, long-stemmed flowers growing in Maître Bachelieu's garden. As the years went by his unsatisfied desire grew so strong that he came to the conclusion that as he need no longer hope to get them by fair means, it might be well worth while to try a little trickery.

Judging the time when the seeds should be ripe the Burgomaster invited himself to see Maître Bachelieu's garden. Unfortunately as he passed the anemone bed his fur-lined civic robe slipped off his arm, and before anything could be said, his servant, who had been instructed in his part, darted forward and picked it up together with such of the fluffy seeds as adhered to it. While the Burgomaster was tendering his apologies the servant took the robe to the carriage and awaited his master, who had to complete his tour of the garden.

We can imagine the glee with which the purloined seeds were picked off and sown, and the care with which they were tended. The Burgomaster was so pleased with the outcome of his strategy that he made no attempt to hide the method by which he had at last come into possession of the coveted Anemones. He is said to have been more generous than the original owner and the following summer distributed seeds and seedlings among all his friends, among whom they came to be known as the French Anemones.

The Garden of an Empress

AMONG the magnificent assemblage of trees growing in the old garden of Malmaison are many that were planted by the Empress Josephine when she chose that quiet house as a place where she could have peace and happiness, away from all the bustle and commotion of official life in Paris. Within a period of three years she laid the foundations of what became one of the richest botanic gardens in Europe, and the many scientists whom she patronized and encouraged spared no effort to collect all the rarest and most interesting plants that could be found. The Empress exerted considerable influence in the development of a taste for new and rare plants in France and became almost a patron saint of flowers. Her love of the strange and the new is enshrined in the names of two of the most unusual species that have ever been brought under cultivation.

Both are still comparatively unknown: Napoleon's Bell, *Lapageria rosea*, because of its peculiar cultural requirements, and the Josephine Lily, *Brunsvigia Josephinae*, because of its tardy methods of reproduction, as it takes about fifteen years to flower when raised from seed. The aristocratic Lapageria, which bears the maiden name of the Empress, is a native of the damp temperate forests of Chile, and is one of the *élite* of that distinguished family, the Lilies. A climber with long, wax-like flowers of pure geranium lake, or the purest white, followed by edible but somewhat insipid fruits. It is very capricious under cultivation, but when provided with the exacting conditions of shade, sunshine, and moisture that it demands, becomes the pride of any garden in which it can be persuaded to become a permanent guest.

The curious *Brunsvigia Josephinae*, with its spidery lily-flowers growing on stems three or four feet high, is one of those singular plants that can always be recognized by reason of their strong individuality. In its native haunts it becomes a sort of "tumble-weed" at the end of the growing season when the whole seed-head breaks off and rolls over the South African veldt, in the wind, like a great ball, scattering the seeds as it goes. The original bulb, that is to said to have been picked up by the Empress while on a shopping expedition in Paris, grew to be thirty inches in circumference, and was the first of its kind to flower in Europe.

From the very beginnings of the Malmaison garden the Empress was interested in Roses and, during the hey-day of the Napoleonic Empire, gave instructions that no specimen grown in Europe was to be left undisturbed, if it was not represented in her garden. In due course a great Rose show was held at Malmaison, and more than two hundred and fifty distinct varieties were represented. The show presented such an inspiration that many French nurserymen set to work raising new and improved varieties, and it is most unfortunate that none of the Scots or Ayrshire Roses, then so popular in Scotland, reached Malmaison. Had that happened they might have contributed something towards the development of our modern varieties instead of being all but lost to cultivation.

During the first half of the nineteenth century all the best Roses were of French origin, or at least bore French names, but it was not until long afterwards that it was realized that this was a legacy from the Empress and her garden. But when the debt became generally known, the French Rose growers brought pressure to bear, and the Rose Garden at Malmaison was reconstructed as far as possible on the original lines, and as many as possible of the Roses of those days were planted there.

Thomas Blaikie, a Scots gardener who had been in the employment of Marie Antoinette, had done much to set the fashion for English gardens during the last years of the old regime, and the Empress Josephine made up her mind to have one of her own at Malmaison. Napoleon is said to have been furious at the suggestion, and to have demanded, "Why an *English* garden?" only to be coldly informed that the grand parterres in the style designed by Le Notre were hopelessly out of date, and anyway, if Marie Antoinette could have Blaikie to lay out an English garden at Bagatelle, why should he not lay out another at Malmaison for the Empress Josephine. When Blaikie was consulted he pointed out that most of the best and rarest plants were grown in England, and he seems to have persuaded the Empress to seek the services of Lee and Kennedy of the Vineyard Nursery at Hammersmith. Lee had died in 1795, and so arrangements had to be made, war or no war, for young Lewis Kennedy to proceed to France for the purpose of developing the new garden being laid out for the Empress of the French. The British seem to have been so gratified by the implied compliment that all officers of the fleet were instructed by the Admiralty that, should any enemy prize captured on the high seas contain seeds or plants addressed to the Empress, their safe and speedy delivery had to be arranged. About that time there had been considerable development of new show and fancy Pelargoniums (Geraniums) in France, and we are told that Kennedy brought home a selection of the new French hybrids from Malmaison that did much to set a new fashion in greenhouse plants.

Seeds and plants collected in Australia and Tasmania by the naturalists attached to Commodore Nicholas Baudin's expedition were sent to the Empress to be grown at Malmaison, and the results are said to have inspired her to send out more collectors. Some were sent independently and others in conjunction with Messrs. Lee and Kennedy, but probably the only one who is ever heard of nowadays is Joseph Niven, a Scotsman, whose name is perpetuated in the pretty purple-flowered Nivenias of South Africa. He collected there for the Empress for about five years, and later for Lee and Kennedy. He learnt to speak the Kaffir language perfectly, and in consequence was forced by the British military authorities to act as guide and interpreter to the troops during the Kaffir War, a service for which he seems to have got neither thanks nor reward.

Among the plants raised from seeds collected by Baudin's expedition was a fine evergreen climbing plant with clusters of scarlet pea-flowers from Australia which was named *Kennedya coccinea* in honour of Lewis Kennedy, by special request of the Empress. When grown as a climber it has long been a great favourite for covering walls and pillars in the conservatory, on account of the attractive foliage and handsome clusters of scarlet pea-flowers.

The Empress was interested in the arts, and was the patron to whom Pierre-Joseph Redouté, the famous flower-painter, dedicated his *Les Liliacées*. About the same time Ventenat published his *Jardin de la Malmaison* with portraits of many of the new flowers that had not previously been grown in Europe. They included "eucalyptus, hibiscus, phlox, camellia, numerous varieties of South African heaths, myrtles, and geraniums, cacti and rhododendrons, certain kinds of Dahlias, not to mention rare tulips and full hyacinths."

Among the most notable features were vases of the highly ornamental *Bonapartea gracilis* from Mexico. A member of the Yucca tribe, this plant is remarkable for the graceful effect of its long rush-like foliage which is armed with yellow prickles and forms symmetrical mounds that are ideal for use in a formal setting. These and many other exotic species were protected during the winter by portable glasshouses. One of the Empress's great favourites was a fine old specimen of the evergreen *Magnolia grandiflora*, but to-day one of the most interesting of all the trees at Malmaison is the Marengo Cedar. This tree was planted by the Empress herself on the day she heard of Napoleon's victory over the Austrians at the Battle of Marengo. Nearly one hundred and fifty years have passed since that June morning. The Triumph of Marengo and all that it stood for have long since passed into history, but this giant Cedar is an abiding result of the Empress's pleasure in the success of her husband.

The fragrant little Mignonette is believed to have achieved much of its early popularity because Napoleon collected seeds during the war in Egypt and sent them home to be grown in the new garden at Malmaison. When Josephine grew it in pots and brought them into the drawing-rooms she set a fashion that spread all over Europe and continued long into the nineteenth century.

With the collapse of the Empire after Waterloo, the gardens at Malmaison were completely neglected for many years, but in course of time a more sane policy was adopted and, their historical value being realized, they were restored to something of their former glory by the French government.

The well-known Rose, "Souvenir de la Malmaison," raised by

Jean Beluze at Lyons in 1843, seems to have had no direct connection with the famous garden whose name it bears, but appears to have been named in its memory by Beluze who, no doubt, had some connection with Malmaison in its great days. There is a certain amount of uncertainty about the origin of the lovely "Souvenir de la Malmaison" Carnations, and so far as can be ascertained there seems to be no truth in the assertion that they originated in the Empress's garden. According to some authorities the name was first bestowed on a very distinctive seedling of the old tree Carnation, which was raised by M. J. Laine, of Naples, in 1857, because of its resemblance to the Rose that was beginning to take its place as a popular variety.

The reason why these popular flowers were originally dedicated to the memory of the lovely old garden designed for Josephine, Empress of France, seems to have been lost in the unrecorded past. There is a distinct possibility, however, that either one or both the raisers of these flowers may have been employed at Malmaison, or at least closely connected with it during the halcyon days when the garden was one of the leading botanical establishments in Europe. In those days it would attract keen young gardeners from all parts of Europe, and nothing is more natural than that some of them should wish to pay tribute to the good old days when the Malmaison they knew was one of the most wonderful gardens in existence.

A Mysterious Root

On account of its long flowering period the modern Dahlia
occupies an honoured place in the garden, and no other autumn-
flowering plant can compare with it in variety of form and
range of colour. Although now acclaimed as the Queen of the
Autumn Garden, the Dahlia has had more than one rise and
fall in public esteem since the days when it was a novelty fresh
from the warm sandy meadows of Mexico. The old-fashioned
show and fancy varieties, sometimes alluded to as Honeycombs,
did not reign very long as popular favourites, and their suc-
cessors the Cactus and Collarette types, although capable of
producing many beautiful blooms, failed in their appeal because
they were of very little use for the production of colour effects
in the mass.

The countless thousands of our modern varieties of Dahlias
are all derived from a handful of seeds that in 1789 were sent
by Vincente Cervantes, of the Botanic Garden of Mexico City,
to his friend and colleague the Abbé Cavanilles, who was at
that time in charge of the Royal Gardens at Madrid.

Some years later the Abbé named this Mexican wildflower in
honour of Dr. Andreas Dahl, one of the leading botanists of

the day, who had been a pupil of the great Linnaeus. Dr. Dahl was very proud of the plant that bears his name, although the flowers of the wild type have but slight resemblance to. the modern beauties that flaunt their gay colours all through late summer and autumn. In fact, no one would be more surprised than he to find it in the first flight of popular favourites, with floral societies in all parts of the world watching its welfare and development. He had visualized a very different future for his namesake, being of the opinion that the tuberous roots should become a highly satisfactory alternative for the potato as a food plant. He tried to popularize it, but his efforts were only partially successful; it found favour in France and some parts of the Mediterranean coast, but the peculiar flavour prevented its adoption as a popular food.

One of the first to appreciate the floral beauty of the Dahlia was the Empress Josephine, whose collection in the gardens at Malmaison was at one time the finest in existence. When the blooms were at the height of their beauty she invited Marie Louise and her entourage to a garden party. Although the Dahlias were greatly admired it was made perfectly clear to everyone that it was out of the question to make any attempt to acquire either root or even bloom from the Empress.

Josephine is reported to have planted the first of her Dahlia roots with her own hands, but as the collection grew it became necessary for her to have some assistance, and this was the undoing of Her Excellency as a Dahlia fancier. One of the Ladies-in-Waiting—according to one version it was the Countess de Bougainville—who had been denied a bloom, made up her mind that come what would she should have as good a show of the new flowers in her Paris garden. Her lover, a young Polish prince, was given the task of obtaining sufficient roots for the purpose. Knowing the futility of approaching Josephine he tackled the gardener, and Pierre, unworthy of his trust, basely sold one hundred Dahlia roots for a gold louis apiece. The lady, with malice aforethought, boasted of her new possessions, and in course of time some kind friend carried it to Malmaison. Josephine was exceedingly annoyed, flew into one of her tantrums, sacked the gardener, excommunicated both the prince and his lady, and turned her back on the Dahlia for ever.

Signs of flower variation appeared during the first summer it was grown in Spain, but it was not until about thirty years later that the double-flowered varieties became known to the florists of Europe. During the next forty years or so the popularity of the flower increased by leaps and bounds, so that about a century ago one New York dealer was able to list over three hundred named varieties, and some years earlier an English catalogue had boasted nearly four times that number. So completely have these earlier types gone out of fashion that it is doubtful if there is so much as one of all that multitude of varieties in cultivation to-day. No one seems to know just how it was that the Dahlia went under a cloud during the latter half of the century, but there can be no doubt that it was rescued from obscurity by the arrival of what became known as the Cactus Dahlia in 1872.

The origin of this peculiar plant is one of the mysteries of the gardening world. Beyond the fact that it came from Mexico, nothing seems to be known about it, and so far as can be ascertained, it has not been found growing wild anywhere. The fact has been established that when J. T. van der Berg, a Dutch nurseryman, received a consignment of plants from Mexico he found this one live Dahlia root among the mass of dead material and semi-decayed bulbs which was all that remained in the case. A number of cuttings were taken and, when they flowered the following summer, were found to be quite different from any Dahlia blooms that had ever been seen before. The plant was assumed to be a new species, and was named *Dahlia Jaureʒii* in honour of the President of Mexico. It soon became better known under the common name of Cactus Dahlia on account of the brilliant scarlet flowers, being very much the same shade of colour as those of *Cereus speciosissima*, a Cactus that was universally grown and was one of the popular favourites of the time. The numerous forms and varieties of Cactus Dahlias grown everywhere are all descended in some way from this one mysterious root. It is a curious fact that the type as we grow it to-day has the florets distinctly tubular in shape, and in this connection *Addisonia* points out that the floral rays of the original Cactus Dahlia were but slightly tubular or fluted, and by a curious ignoring of historical precedent *Dahlia Jaurezii* would now qualify as a hybrid Cactus rather than a true Cactus Dahlia.

About the turn of the century the Dahlia again began to lose favour, but the advent of the new race of dwarf bedding varieties proved so useful that they inaugurated a new era of prosperity for the clan. Ever since then Dahlias have soared to ever greater heights of popular favour until they have deposed the Chrysanthemum from the proud position of the Queen of the Autumn Garden.

Two Trees from China

THE Willow seems to have been considered the Emblem of
Spring long before it was adopted as the "Palm" used in pro-
cessions on Palm Sunday in some of the colder parts of northern
Europe where the early Christian people were unable to find the
true palm leaf. The Weeping Willow, now so familiar in our
parks and gardens, reached Europe during the early part of
the eighteenth century, and Linnaeus gave it the name *Salix
babylonica*, under the impression that he was dealing with the
tree referred to in Psalm 137—"By the waters of Babylon, there
we sat down, yea, we wept, when we remembered Zion. We
hanged our harps upon the willows in the midst thereof."

A native of Eastern Asia, it is very doubtful if this species
had reached the Levant in the days of Babylon, although there
is evidence that it was well known in that region long before
the dawn of Christianity, having found its way across Asia by
means of the age-old caravan route from China. Peter Collinson,
the Quaker botanist, recorded its arrival in England, "Mr.
Vernon, Turkey Merchant at Aleppo, transplanted the Weeping
Willow from the River Euphrates and brought it with him to
England. It was planted at his seat at Twickenham Park where

I saw it growing in 1748. This is the original of all the willows in England." A few years later the poet Alexander Pope begged a green withe from Lady Suffolk while she was untying a package of figs sent by an admirer in Smyrna. With the remark, "Perhaps this will produce something we have not in England," he took it home and planted it in his garden in Twickenham. The tree grew there until about 1801, and according to one version of the story was destroyed because a subsequent owner resented being disturbed by visitors who wished to see Pope's Willow. The *Dictionary of National Biography* discredits this tale, however, and states that after the poet's death the property was acquired by Sir W. Stanhope and when the tree was blown down in a storm in 1801 he had it made into relics.

Although there may be some doubt about the history of Pope's tree, it played a great part in the distribution of the Weeping Willow as an ornamental tree throughout the world. A young British officer is believed to have taken a twig of it to America, where it was planted at Abingdon, in Virginia, and grew to become the ancestor of most of the Weeping Willows in the United States. Another authority records that a General Bateson took another twig to St. Helena during the last years of the eighteenth century.

During his six weary years of exile on the island Napoleon came to love this tree, and spent many hours in its shade, where a seat was placed by his special request. Overthrown by a violent storm about the time of his death, the tree was destroyed, but Madame Bertrand planted a few twigs of it around his grave. One of them lived, and many years later, when sailing vessels carrying the pioneer settlers to Australia and New Zealand broke their voyage there, it was gradually spread to those countries and to Europe. It became the custom to place a few twigs from Napoleon's tree in bottles of water so that they were rooted and ready for planting out at the end of the voyage.

In this respect it is of interest to note that Napoleon's Willow was considered one of the treasures of Kew a century ago. At that time the Royal Gardens could be visited only by approved visitors who were armed with a permit, but even so entrance was not at all easy, and was not encouraged. According to Dr. Lindley, "You rang a bell by the side of a small wooden gate which was of itself emblematic of the secrecy, the unnatural privacy, of the working principle within. You were let in by stealth as if the gatekeepers were ashamed to see you come . . . and when you were there you were dogged all the time by an official as if you were likely to walk off with the St. Helena Willow in your button-hole."

The gnarled old Willow has always been a great favourite in its native land, China, and is generally believed to be the tree represented in the "willow pattern" china of old Canton, but some students of the Orient believe that it may be *Ginkgo biloba*, the Maidenhair Tree. The Ginkgo is an ancient tree dating back almost to the Coal Age, and has been termed "a living fossil" because it has no near relatives other than those found in fossilized form. This proves that this tree had its heyday in the days when the giant reptiles roamed the earth, many millions of years ago. It has never been seen growing wild in any part of the world, although it is grown as a planted tree all over China and Japan, being especially associated with palaces, temples, and historical sites. It is the world's oldest nut tree, having been grown for its seeds, known in China as White or Silver Nuts, from time immemorial. As may be expected in the changeless East the seeds may still be bought as nuts in almost any bazaar in China.

The oldest specimen in Europe grows in the Utrecht Botanic Garden, having been planted there about the time the Weeping Willow arrived in England. Another specimen had been growing for more than thirty years in Britain before the species was introduced into France by Monsieur R. Petigny in 1780. A very keen amateur gardener, M. Petigny paid a visit to England, where the famous nurseries of Lee and Kennedy of Hammersmith, Conrad Loddiges of Hackney, and James Gordon of Mile End had the most comprehensive collections of new and rare plants available anywhere. In those days, for example, Messrs. Lee and Kennedy listed no fewer than 228 different South African Heaths.

The story goes that when the Frenchman visited James Gordon, who is credited with introducing the Ginkgo into England, the nurseryman was the proud possessor of five young Maidenhair Trees that were growing together in one pot, having just been raised from seeds imported from Japan. M. Petigny made strenuous efforts to buy at least one of them, but all his attempts were unavailing, until he tried the effects of abundant hospitality at a nearby tavern. This line of attack was successful, and it was a very jubilant Frenchman who paid his six hundred francs for the potful of seedlings and bore them in triumph to his lodgings. Next morning the nurseryman was on the doorstep with the milk, bitterly regretting his bargain and trying to buy back some of the young trees. The wily Frenchman declined to part with any of his ill-gotten gains, although Gordon finally offered the six hundred francs for a single specimen. When Petigny returned to Paris with his trophies, he took great joy from amusing the gardening fraternity with his tale of how he had befooled the stupid John Bull.

Romance of the Trees

BELOVED alike for its handsome leaves, attractive fruits, and historical associations, the Mulberry is one of the most pleasing of ornamental trees and, being known from the very earliest records of antiquity, may be one of the first trees to be cultivated by man. Its home was long believed to be somewhere in the Orient, but nothing definite was known until about eighty years ago a French missionary cleared up the mystery by finding wild silk-worms living on wild Mulberry trees in the mountainous region where northern China merges into Mongolia.

The story of the Mulberry is inextricably intertwined with that of silk, and although the Chinese have many legends that account for the origin of silk, many thousands of years ago, no authentic records have come down to us. No one knows when the Mulberry tree first reached the Western World, but old traditions tell that it was brought from Persia by two travellers who had to smuggle the young plants out of the country. Slowly the knowledge of silk and its manufacture percolated through Venice, Genoa, and Milan, and northwards to England, where the idea of growing his own silk was one of the dreams of King James I. One of the fashionable haunts of eighteenth-century London was the "Old Mulberry Garden," somewhere near the site of Buckingham Palace, which got its name from "a garden of Mulberrie trees planted by King James I in 1609 in which yeare £935 was expended by the said King in planting Mulberrie trees neare the Palace of Westminster." The fashion was probably instigated by the Huguenot refugees from the Low Countries, many of whom were silk merchants and weavers. In an effort to found the industry a Belgian contractor was authorized to plant one hundred thousand trees in the south of England and the King himself wrote a treatise on their care and cultivation. This is one of the first official bulletins on plants. Unfortunately the climate was too cold for the silkworms, and then it was found that the trees were all Black Mulberries, *Morus nigra*, whose leaves are not so palatable to the parasites as those of the White Mulberry, *M. alba*.

The Black Mulberry is a long-lived tree, and many of King James's trees are still alive in England. One of the most famous of Mulberry trees was one planted by Shakespeare in his garden at Stratford-on-Avon in 1609. Alas! this tree is no more, and one writer expresses the indignation that all must feel who read of its destruction. "That Shakespeare planted this tree is as well authenticated as anything in nature can be . . . and till this was planted there was no mulberry tree in the neighbourhood. The tree was celebrated in many a poem, especially one by Dibdin, but about 1752, the owner of New Place, the Rev. Mr. Gastrell, bought and pulled down the house, and wishing, it would seem to be damned to everlasting fame, he had some time before cut down Shakespeare's celebrated Mulberry tree, to save himself the trouble of showing it to those whose admiration of our great poet led them to visit the poetick ground on which it stood." Some pieces were rescued by a neighbour from the fire and were made into snuff-boxes and other relics, and inscribed with the punning motto, "Memento Mori."

Another tree that has carved a niche for itself in our history is the Common Hawthorn or May. In Scotland there is a well-beloved variety that is known as the Queen's Tree, *Crataegus monogyna Reginae*, which, although not very different from the common sort, is descended from a fine old specimen that used to grow in the gardens of Holyrood House. Away back in the middle of the sixteenth century, Mary, Queen of Scots, and her four Maries, are said to have sewn their tapestry under its shade, in the few happy years before all was lost. Centuries before Queen Mary's time the best-known tree in Britain was the Holy Thorn in the grounds of Glastonbury Abbey, a remarkable form of the Common May that, instead of bearing its crop and blossom in early summer, begins to flower and produce young foliage in midwinter.

The old legend of its origin is that, after the Crucifixion, Joseph of Arimathea and the Apostle Philip wandered over Europe until they reached England, arriving there in the dead of winter. At Glastonbury their exhortations had so little effect on the people that Joseph prayed to God to give some sign which could be taken as definite proof of his divine mission. When he turned to pick up his staff he found that it had burst into leaf and flower, and the wonder was repeated every winter on the anniversary of that day.

The Holy Thorn of Glastonbury Abbey was reverenced in monkish times, and the sale of twigs, flowers, and berries was a fruitful source of revenue. The ancient tree had two trunks, but one was destroyed by a gale in Shakespeare's time and the other was felled by the Puritans during Cromwell's regime. Some years later a sucker appeared, and it lived until the beginning of last century. Plenty of seeds had been saved before the tree died, and it is still to be met with in gardens, and is well worth growing not only for the fragrant white flowers that appear during the shortest days of the year, but also because it takes us back through the turbulent centuries to the days when pilgrims travelled from far and near to see the Holy Thorn of Glastonbury.

One of the most beautiful of our flowering trees is the double-flowered variety known as "Paul's Scarlet," which originated in the garden of Christopher Boyd at Waltham Cross near London in 1860. One May morning Mr. Boyd noticed that one of his pink-flowered Hawthorns was bearing one branch of large scarlet flowers. He mentioned the fact to his neighbour, Mr. William Paul, who secured a few buds and showed some flowering specimens at the International Horticultural Exhibition held in London in 1866, where it was greatly admired and was awarded a First Class Certificate of Merit. This was the first of many awards and the new tree created a great deal of interest wherever it was shown.

One enthusiast who visited Mr. Boyd's garden to see the original branch has left a description of the parent tree. He says it was about twenty-five feet high and the same in the circumference of its canopy. The coloured branch was a strong one growing from the centre of the tree, with both leaves and flowers quite distinct from the parent. In fact "so great was the contrast between the sport and the original that we could not rid ourselves of the impression that the parent variety was much paler than usual, and we asked ourselves whether the colouring matter had been drawn from the larger surface and intensified in that particular branch by some secret process of Nature."

The variety became known the world over as "Paul's Scarlet," and there seems to have been a good deal of undignified bickering between the two nursery firms, Messrs. George Paul & Sons and William Paul, as to whose tree it was. Every effort was made by the nurserymen to convince the public that there were two varieties, and that one or other of them was the better. The matter was finally settled by an impartial committee of the Royal Horticultural Society, which found by comparison that all were identical and had originated from Mr. Boyd's tree.

Cedar of Lebanon

WE know that when Babylon and other great cities flourished in that ancient land through which the Tigris and the Euphrates flow much of the surrounding country was covered by forests, and although no records exist there is little doubt that one of the dominant trees of those forests was the Cedar of Lebanon. Centuries of heedless exploitation have long since reduced those verdant forests to barren hillsides, and the cities that were dependant upon them to dust, but fortunately a few groves of trees exist in some of the more inaccessible places.

The glory of those old forests is reflected in the Bible, Ezekiel symbolizing the Assyrian as a great Cedar "in Lebanon with fair branches, and with a shadowing shroud, and of a high stature. The waters nourished him, the deep made him to grow, therefore his stature was exalted above all the trees of the field: the fir trees were not like his boughs, and the plane trees were not as his branches; nor was any tree in the garden of God like unto him in his beauty, so that all the trees of Eden, that were in the garden of God, envied him." Unfortunately the fall of the Cedar was also well known, and Isaiah likened the fall of the Assyrian to that of the great tree, knowing that it signified total extinction, because once the tree was cut down the complicated system of roots that had fed it for a thousand years was incapable of sending up so much as a single living shoot.

Some of the trees rejected by Solomon's axemen while selecting timber for the Temple of Jerusalem are still growing on the slopes of Mount Lebanon, and it is from there that the tree has come to our gardens. A recent visitor tells of seeing them. He had reached the summit of Mount Lebanon, 10,200 feet above sea level, and looked down on a valley where they grew. "Far below us a river ran straight to the Mediterranean, which we could see in the blue distance. At one time all this country-side must have been covered with Cedar forests, but all are gone save a few remnants, but from where we stood we could see a small grove straight below us at a height of little more than 6,000 feet. A beautiful Maronite Chapel stood beside the grove with a wall enclosing the lot. The Maronites, a Christian sect with some curious beliefs, consider the trees more or less sacred and visit them each year and hold some sort of festival."

One of the first Europeans to visit Mount Lebanon was Pierre Belon, a Frenchman who went to see the trees in 1550 while gathering material for his *De Arboris Coniferis*, believed to be the first book ever written on the Coniferae. Then, as now, the trees belonged to the Patriarch of the Maronites, and he states that, after celebrating High Mass at a special altar erected under one of the trees, the Patriarch issued a solemn warning to any who presumed to harm the trees in any way.

Shakespeare mentioned the proud Cedar that "stoops not to the base shrubs' foot, but low shrubs wither at the Cedar's root," but he was evidently thinking of the tree as the classical type of majesty and grandeur, as it is almost certain that he never saw a living specimen of the Cedar of Lebanon. It was not until 1641 that Edward Pococke, who spent some years as a chaplain at Aleppo, introduced the first one into England.

Tree lovers from all over the world have climbed Mount Lebanon to see these magnificent old trees, but there is a good story of the trouble taken by Bernard de Jussieu to bring home a young specimen. Jussieu held the position of Director of the famous Jardin des Plantes in Paris for many years, and in 1734 visited North Africa and the Levant in search of new flowers and plants for the gardens. As the story goes he was so enthralled by the majesty of the giant Cedar trees on Mount Lebanon that he made up his mind that at all costs he would carry back a specimen to the Jardin des Plantes.

Carefully he selected a robust little seedling and forthwith planted it in his hat. While crossing the desert his caravan is reported to have been overtaken by a sandstorm. The heat was so terrific that Jussieu was compelled to abandon all his plants with the exception of the young Cedar. This he wrapped in blankets so that the scorching winds would not shrivel it up.

While crossing the Mediterranean his ship was held up by contrary winds for so many days that the water supply almost ran out and water had to be rationed at the rate of half a glassful per person. Having shared this scanty supply with the young tree Jussieu thought that all his troubles were over when at last the shores of France were reached. He was soon disillusioned, however. The customs officials were not long in coming to the conclusion that he must be attempting to smuggle some article of great value into the country, hidden in that hatful of soil. Nothing the Director of the Jardin des Plantes could say would convince them of the truth of his story. The statement that this small green object had been brought all the way from Mount Lebanon in the hat was a highly remarkable tale! But were there not plenty of trees in France, and what difference could such a tiny seedling make. Jussieu was driven to distraction as he saw their clumsy fingers fumbling among the tender roots of his precious little tree. At long last the inquisition was over and he was able to hasten off to Paris. There he planted the young tree which has stood for over two centuries of French history and has slowly grown into one of the finest specimens of its kind in Europe and one of the historical trees of France.

It is a good story and "founded on fact"—but the fact is that de Jussieu grew the famous tree in the Jardin des Plantes from seed he got in England in 1735.

Sir Joseph Banks

In the long history of our gardens few men have been able to exert such a wide and beneficent influence in their development as was wielded by Sir Joseph Banks throughout the long reign

of George III. For more than fifty years he was Honorary
Director of His Majesty's Garden at Kew, and not only did he
send collectors to all parts of the world in search of new plants,
but arranged a special course of training so that young men
from Kew could be relied upon to take charge of plants on
board ship during the long voyage home from the Orient or the
Antipodes.

His interest in plant life began while still a schoolboy. He did
not like lessons but preferred the open air, and on one occasion,
while swimming with his school-fellows in the Thames, he
enjoyed himself so much that by the time the others were ready
to return to school he had barely begun dressing. As he made
his way back along the banks of the river he was so struck by
the beauty of the English wildflowers that he felt he ought to
know something about them. Soon afterwards he met some
women collecting herbs for the druggists, and was so interested
in what they told him that he made arrangements to pay sixpence
a time for all the information they could give. This was supplemented by an old torn copy of Gerard's *Herball* that he found
in his mother's dressing-room, and the following summer he
surprised his teachers by his knowledge of the local wildflowers
and their virtues.

He inherited an income of £6,000 a year when his father died
in 1761, and soon afterwards went to live at Chelsea, where he
was able to make such good use of the Physic Garden and
Philip Miller's great knowledge of plants that he was enabled to
lay the foundations of Kew as a botanical institution of international importance. It was about this time that he had the
misfortune to be arrested as a highwayman. A coach had been
robbed on the lonely Hounslow Heath, and when the servants
gave chase they came upon a young man with his head in a
hedge. It was no use protesting that he was merely looking for
wildflowers; he was taken to Bow Street, and it was only by

convincing the Magistrate that he was Mr. Banks, a respectable citizen of Chelsea, that he was allowed to go free.

About five years later he visited Newfoundland and spent a very interesting summer exploring and collecting its flora. Unfortunately, most of his collections, including notes and living plants, were lost when the ship ran into a violent storm on the homeward voyage and barely escaped shipwreck. Nevertheless, Mr. Banks was able to hand over to Mr. Aiton, of Kew, a few small plants and much information about the swamps of north-eastern America. Among the plants he brought back were the Rhodora and *Kalmia glauca*. The former is one of the brightest and most pleasing shrubs from that part of the world, heralding the spring with festoons of rosy-purple blossoms which adorn its quaintly tapered twigs. The Kalmia is another of those swamp plants belonging to the Erica family, and is notable for its beautiful evergreen leaves, glaucous beneath, that in due season are eclipsed by a halo of lovely rose-pink flowers.

Accompanied by Dr. Solander he was attached to Captain Cook's great voyage of exploration through the Pacific and in his *Journal* tells of a most unpleasant experience while plant-hunting among the hills of Tierra del Fuego. One January day in 1770 a small party set out to reach the uplands and find out something of the plants that grew there, above the forests. Suddenly they were overwhelmed by a blinding snowstorm, and in their hurried scramble for the shelter of the woods, lost all knowledge of their whereabouts. Two men died of exposure and several others, including Dr. Solander, had a very narrow escape as they spent a cold and cheerless night around a fire in the midst of the trackless forest. They had no food beyond a vulture which was divided into ten equal parts, each man cooking his own portion as he thought best. The weather eventually cleared up and they were able to make their way back to the beach and reached the ship in the last stages of exhaustion. Over a hundred new plants were collected, and among those which attracted some attention were "Cranberries both white and red," that are now held in high esteem on account of their neat evergreen foliage, dainty lily-of-the-valley flowers, and attractive fruits which range from pure white through pink and cerise to the deepest purple and black. Now known as *Pernettya mucronata*, Banks's Cranberries have the distinction of being the only shrubs whose fruits have been developed for their beauty rather than their economic value. Most interesting of all, however, was *Drimys Winteri*, the famous Winter's Bark tree with its long pale leaves and fragrant trusses of ivory coloured blossom. The aromatic bark was well known in England, having been used as a spice "no less pleasant than wholesome," besides having had a great reputation among the medical fraternity ever since it had been brought home by Captain W. Winter ten years before the defeat of the Spanish Armada.

After many adventures they reached New Zealand and the east coast of Australia, where they were so delighted by the multitudes of new and strange forms of plant life that they named their principal stopping place Botany Bay. Soon after his return Mr. Banks became Honorary Director of Kew, and later became President of the Royal Society. Through his efforts Kew was the first botanical institution to attempt anything in the nature of a systematic exploration of the flora of the earth. For about half a century Sir Joseph Banks sent plant collectors to all parts of the world and inaugurated an era of plant introduction such as had never been known before. Young men trained at Kew searched every part of the newly discovered lands in the Pacific, besides South Africa and eastern Asia, for new plants for the Royal Gardens, and although they have long since passed to their rest their names are enshrined for evermore among the wildflowers of the lands they explored.

Massonia latifolia, a curious plant from the deserts of South

Africa, bears the name of Francis Masson, the first collector to be sent out from Kew; *Burtonia scabra*, a heath-like shrub, with pea-blossoms of pink and deep red, and narrow downy leaves, commemorates David Burton, who was killed in Australia. It was introduced to Kew by Peter Good, another Kew collector, whose memory is kept green in the golden-flowered *Goodia loti-folia*. The well-known *Kerria japonica* reminds us of William Kerr, who sent home a number of Oriental plants, including Lady Banks's Rose, whose dainty blossoms are among the joys of early summer.

These are some of the better known of the collectors sent out by Sir Joseph Banks, but there are many more, men whose names are all but forgotten and whose history is unrecorded, beyond a scanty reference in some long-forgotten periodical stating that such-and-such a plant was introduced by him. Any survey of the eighteenth-century collectors shows that there is a remark-ably large proportion of Scots names among them, and indeed that may be termed the Golden Age for Scots gardeners working in England. Early in the century Philip Miller had been appointed Curator of the Physic Garden at Chelsea, and he made a rule that only Scotsmen were to be employed there. Some twenty years later Aiton, one of Miller's young men, took over the control of Kew and followed much the same course. When Sir Joseph Banks came upon the scene he endorsed this policy, saying, "So well does the mind of a Scotch education fit Scotsmen to the habits of industry, frugality and attention that they rarely abandon them at any time of life, and I may say, never while young."

Always on friendly terms with the Royal Family, he was knighted in 1781, not because he took any interest in either politics or in politicians, but in recognition of his interest in Natural History and his many valuable contributions to the sciences. His private garden at Spring Grove was one of the show places of London, and he was proud to show his new and rare plants to visitors. One of his biographers tells an amusing story of this period. Sir Joseph was showing two American ladies over the gardens, and in due course they came to the fish pond. Goldfish were great rarities in those days, and the host enquired if his visitors knew what sort of fish these were. We may imagine his amusement when the younger lady exclaimed, "Oh, red herrings! I have often heard of them but this is the first time I have ever seen red herrings."

Early in the new century Sir Joseph began to suffer from ill-health, and from about 1805 had to be wheeled about in a chair. After his death in 1820 Kew fell from its high estate, Government grants were gradually withdrawn, and the task of sending out plant-hunters was taken up by the Royal Horticultural Society.

Hosts of new plants found their way to Kew while Sir Joseph Banks was the presiding genius there, but so far as we can find out he was only directly responsible for the introduction of the two species that are already mentioned as coming from New-foundland. Quite a number of plants from the Antipodes have been dedicated to Sir Joseph Banks, but it fell to the younger Linnaeus to dedicate a genus of Proteaceous plants from Australia. More than fifty species of Banksia are now known, and all are odd-looking specimens, very different from the ordinary run of plants. In the land of their origin they are known as Honeysuckles, on account of the vast quantities of nectar produced in the quaint flowers; some species are so well provided as to burst open the florets before they are ready. The abundance of this supply was so well known to the Australian aborigines that they used to collect the inflorescences and either suck the nectar or soak the flowers in water to produce a sweetish liquid that was drunk either before or after fermentation. *Banksia integrifolia* and *B. ericifolia* were the first species to arrive at

Kew, having been sent home in 1788, and they are probably the best-known species in cultivation, although by no means the most attractive. *B. integrifolia,* with dark green leaves, silvery on the undersurface, produces its sulphur-yellow cones of blossom throughout the year, but *B. ericifolia* is the more ornamental, being an ornamental bush with slender cone-like spikes of yellowish-red flowers garnished with strands of yellow silk.

Pioneer Plant-Hunter

THE Queen of the Gentians is *Erythraea Massonii*, a neat little plant whose clumps of small shiny leaves are hidden in summer-time by a profusion of bright pink stars that flutter on stems a few inches high. This lovely species from the Azores bears the name of Francis Masson, who brought the first of its kind to Kew in 1777. He was the first of the plant-hunters sent out by Kew, and the amount of material he collected, over four hundred species that were new to the scientists of Europe, gave Kew that early pre-eminence in botanical affairs which has made it one of the great institutions of Europe.

All through the early months of 1772, while preparations were
being made to despatch Captain Cook on his second voyage of
discovery in the South Seas, Francis Masson was quietly attend-
ing to his work at Kew. Then came the day when he was
informed that he had been selected by Sir Joseph Banks as the
most suitable person to go plant-hunting in South Africa, and
that he would be expected to sail with Captain Cook on April
9th. Considering the value of money in those days, when a
leader such as Captain Cook was in receipt of a salary of less
than £200 a year, we may be sure that this quiet industrious
Scotsman of thirty-one was quite satisfied with his £100 a year
and the right to run up expenses to double that amount.

Besides exploring Table Mountain and the country around
Cape Town, Masson made several journeys into the hinterland,
his ample funds enabling him to hire an ox-wagon and the
services of a Dutch guide as interpreter. He was fortunate in
meeting Carl Thunberg, a pupil of the great Linnaeus, and the
two plant-hunters had a most profitable, if somewhat uncom-
fortable, journey in Masson's ox-wagon until they were turned
back at the Sunday River by a tribe of hostile natives. During
the three years he spent in South Africa Francis Masson sent
home many plants that have since become great favourites.
Among them were the first of the South African Heaths to reach
England, *Erica concinna*, with pink flowers, and the white-
flowered *E. marifolia*, that did so much to develop a taste for
Cape and New Holland plants during the next century or so.
He was impressed by the scarlet-flowered tree, *Erythrina caffra*,
and sent home seeds along with bulbs of the handsome red
Buphana disticha, several species of Proteas, *Stapelia grandiflora*,
Aloe dichotoma, and the Green Ixia, *I. viridiflora*, which was
one of his greatest triumphs and created a sensation when its soft
pea-green flowers were seen for the first time at Kew.

Table Mountain was a wild place in those days, and on one

occasion he narrowly missed being waylaid by a gang of escaped slaves. He lost his bearings in the excitement of the chase and was resigning himself to the discomfort of a night in the open, with many wild beasts prowling around, when he found a shepherd's hut. Being unable to lock it he barricaded the door, and went to sleep with a clasp-knife under the knapsack he was using as a pillow. In one of his journeys he found *Aloe succotrina* forming thickets five or six feet high, and noted that the settlers were preparing a sort of gum-aloes from the leaves and selling the substance in Cape Town for five shillings a pound. He sent home many new plants, including fifty species of Cape Pelargoniums that gave rise to the Garden Geraniums that were so popular as bedding plants in the domains of the rich and as pot plants in the homes of the poor, throughout the greater part of the nineteenth century. His work in South Africa is commemorated in the lovely *Erica Massonii* whose viscid scarlet flowers are tipped with green and yellow.

Within two years of his return to Kew he was off again, this time to explore the wildflowers of Portugal, the Canary Islands, Madeira, and the West Indies. From that expedition he sent home some of the curious Echiums and the Canary Island Broom, *Cytisus canariensis*, whose golden plumes of fragrant blossom are so popular that in early spring pot plants in blossom can be bought from a coster's barrow in almost any town in Britain. His greatest gift to the modern garden is probably the gay Cinerarias that are so valuable in greenhouse and conservatory during winter and early spring. The many lovely colours that we grow to-day are all developed from wild species of Senecio that Francis Masson found growing in South Africa and the Canary Islands.

When Masson reached the West Indies international affairs forced him to forget all about flowers and gardens in order to do battle for his freedom. War had broken out with France again, and Masson was actually taken prisoner, while fighting in the trenches, at the fall of New Grenada. In 1785 he was back in South Africa, and there he remained for about nine years, but the growing hostility between Dutch and British settlers prevented his going beyond a forty-mile radius of Cape Town. On the advice of Sir Joseph Banks he established a garden where his new plants were acclimatized, and stocks of the rarer and more desirable species were raised under the most favourable conditions before being exported to the homeland.

Some time during 1797 he went to North America, but the constant wars against the French were still in progress and the journey across the Atlantic took more than four months. Such conditions prevented satisfactory communication with Sir Joseph Banks, and so far as can be ascertained there is no record of whether or not Francis Masson undertook any plant-collecting in Canada. If he did and sent seeds or specimens to Kew they seem to have failed to reach their destination. Nothing seems to have come down to us of his work in later years, and even the exact date of his death is in some doubt, although it evidently took place during the winter of 1805–6.

Golden Flower from China

LONG centuries before the Romans began to tend Roses and Carnations in their quiet villa gardens by the blue Mediterranean, the wise old gardeners of far Cathay had cultivated some of their common wayside weeds and developed them into the flowers we know as Chrysanthemums. From time immemorial Chrysanthemums have been regarded as sacred flowers in the East, having been used not only as decorations for the temple, but also as popular ornaments painted on porcelain, hammered in metal, woven in rugs and embroidered in brocades in much the same way as the Rose is used in the West.

About the time the Roman legions were being recalled from Britain there lived in China a poet, T'ao Ming-Yang, who is credited with having done more than any other man in the Far East to improve the colour and form of the Chrysanthemum. He raised so many new and improved varieties that after his death his fellow-citizens commemorated his work by renaming their town "Chuh-sien," the City of Chrysanthemums.

The Chrysanthemum has often been called the national flower of Japan, an honour that actually belongs to the Cherry blossom. The misunderstanding has arisen from the fact that a sixteen-petalled Chrysanthemum flower is the emblem of the Mikado, but the flower is not a native of Japan. At some time away back in the dim mists of antiquity some of the improved forms of this Chinese wildflower were taken to Japan and were so well received that the Emperor adopted the bloom in a conventionalized form as his symbol, and it is used in all state documents, much as the Royal Arms are used in the British Commonwealth.

Before their contact with western civilization the social life of the countries of the Far East accepted Chrysanthemum growing as a pastime to be indulged in by all sections of the community, and almost every household had some part of the garden reserved for this favourite flower. A young Manchu Lady-in-Waiting to the old Empress Hsu of China has recorded how the Empress personally selected the plants used to decorate the various rooms of the palace, and allowed the ladies of the Court to arrange them, encouraging a friendly rivalry by giving some trinket for that which was thought to be the best. She goes on to say, "Early in the eighth month the Empress personally attended to the transplanting of the Chrysanthemums, which were her decided favourites. Every morning we, that is the whole train of ladies and Court eunuchs, accompanied her to the western shore of the lake. Under her direction we cut twigs from the young plants and put them in pots. At first I was greatly astonished at this method, but Her Majesty assured me that these little shoots would soon grow into splendid plants. Every day we went to water the young plants until they began to sprout.

"Occasionally during a heavy rainfall Her Majesty would order the eunuchs to cover the Chrysanthemums carefully with thin straw mats to protect the delicate shoots from the impact of the shower. It was characteristic of the Empress that, no matter how many pressing matters of State awaited her attention, her first thought nevertheless was for her flowers, particularly her Chrysanthemums. At times she sacrificed her accustomed noon rest to care for her flowers."

Nothing very definite seems to be known as to how or when the first of these flowers arrived in Europe, but in all probability they were among the treasures brought home by keen Dutch traders who for so long had a monopoly of Oriental trade. Known to have been grown in the Chelsea Physic Garden in 1754, Chrysanthemums were evidently lost by some unfortunate accident and were not seen again in the British Isles until they flowered in Colville's nursery in the King's Road, Chelsea, in 1796. This was the variety known as the "Old Purple," which had been brought to France by Captain Blanchard of Marseilles some five years earlier. The potentialities of the Chrysanthemum as an autumn flower were quickly realized, and the wealthy East India Company asked John Reeves, their resident tea-buyer in Canton, to send home a selection of these oriental Daisies. Many new forms arrived in England during the next few years, and within a generation about sixty varieties were being grown by the Royal Horticultural Society in its Chiswick garden, although barely a quarter of that number were known in France.

In the early days there seems to have been considerable difference of opinion among the botanical fraternity as to the correct designation of these gaily coloured Daisies from the Orient. Some botanists thought they should be included among the Pyrethrums, and while others believed their place was among the Anthemis, a third group asserted that they should be listed with Leucanthemum. The controversy was finally settled by calling them *Chrysanthemum sinense*, the Golden Flower from China.

About a century ago Robert Fortune went to the East for the purpose of introducing the China Tea into India, and when he returned he brought a number of new flowers for our gardens.

Among them was a dainty little Daisy with semi-double flowers of a rich mahogany-red. Under the name of Chusan Daisy, from the island on which it had been found, the new flower was distributed among the members of the Royal Horticultural Society, but its petite charm found little or no response in Britain. In France, however, it was greeted with enthusiasm, and became the parent of a race known as the Pompon Chrysanthemums. This group, which is thought to have got its name from the resemblance between the miniature flowers and the tufts or pompons worn on the hats of French soldiers, is now coming into its own again after having dropped out of general cultivation for more than half a century.

Although many attempts had been made to introduce the type known as the "Hairy Japanese," they had defied all attempts to introduce them into western gardens until they made their appearance in America in 1888. Some twenty years earlier a Yankee skipper, Captain Alpheus Hardie of Boston, homeward bound from Yokohama, had found a lonely little Japanese boy as a stowaway on his ship. Shocked by his pitiful condition, the American took the lad home, clothed and fed him and sent him to a good school. When the young man returned to his homeland in 1887 he did not forget the kindness of Captain and Mrs. Hardie, and sent his foster-mother a gift he knew she would appreciate, some Japanese Chrysanthemums such as he had not seen grown in America. Mrs. Hardie raised cuttings, and when they bloomed showed some of the flowers at the Boston Flower Show in November 1888. The lovely white flowers created widespread enthusiasm, and the announcement that the whole stock of the new variety had changed hands for $1,500 was widely discussed and commented upon, as no one had ever heard of such a price being paid for a Chrysanthemum. The astute buyer knew the value of advertisement, and capitalizing on the story of the stowaway he placed it on the market under the name of Mrs. Alpheus Hardie. With such a history behind it the variety soon became a universal favourite, and by the records it appears that it was not until two years afterwards that there was sufficient stock available to send some plants to the eager growers of Europe.

The Two Forsters

FROM the alpine heights of the Southern Alps of New Zealand, more than five thousand feet above the blue Pacific, come the Forsteras, a dainty group of three species of mountain gems that rarely reach more than six inches in height even when the slender flower-stems rise above the overlapping leaves. *Forstera sedifolia*, with fairy-like blossoms borne singly or in pairs, is the most attractive species and in its finest forms the flowers have an attractive maroon eye in the centre. This small genus of alpines that prefers a shady pocket in the rock garden commemorates the work of Johann Reinhold Forster and his son Johann Georg,

who were the naturalists attached to Captain Cook's second
voyage of discovery that sailed the South Seas during 1772–5.

J. R. Forster was a German of English descent who had been
a Lutheran minister in East Prussia, where he adopted the brusque
and hectoring manner of the ruling classes. He had always been
something of a naturalist and had gravitated to Kew which, even
in those days, was beginning to take its place as one of the leading
botanical gardens in England. Being unable to make a living by
means of his pen, Forster senior was forced to become a school-
teacher and spent his spare time translating Bougainville's
Voyages. This proved so popular on publication that Forster
was hastily selected to accompany Captain Cook after Sir
Joseph Banks withdrew at the last moment as a result of the
endless obstacles placed in his way by the Comptroller of the
Navy.

Forster has been described as a "man possessed of vast
information in natural science, philosophy and general literature,"
but his behaviour throughout the voyage was a constant source
of irritation to the Commander and his officers on account of
his complete lack of co-operation combined with his failure to
make any effort whatsoever to understand any point of view
except his own, which was always right. While the ship was
lying in Plymouth Harbour she somehow came adrift, and Forster
hastened to claim that he was the first to discover the mishap
and that it was only through his vigilance that she was saved
from complete disaster. In actual fact there appears to have been
no danger at any time, and the situation was well in hand by the
time Johann Reinhold Forster was aware of the position, and his
only knowledge of the incident was what he surmised. This was
not an auspicious beginning, and the officers were not long in
lodging complaints about his interference and his continual pin-
pricking on matters that were no concern of his. Within a few
weeks the Forsters had made themselves thoroughly unpopular.

Forster was very discontented with the accommodation provided, and offered Lieutenant Cooper £100 for the use of his
cabin. This offer was joyously declined, and then the naturalist
attempted to force the Master to give up his cabin. This was
rejected with a few home-truths, and Forster made a very unpleasant scene, threatening to have him hounded out of the
Service on their return to England. So fond did the naturalists
become of this threat that it became the joke of the lower deck,
but the Forsters in their pompous self-satisfaction failed to
realize that they were merely making themselves ridiculous.
Forster did not approve of anyone on board, and recorded of
the seamen that they "recited droll stories intermixed with
hearty curses, oaths and indecent expressions, but seldom without real humour" while at their meals. But when battling with
the storms he heard their "voices louder than the blustering
winds or the raging ocean itself, uttering horrible volleys of
curses and oaths. They execrated every limb in varied terms,
piercing and complicated beyond the power of description.
Inured to dangers from their infancy, they were insensible to its
threats, and not a single reflection bridled their blasphemous
tongues. I know nothing comparable to the dreadful energy of
their language." When this tribute to the British sailor was
published another writer sprang to their defence, saying, "Who
does not know that sailors sometimes sing and swear? . . . but
the Doctor swears so dreadfully himself at times that there was
not a soul on board who ever dreamed that it gave him the least
satisfaction."

Father and son were greatly incensed by the decision of the
Admiralty, acting on the advice of Captain Cook, that J. R.
Forster was not a fit man to record the history of the voyage, as
had been originally intended. Despite the ban, however, Forster
proceeded with his version of the story and had it rushed through
the publishers so that it appeared, with the son's name on the

title page, some months before the official record. This effort to spoil the sale of Captain Cook's book and blacken his reputation aroused so much public indignation that the Forsters thought it advisable to seek sanctuary in Germany. There they were hailed as great men, and Forster senior was appointed Professor of Botany at Cassel. Within a year he published a treatise dealing with the plants he had collected during the voyage, and it was so well received that Frederick the Great made him Professor of Natural History at Halle University, a position that he held until his death twenty years later.

Among the many well-known plants dealt with by the Forsters were specimens from the South American coast, New Zealand, and many of the islands of the South Seas. Among those that were named and described were several species of Brazilian plants, the Chilean Fire Bush, *Embothrium coccineum*, a shrub or small tree whose glowing colours are rivalled only by the finest of the Rhododendrons. It was he who named the famous *Drimys Winteri*, well known as the source of Winter's Bark, which Captain Cook found so useful against scurvy when the bark had been steeped in honey to remove the acrid taste of the fresh substance.

The wildflowers of New Zealand were well represented in the Forsters' collections because that country was Captain Cook's main haven of rest after long months of buffeting across the Pacific. They discovered *Hebe elliptica*, which grows on the Straits of Magellan as well as around the New Zealand shores, and is well worth growing for the neat box-like foliage and trusses of fragrant white or violet-coloured flowers that bloom for months on end. Another of their plants with the same distribution is *Coriaria ruscifolia*, notable for its long racemes of black fruits that glisten like jet beads. On shingly riverbeds they found the graceful *Arundo conspicua*, a slender edition of the Pampas Grass, while the dry tussocky hillsides gave them a number of new plants, including the New Zealand Flax, *Phormium tenax*, with spikes of bronzy-red flowers carried twelve or fifteen feet in the air and clumps of large iris-like leaves that were put to a multitude of uses by the Maoris. One of their greatest contributions to the glasshouse was the lovely white *Clematis indivisa*, which drapes the highest trees of its native forests with garlands of blossom. In captivity it is usually grown in a cool greenhouse, and under suitable conditions a single plant has been known to produce over seven thousand white stars, each between two and three inches in diameter, at one time. Truly a sight never to be forgotten. But the plant that has made their name familiar in gardens the world over is the popular Thatch Palm, *Howea Forsteriana*, probably best known among gardeners as the Kentia. From being one of the dominant features of the lonely Lord Howe Island its accommodating disposition has made it the favourite of ornamental plants in halls, hotels, conservatories, ballrooms, and restaurants in all the big cities of the earth. The first seeds arrived at Kew in 1872, and the airy grace of the young plants soon attracted attention. So popular has the Kentia become that the export of its seeds is one of the staple industries of its homeland, and in due season the whole population takes part in collecting, cleaning, fumigating, and packing them so that they may arrive in the northern hemisphere in the spring of the year.

On their return the Forsters were allowed £4,000 for their scientific work, but their extravagant tastes soon frittered this away and they got so deeply into debt that Sir Joseph Banks took pity and advanced £250. This sum does not seem ever to have been repaid, although there was a long and not altogether amiable correspondence about it over many years. The son was a true "chip of the old block," who, after failing to pay his subscription to the Royal Society for more than ten years, had the effrontery to ask that it be written off. This was declined, but in

1786 Sir Joseph assisted him to publish a book dealing with six hundred of the plants collected. It was well received at the time and helped to relieve the financial position of the author, but is not held in high esteem to-day. One authority complains that "the illustrations are so badly executed as to be practically useless, while the descriptions are short and unsatisfactory and usually quite insufficient for the proper identification of the species."

David Nelson

IN the great days of exploration, when the greater part of the world was still almost unknown, David Nelson, a young man employed in His Majesty's Garden at Kew, had the good fortune to be selected as the assistant who was to accompany Dr. William Anderson, the surgeon-botanist, on the *Resolution* during Captain Cook's third expedition. Four adventurous years passed before he saw England again, and in the meantime he had collected wildflowers in some of the most inaccessible parts of the world from the lonely rock known as Kerguelen's Land in

the sub-Antarctic, through the tropical islands of the South
Seas to the desolate shores of the Aleutian Islands and the
Bering Sea.

He is commemorated in *Ranunculus Nelsoni*, one of the commonest buttercups of the Aleutian Islands, and in the far better
known *Nelsonia campestris*, a pretty little perennial from the
tropics that is well worth growing for its felted leaves rather
than the violet flowers. He did not actually bring many plants to
our gardens, but those we are sure of include *Oxylobium ellipticum*, a compact little shrub from Tasmania, with its leaves in
clusters along the stem and bright yellow pea-flowers in dense
racemes; *Melaleuca squarrosa*, with stiff little leaves and oblong
bottlebrushes of pale yellow; but best known of all is the South
African Satin Bush, *Podalyria sericea*, popular on account of
the silvery lustre of its compact box-like foliage and pleasing
pea-flowers of an attractive delicate pink.

Christmas 1776 was spent at Kerguelen, where the only plant
of interest is *Stilbocarpa polaris*, better known to the sealing
and whaling fraternity of last century as Macquarie's Cabbage
because it is the only edible plant that can stand up to the rigours
of the sub-Antarctic climate. This striking species is all too rarely
seen in cultivation, but its great bristly rhubarb-like leaves and
upright bunches of waxy yellow florets are worthy of a place in
any bog garden. No shrubs or trees grow there, and Captain
Cook noted that, "from its sterility I should with great propriety
call it Island of Desolation, but I would not rob Monsieur de
Kerguelen of the honour of its bearing his name."

On their arrival at Adventure Bay in Tasmania, Nelson saw
for the first time the New Zealand Tea plant, *Leptospermum
scoparium*, which the commander had found so useful during his
earlier voyages in his continuous fight against scurvy. David
Nelson has the distinction of having been the first to take home
specimens of the Acacias and Eucalypts that are so widespread

in Australia and Tasmania. One of them, *Acacia verticillata*, long known as Nelson's Mimosa, is still a great favourite in the conservatory where its dark prickly foliage and fluffy cylinders of lemon-yellow blossom are of great decorative value during the winter.

During a comparatively short stay in New Zealand few new plants were found, although they again noticed the ubiquitous New Zealand Tea with its aromatic foliage and pretty white flowers. Among the swamps grew the giant flax with its long, sword-like leaves and a Bulrush very similar to the form so familiar in the south of England. On dry sunny hillsides flourished *Cordyline australis*, now one of the most popular of all New Zealand plants because its seedlings are so valuable for sub-tropical bedding or as accent plants in all manner of decorative schemes.

Although Captain Cook was killed at Tahiti the quest for the North-West Passage had to go on, and later, when Dr. Anderson died at sea, David Nelson acted as botanist, being one of the first naturalists to explore the flora of the Aleutian Islands. In that far-off corner of the earth he was surprised to find an abundance of Vacciniums and other berry-bearing plants, many of which were very similar to those growing in the moorlands at home. By the margin of streams grew the lovely *Iris setosa* and many lovely ground Orchids, while the lush growth of the damp meadows included a giant Cow-Parsnip, a lovely golden Senecio, the familiar *Epilobium angustifolium* growing five feet in height, and on drier ground *Geranium erianthum* painted the hillsides with myriads of large purplish-crimson flowers. Around the primitive villages grew clumps of the sapphire-coloured *Aconitum delphinifolium*, whose roots formed a convenient source of the deadly poison used for tipping the poison arrows of the populace. At Kamtschatka he found the natives eating the bulbs of a plant with solitary flowers of "an exceeding dark red colour" which later travellers tell us may have been either a form of *Lilium davuricum*, or more probably the Eskimo Potato, *Fritillaria kamtschatkensis*, which has handsome flowers of wine-purple or maroon that may grow singly or in threes.

Dampier's description of the Breadfruit tree of the tropics had interested some of the London merchants concerned with the development of the West Indies, and caused them to ask the Government to do something about it. In 1787 Captain William Bligh was appointed to command the *Bounty*, in order to bring a shipment of Breadfruit trees from Tahiti. Included in the ship's company were "two skilful and careful men recommended by Sir Joseph Banks, to have the management of the plants intended to be carried to the West Indies and others to be brought home for His Majesty's Garden at Kew. One was David Nelson who had served in a similar situation in Captain Cook's last voyage; the other William Brown as an assistant to him." A great many people were most anxious to grasp such an opportunity of seeing the world, and in accordance with established custom the principals were either appointed by the commander himself, or by his personal recommendation. Bligh had been sailing-master on the *Resolution* seven years before, and in the light of later events there seems to have been some degree of friendship between him and David Nelson.

The long voyage to Tahiti was comparatively uneventful, although a full month was spent in the struggle to round Cape Horn. A short stop was made at Adventure Bay in the south of Tasmania, and a number of fruit trees from South Africa were planted. A little exploration was done, and Bligh recorded that Mr. Nelson had found "a tree in a very healthy state which he measured and found to be 33½ feet in girth, with height proportionate to its bulk."

On their arrival at Tahiti Nelson soon discovered that there would be no difficulty in securing the requisite number of young

Breadfruit trees, and that the natives were prepared to assist in collecting them. He was elated to find that two Shaddock trees—a sort of Grape-fruit brought to the West Indies from India by a Captain Shaddock in the seventeenth century—he had planted in 1777 had flourished and were bearing a good crop, although the fruit was not quite ripe.

Six very happy months were spent there, and when the *Bounty* set sail for home she had on board over one thousand young Breadfruit trees and some seven hundred other plants destined for the Royal Gardens at Kew. Suddenly in the early hours of an April morning the crew mutinied, and before Captain Bligh knew what had happened he was dragged out of bed and set adrift in an open boat on the broad Pacific. David Nelson was among his seventeen companions, and this may have saved the Captain's life when mutiny again raised its head. Bligh steered for the Dutch settlement of Timor, 4,500 miles away, and reached it forty-seven days later. The party had rested for a few days among some of the coral islands off the coast of Australia, and there was considerable discontentment among the crew. The ship's carpenter appears to have been the leader, but the trouble passed over when Bligh challenged him to a duel with swords. During these difficult days Bligh records, "I was assisted only by Mr. Nelson."

On the day after their arrival at Coupang, July 20, 1789, David Nelson died "of an inflammatory fever" brought on by the privations and hardships he had undergone. Bligh recorded in his Journal—"The loss of this honest man I much lamented; he had with great care and diligence attended to the object for which he was sent, and had always been ready to forward every plan that was proposed, for the good of the service for which we were engaged. He was not less useful in our voyage hither, in the course of which he gave me great satisfaction, by the patience and fortitude with which he conducted himself." Bligh gives an account of the funeral which took place the following day. "The corpse was carried by twelve soldiers dresst in black preceded by the minister; next followed myself and the second Governor; then the gentlemen of the town and the officers of the ships in the harbour, and after that my own officers and people."

With the regret that he was "sorry I could get no tombstone to place over his remains," Captain Bligh goes on to say, "This was the second voyage Mr. Nelson had undertaken to the South Seas, having been sent out by Sir Joseph Banks to collect plants, seeds, etc., in Captain Cook's last voyage. And now after surmounting so many difficulties, and in the midst of thankfulness for his deliverance, he was called upon to pay the debt of Nature, at a time least expected."

Bligh returned to England and, with characteristic energy, was back at Adventure Bay by the beginning of 1792 on his way to Tahiti to complete the job he had undertaken. He found "only three of the fine young apple-trees" planted by David Nelson were alive, and a few days later, on February 12, 1792, recorded that "Our Botanists were zealously employed and have travelled back as far as the top of Nelson's Hill which I named after Mr. Nelson who was Botanist in my last voyage and the first man ever on it."

He gives a description of the hill, saying it lies "three miles distant as a bird flies from the west end of the beach. The top is covered with smaller trees than the parts below, but none of the forest kind so that the top appears bare. On the top of the hill is a large oblong rock, on which a dozen men may stand with ease." Mr. Joseph Pearson, Director of the Tasmanian Museum, of whom I enquired if the hill has been identified and whether it is still known by the name given by Captain Bligh, says, "This hill is known locally as Cook's Lookout, and occasionally as Mount Cook. It is a prominent landmark from the beach and is about 1,100 feet high." He also informed me that although he had no photograph available, I might be able to get one from a local resident, Mr. T. H. Dorloff, of Adventure Bay. Mr. Dorloff very kindly procured these photographs and he says he has been settled in this beautiful bay for more than forty years, and has Blackcurrant and Gooseberry plantations near where Captain Bligh planted the first fruit trees in Australia.

The subsequent history of William Brown, Nelson's assistant, is of some interest. He has been described as a small, shy man of thirty, gentle of voice and manner, who enjoyed to the full the opportunity of studying the tropical flora of Tahiti under the able tuition of his chief. He appears to have been one of those quiet studious men who are slow to make decisions, and who prefer to look to others for guidance. Apparently it was just this lack of independence that led to his being numbered among the mutineers. He was awakened by a sailor who thrust a rifle into his hands and told him to go on deck immediately, and before he realized what was taking place, and the implications of his actions, Bligh was overboard with a mental note that Brown was "among those who bore arms."

Long before the mutineers had reached Tahiti William Brown had transferred his allegiance to Fletcher Christian, and on their arrival there he took aboard his Tahitan wife, Jenny, and went with the others to the lonely Pitcairn island. This quiet and industrious man was out of his element among the mutineers, but was of great assistance to the leader in many ways. During the early days of settlement he was able to identify trees and plants of economic value and taught them how to grow crops. He was a member of the first party to explore the island, and it was he who discovered an ample water supply, the supply that is still in use and known to this day as "Brown's Well." Some years later trouble broke out in the small colony over the ownership of land, and William Brown was shot while peacefully working in his garden.

The Story of the Frangipani

THE art of perfumery began in the distant past and reached the Valley of the Nile in very early times; from there it spread to Greece and to all parts of the western world by way of Rome, Milan, and Paris. Even so early as 1190 the perfumers of Paris had secured a Royal Charter from Philip Augustus of France, but the trade does not appear to have reached Britain and America until the last great wave of Huguenot refugees at the end of the seventeenth century. The appreciation of perfumes and savoury odours was not confined to Europe or to highly civilized communities; they were of great religious importance in all parts of the world from the Aztecs of Mexico to the Brahmins of India. In Mexico and Peru the flowers that were thought of most value for use in religious rites were the various sorts of Frangipani, and it was forbidden under the penalty of death for anyone to touch or even smell the blooms that had been so dedicated, as it was believed that this would defile the spirit of the offerings.

The various species of Plumiera, better known as Frangipani, are essentially plants for the warm conservatory or sub-tropical garden. Although there are several wild species from tropical America and the West Indies, the two that are commonly known as Frangipani, *Plumiera acutifolia* and *P. fragrantissimum*, are well known in every warm country on account of their handsome flowers and exquisite perfume. Perching Orchids prefer them above all other plants, and in many collections Frangipani plants are grown in quantity for the purpose of acting as hosts. They have found their way into almost every tropical land, being popular as garland flowers in the islands of the South Seas, while in Malaya and farther east they are extensively planted in graveyards and by the entrances of pagodas and temples. In India and Ceylon the Frangipani has long been known as the Temple flower, and on feast days carpets of the fragrant blossom are spread in front of the statues of Buddha.

It is in Australia, however, that the cultivation of the Frangipani has been brought to the greatest perfection. In the genial climate of Queensland and New South Wales it is treated as a shrub of some six feet in height, and its habit of dropping the large leathery leaves to assume the appearance of a spineless candelabra Cactus has given it another common name, Dead Man's Fingers. Shortly after the leaves have dropped three young shoots make their appearance at the tip of the old branch and within a short time each of these is wearing its tribute of blossom. The large waxy blooms have something of the appearance of overgrown Jasmine flowers with five spreading petals of gold, rose-pink or pure white or a combination of all three colours. Well-grown plants may have clusters of more than twenty flowers, each of which is between two and three inches in diameter. The blooms last well in water, and in consequence are much in demand as cut flowers, so that Frangipani has been greatly improved by the Australian nurserymen who have developed many new and improved varieties.

The botanical name *Plumiera* commemorates a French priest,

Charles Plumier, who made three voyages of discovery to the West Indies and Central America during the closing decades of the seventeenth century. He died suddenly at Cadiz, in Spain, while fitting out a fourth expedition in 1706. The preceding year he had published the results of his travels in what is now a rare old book, *Nova Plantarum Americanarum Genera*, in which he named and figured about one hundred of the plants he had discovered. In the preface he recorded something of his life. He states that from earliest childhood he had an innate love of trees, plants, and flowers, and shows that some of his happiest hours were spent seeking and describing new and strange forms that had never before been found by civilized man. Plumier was not one of the bold adventurers who crossed to the New World in search of gold or fame. He was a humble member of the Order of Minims, but with a vocation for botany acquired when he met Paul Boccone in Rome and developed by study under Tournefort in Paris. His superiors wisely gave him leave to pursue this calling.

The origin of the common name, Frangipani, is not so easy to define. One account states that it is merely an adaptation of the French *franchipanier*—coagulated milk—and simply refers to the thick milky sap that flows so freely from the slightest injury to leaf or branch. According to some authorities it is derived from the name of an Italian perfumer, named Frangipani, who compounded a perfume from a mixture of spices, orris root, and musk. This is said to have been a favourite scent used by Catherine d'Medici as a good imitation of the characteristic aromatic fragrance of the Plumiera flowers. The scent became known as Frangipani, and in course of time became better known than the plant, and so was transferred to the flowers.

Another version of the tale says that the flowers bear the name of a Count Mercuteo Frangipani, an Italian adventurer who sailed to the Americas within a year of their discovery by

Columbus. As his ship neared the shores of Antigua the sailors noticed a strong fragrance in the air and as soon as land was reached the Italian leapt ashore and returned soon afterwards with masses of the fragrant flowers, which were used to decorate an improvised altar during the thanksgiving service. He is said to have taken home some plants so that the Frangipani was well established in some of the warm gardens on the Mediterranean coast. The first of the Plumieras did not reach England until 1790, when Sir Joseph Banks received some plants from the Botanic Garden of St. Vincent in the West Indies and presented them to Kew. When they flowered in a warm greenhouse towards the end of the eighteenth century they were greatly admired and did much to awaken an interest and develop the fashion in tropical plants that was such a feature of the Victorian era.

Vice-Regal Nuts

DURING the eighteenth century the mariners of all the seven seas and the geographers at home were of the opinion that a north-west passage between the Atlantic and the Pacific only awaited discovery and great was the disappointment when Captain Cook's last expedition returned in 1780 only to report that the quest had been in vain. The British Government felt that another effort should be made but the many troubles of the day prevented any action for ten years. Then, in 1790, a small British colony was ejected from Nootka Sound by the Spaniards, who claimed the territory. This claim was withdrawn when the British prepared to fight, and it became necessary to send someone to take formal control of the disputed region. Thus it came about that Captain George Vancouver was despatched to attend to the matter, but, "principally with a view to ascertain the existence of any navigable communication between the North Pacific and Atlantic Oceans."

On the deck of the *Discovery* gleamed a most unnautical object, a glass frame, built on the advice of Sir Joseph Banks so that the surgeon-botanist, Archibald Menzies, should be able to bring back living plants from the strange lands they were to see. Although a fully qualified naval surgeon, who had seen active service on the high seas, Menzies was much more interested in plants than in medicine. Menzies made good use of his time, and when the voyage ended Sir Joseph Banks had reason to congratulate himself on his choice. Many new species of plants were discovered and wildflowers from Australia, Tasmania, New Zealand, and the far north-west coast of America have been dedicated to him in recognition of his explorations.

His plant-hunting began in earnest when they reached the south-west corner of Australia, and while the commander added an additional three hundred miles to the knowledge of that uncharted coast, Menzies went off in search of wildflowers. His brief month of botanizing is very well commemorated in a number of them, including one of the commonest trees of the area, *Banksia Menziesii*, known locally as the Honey-flower. It is a rough, ungainly tree, but certainly does not fail to attract attention in autumn when it covers itself with cone-like inflorescences of a peculiar bronze-red. One of the most interesting is the climbing Sundew, *Drosera Menziesii*, a straggling plant of some thirty inches that scrambles over low shrubs and ekes out a precarious existence by catching small insects on its sticky leaves. In summer it produces clusters of bright pink Helianthemum flowers.

Barely three weeks were spent in New Zealand, and, of course, the first plant he looked for was the famous Tea Plant so highly recommended by Captain Cook. His visit is commemorated in *Dracophyllum Menziesii*, a very curious shrub with masses of dainty white heath-flowers borne at the ends of branches furnished with tufts of leaves reminiscent of pine-apples. While scrambling on the hillsides above Dusky Bay he found the neat little *Hebe Menziesii*, notable for its broad clusters of lilac-coloured flowers.

In April 1792 Captain Vancouver sighted the tall trees of Drake's New Albion, discovered a little over two hundred and twenty-five years before, and began the long task of charting its coastline from California to far Alaska. Menzies set to work collecting and studying the flora, and among the plants he made known to us are many garden favourites, including *Zauchsneria californica*, sometimes called the Californian Fuchsia on account of some resemblance to *Fuchsia triphylla*, although the brilliant vermilion-coloured flowers are upright rather than drooping. He was greatly impressed by the masses of blossom produced all through the long dry summer by plants perched in the vertical ledges of rocks, where scarcely a drop of rain reached them. In the warmer parts of California he found the Tree Lupin, *Lupinus arboreus*, covering the sandy shores with its masses of sage-green foliage lighted up in due season by myriad candles of fragrant sulphur-yellow blossom, while farther inland grew *Ribes speciosum*, a plant of rare distinction and beauty when seen in all the glory of its slender arching branches laden with pendant clusters of rich crimson fuchsia-like flowers.

The explorers had many adventures, but their narrowest escape came when they were set upon by a party of Wolf Indians off the coast of Alaska. The shore party was endeavouring to trade with the natives, and before they knew what was happening the Indians had lashed one of their canoes to a boat and had set to work transferring what they could of the movable articles. Vancouver noticed that his launch was not too far away, and with no little ingenuity managed to keep the attackers from direct action until it came within pistol shot. Immediately the explorers began firing their arms, the Indians leapt overboard and swam for the shore, hiding under their canoes. Back in the *Discovery* the captain commemorated the incident by naming the inlet Traitors' Bay, the name by which it may be found on the map, while Dr. Menzies attended to the wounded.

From that moist and rainy land he brought specimens of the Sitka Spruce, *Picea sitchensis*, which can always be relied upon to grow in wet and water-logged soils; the graceful *Cupressus nootkatensis*; and the noble *Acer macrophylla* or Oregon Maple, a fine tree with handsome leaves that turn a pleasing reddish-yellow in the autumn. In those wet woods he also found the small inconspicuous *Menziesia ferruginea*, a mass of narrow tapered leaves above which nod small pinkish-white flowers. But this is not the only plant from that part of the world that bears the name of Archibald Menzies. There are *Tolmiea Menziesii*, with white flower spikes and lovely cordate leaves; *Spiraea Menziesii* of which the variety "Triumphans" is the most attractive form, a fine shrub of six feet with large terminal panicles of rose-pink flowers; the dainty *Penstemon Menziesii*, that follows the contour of every rock in its path and hides its small shiny leaves beneath a sheet of soft violet-blue blossom. Most worthy of mention is the Madrona, *Arbutus Menziesii*, that has been termed the noblest member of the Heath family, a lovely evergreen tree of which one writer says, "The traveller, forester, hunter, artist, and botanist is held by the spell of its crown of flowers, masses of red fruits, its terra-cotta bark and its burnished foliage."

By the time the weary mariners had reached the Chilean coast on the homeward run they were greatly in need of fresh water and food, so they put in at the Spanish port of Valparaiso. When brought into the presence of the Viceroy of Chile they were astounded when His Excellency addressed them in a rich Irish brogue. They learnt presently that he was an Irishman who had gone to Spain in search of adventure, become a naturalized Spaniard and had risen so high in the favour of the king as to be appointed his representative in Chile. A vice-regal reception was arranged for them, and when it was discovered that the guests were very conscious of their travel-stained uniforms His

Excellency made a public announcement of their achievements and adventures.

It was during this reception that Dr. Menzies noticed some peculiar nuts being served as dessert and, in the cause of science, quietly wrapped a few of them in his handkerchief and put them in his pocket. It was found out later that a wandering Spaniard had penetrated far into the dry hinterland of Chile a few years earlier, and found some fine territory dominated by the Araucanos Indians, whose staple food was the seeds of a tree whose peculiar habit of growth was quite unlike any he or any other white man had ever seen before. The nut-like seeds were borne in great cones, and the crop was skilfully controlled by the wise men of the tribe. The giant trees, towering one hundred and fifty feet into the air, were under a kind of taboo, and at certain times of the year the Araucanos were gathered under them to perform their strange religious rites and harvest the season's yield.

Menzies sowed his nuts in the frame on board ship, and by the time England was reached he had four young nut trees to hand over to Sir Joseph Banks. At first they were known as the Banks' Pine, but later became more popular as the Monkey Puzzle, receiving the botanical name *Araucaria imbricata* in recognition of the fact that they came from the land of the Araucano Indians. About half a century later seeds were introduced in quantity from South America, and when the trees became available in the open market their stiff architectural structure had a universal appeal, coming as they did when the ribbon border and the carpet bed ruled the garden. This is one of the tributes paid to this peculiar tree about the middle of the nineteenth century. "The Araucaria is very generally used, and is much and justly admired in localities where it grows freely; it is to be found planted in almost every villa garden; on the lawns and pleasure grounds of our nobility it is a great favourite. The symmetrical outline, the distinct and unusual appearance of the tree, combined with the regularity and order which is observable in the beautiful arrangement of its branches and foliage, causes it to harmonise well with architectural erections and to be frequently planted in their vicinity; as a single specimen planted on a lawn it has few equals."

During the last lap of the homeward voyage the latent antagonism between captain and surgeon flared up into an open breach. The unpleasantness following Captain Cook's second voyage, when the Forsters defied the Admiralty and published their own account of the expedition, had caused an edict that all diaries and notes relating to any voyages of His Majesty's ships were to be handed over to the commander before the home port was reached. This Menzies declined to do, and it was only after he had been placed under arrest that he saw reason, and decided to conform. By the time England was reached friendly relations had been established, and the commander of the *Discovery* is remembered in a genus of pretty little wildings from the forests of North-west America. Perhaps the most alluring species is *Vancouveria hexandra*, with distinctive foliage like a giant maidenhair fern surmounted by airy panicles of thirty or forty buds that open to display pretty lilac-tinted flowers which give a quaint suggestion that some mischievous fairy has turned them all inside out.

George Caley

WHEN the mid-winter garden rests under a covering of snow we turn to greenhouse and conservatory for the gay blossoms, sweet scents and luxuriant verdure of the summer garden, and of the plants that give of their best at this season none can excel the Australian Wattles. With their great variety of growth and leafage and flowers that ring all the changes between little balls of golden down to dainty catkins of the palest canary-yellow, some of the species such as *Acacia armata* and *A. verticillata* make highly desirable pot plants while others are more suitable for training up pillars or over the back walls of conservatories. One of the most valuable species where such freedom of growth may be permitted is *A. podalyriaefolia*, whose long slender growths and neat little leaves, all dressed in pearl-grey felt, may be relied upon to produce graceful clusters of fragrant yellow balls all through the dullest days of the year.

At one time known as *A. Caléyi*, this old favourite was discovered by George Caley, one of the first plant-hunters to be sent out to Australia by Sir Joseph Banks. The son of a Yorkshire horse-dealer, young George is said to have been a "chip off the old block," a man of sterling honesty whose brusque eccentricities and tactless manner led most people to prefer his room to his company. As a boy he began to take an interest in plants by looking at the veterinary books belonging to his father, and was led on to study the wildflowers of the English countryside. In 1795, when about eighteen years of age, he wrote to Sir Joseph Banks, stating that he wanted to become a botanist, and enclosed some plants. One or two of those turned out to be new to science, and Sir Joseph informed the young man that although botany was not a profession that paid big dividends, an opening was available for him at Kew at ten shillings a week, and no doubt opportunities of advancement would occur. Two years later Caley threw up his position on account of the "poor pay and bad prospects," but Sir Joseph arranged that he be given a free passage to Australia as a plant collector. He prepared the way by writing to the Governor that this young man was "hardy and bold" and that his "skill in botany is beyond what his appearance promises, and he has some knowledge of the sciences."

Caley spent the greater part of the next ten years exploring the lonely valleys, the forests and the mountains of south-western Australia, and most of his expeditions were monotonous in the extreme. On returning from one of them a companion told the Governor that the only living things they had seen had been two solitary crows, and in his opinion even they had lost their way. Caley was a voluminous correspondent, on one occasion enclosing 318 pages of botanical notes to describe 31 packets of seed. He sent many New Holland plants to Kew, including Acacias, Eucalypts, Grevilleas and Banksias, and *Epacris purpurascens*, a dainty little shrub from the Blue Mountains. It was the first Australian Heath to reach England, and was one of the most popular of all Caley's plants on account of its neat habit and plentiful supply of white or rosy-purplish flowers.

George Caley seems to have been something of a character

in the small community, and if his many quarrels did not exactly endear him to the neighbours, they certainly provided something to talk about. His tiff with the missionary Samuel Marsden was typical of them all. Caley was very fond of dogs, and when Marsden's rabbits began to disappear the missionary threatened to shoot the dogs. Caley complained to the Governor, who, being tired of the continual squabbling, gave him little satisfaction. Caley then said he would thrash Marsden, and so the game went on over many weary weeks. The Governor in turn complained to Sir Joseph Banks, who replied to the effect that "I feel a particular obligation to you for bearing with the effusion of his ill-judging spirit. Had he been born a gentleman he would long ago have been shot in a duel. As it is I have borne with much more than even you have ever done under the conviction that he acted under strong though mistaken feelings of a mind honest and upright."

His efforts towards matrimony seem to have been the cause of much gossip. He had barely landed before he began to get himself talked about on account of an infatuation with a Mrs. Wise, the widow of a weaver who had died on the voyage. Again, about 1808, his affairs were in the public eye. This time he was enamoured of Margaret Catchpole, a convict who had been assigned to the household of Mr. John Palmer, the Commissary of New South Wales. This young woman had been convicted of stealing a horse from Ipswich and riding to London in about ten hours. She and Will Land, her sweetheart, escaped from prison; he was shot and she was deported to Australia. The lady seems to have been indifferent to George Caley's attentions, preferring to remain true to the Ipswich smuggler who had been her sweetheart.

During Captain Bligh's regime as Governor, Caley seems to have settled down in a farm some miles from Sydney. He became very friendly with the new Governor and sent home voluminous reports about the conditions in Sydney before Bligh was deposed. During the period while the Governor was in prison Caley visited him many times, and did all he could to sway public opinion, both in Australia and at home, in favour of Bligh.

About 1810 Banks cut off supplies, offering a choice of remaining in Australia or returning home; Caley chose the latter and arrived in England in 1811, accompanied by Dan, an Australian aboriginal, as his personal servant. Soon afterwards he took up the position of Superintendent of the Botanic Garden at St. Vincent, but was not a social success there either. The Pukka-Sahibs were most indignant because he closed the garden, then a fashionable parade ground, to Sunday visitors because he found that they were helping themselves to plants and seeds. In 1819 he returned to England, and on his death ten years later left enough money to allow Dan to return to Australia and provide him with a small annuity for life.

George Caley did not publish anything on the results of his plant collecting in Australia, but Alan Cunningham and Robert Brown, who covered the same field in later years, acknowledged his work and valued it very highly. His name is remembered in quite a number of Australian wildflowers, of which the most important are the aromatic *Prostanthera Caleyi*, the dainty white *Viola Caleyana*, the tiny Caleanas, a genus of curious little cockatoo Orchids, and *Grevillea Caleyi*, a handsome evergreen shrub of elegant habit with deeply cut pinnate leaves and red flowers borne in odd-looking, one-sided racemes.

The Cape Primrose

DURING the past three hundred years South Africa, out of the infinite variety of her wildflowers, has given us many strange and beautiful plants, but one of the most curious is *Bowiea volubilis*. This remarkable species has an onion-like root, that may grow up to twenty inches in circumference, and a graceful twining stem that looks just like a trail of Asparagus and is out of all proportion with the massive root. This peculiar plant was found by James Bowie where the Umzimkulu River flows, in the south of Natal, and was dedicated to the finder by Dr. Harvey on account of "the many years of patient labour in the interior of South Africa, by which he enriched the gardens of Europe with a greater variety of succulent plants than had ever been detected by any other traveller."

The son of a London seedsman, James Bowie entered Kew in 1810 and within four years had been sent to South America with Alan Cunningham to look for Orchids. Two years later he was sent to South Africa, but was forced to return home when the prestige of Kew began to decline after the death of Sir Joseph Banks in 1820, the House of Commons having cut the plant collectors' allocation in half. After a few years of the quiet life in England he returned to South Africa as gardener to Baron Ludwig of Ludwigsberg, but about 1841 terminated this employment and endeavoured to build up a business as a professional collector again. His later life seems to have been rather unhappy —much living alone had made him eccentric and he appears to have endured extreme poverty, an outcast from the white community, until his death about 1853.

He sent home a great variety of plants, including the parents of our modern Gladioli, many kinds of Aloes, Euphorbias, and species with bulbous roots. One of his greatest favourites was *Clivia nobilis*, sent home in 1823 and known ever since as one of the most ornamental plants for the warm greenhouse during late winter and early spring. From the bold clumps of dark foliage arise handsome umbels of fifty or more flowers, each about an inch long and of a deep orange-yellow shading off to vermilion and buff, tipped with the brightest pea-green.

James Bowie's greatest contribution to the twentieth-century garden is the pretty little Cape Primrose that flowered for the first time in the northern hemisphere in the glasshouses at Kew in 1823. The flowers are usually solitary, although sometimes borne in pairs, and are of a soft blue colour, nodding on their wiry stems six or eight inches above the tufts of bright green leaves. The plants are very floriferous, and they produced so much seed that it was not many years before seedlings were appearing as weeds in the adjacent pots or in the moist gravel beneath. When the Cape Primrose came to be named Bowie requested that it should bear the name of his friend, George Rex, on whose property at Knysna, on the south coast of Cape Colony, it grew as a wildflower among the rocks.

George Rex was a strange character who was in reality

another of Queen Victoria's "wicked uncles." He was a natural son of George III, and about the turn of the century had been sent to the Cape to be out of the way, being provided with the position of a minor official and a pension on condition he did not again set foot in England. When the Dutch took over Cape Town in 1803 he was forced to migrate to Knysna, where he seems to have adopted much the same mode of life, complete with plural wives, as the "wicked uncles" were then enjoying in England.

Within a few years *Streptocarpus Rexii* became a very popular greenhouse plant, and for the next thirty years was the only species of its kind in cultivation. The next to appear was *S. polyanthus*, an extraordinary plant with only one leaf, which seems to be a continuation of the seed-leaf, six or seven inches long and about three inches wide. Along the mid-rib a continuous succession of flowering panicles is produced throughout the summer, each inflorescence bearing fifteen or twenty pale-blue flowers. As the flora of South Africa became better known about sixty different species were discovered, and when many of them were found to belong to the group with only one leaf they received considerable attention from both growers and plant-breeders.

In 1884 Mr. E. G. Dunn of Cape Town sent seeds of a splendid new species to Kew, and the resultant plants, which became known as *S. Dunnii*, were of great interest on account of their solitary leaf being about three feet long, and the multitudes of dainty flowers were mostly of a deep brick-red or dark rose colour. About four years later *S. parviflorus* appeared upon the scene with its clouds of pretty little blossoms of white, yellow, and pale violet. Working with these four species William Watson of Kew began to experiment with the intention of producing a new race of greenhouse plants that combined the large flowers of *S. Rexii* with the floriferous panicles and gay colours of the other species. He was quite successful, and some of his hybrids such as *S. kewensis*, although they may appear small and rather insignificant in comparison with our modern varieties, were hailed with acclamation half a century ago.

The long and continuous improvement in the size and colour of the modern Streptocarpus has produced a race of sturdy greenhouse plants with handsome flowers of many delightful colours from attractive shadings of spiraea red and persian rose through tonings of cobalt-violet and heliotrope to the most exquisite tints of wistaria blue. Perhaps the greatest improvement has been the elimination of the dull throats and cinnamon-brown stripes of the old-fashioned hybrids. These have now given way to bright clean colours and centres of the purest white, cream or yellow that are sometimes relieved by the laced and reticulated pencillings of bishop's violet and maroon.

Alan Cunningham

In a secluded corner of the Sydney Botanic Garden stands an obelisk dedicated to the memory of one of Australia's greatest explorers, Alan Cunningham, who spent the best years of his life opening up the hinterland and studying the flora of that vast new land. In 1810 William Aiton of Kew advertised for an assistant to help with the second edition of his *Hortus Kewensis*, and the successful candidate was Alan Cunningham, a young man who soon let it be known that he had no desire to spend the rest of his days as a clerk in an office. Within four years he was despatched on a plant-hunting expedition, accompanied by James Bowie. They journeyed through various parts of South America and were the first collectors to explore the Organ Mountains in southern Brazil. They achieved great success, bringing back the Brazilian Prickly Pear, various species of Bromeliaceous plants, including *Billbergia pyramidalis*, notable for its clusters of red flowers, the true *Cattleya vera*, and *Verbena erinoides*, the Moss Verbena, now rather rare in cultivation although well worth growing for the beauty of its finely cut foliage and scarlet, rosy-lilac or deep purple flowers. This species has played little or no part in the development of our hybrid Verbenas, but it was the first species in cultivation and did much to stimulate an interest in the genus as a source of bedding plants.

Within a few months of his return to Kew Cunningham was off, in the capacity of King's Botanist, to Australia, and with characteristic energy he lost no opportunity to see something of the unknown interior. The venture ended in disappointment, the leader complained bitterly of the heart-breaking monotony of the whole region, saying, "One tree, one soil, one water and one description of bird, fish and animal prevails alike for ten miles and for one hundred." Cunningham continued his explorations, however, for another fourteen years, and added a large number of New Holland plants to the garden flora of Europe. He twice circumnavigated the island-continent, and made many long and difficult journeys into the strange hinterland, besides visiting Tasmania, New Zealand, and Norfolk Island.

Although Alan Cunningham discovered many new species of Australian plants and sent most of them home to His Majesty's Garden at Kew, his greatest claim to fame is as an explorer. In 1823 he penetrated far beyond the Blue Mountains, and had the satisfaction of passing a lonely cairn known as "Caley's Repulse," perched on the summit of a sharp outline and long believed to mark the spot where George Caley had turned back for lack of provisions, twelve years before. He pushed on and found the Pandora Pass, whose discovery was recorded in *The Times* of London on Friday, August 24, 1824.

> The last letters from New South Wales state that Mr. Cunningham, Botanical Collector for Kew Gardens, has discovered a valuable tract of country, abounding in well-watered plains, and fine timbered land, to the north of Bathurst, and a pass through a ridge of mountains. . . .

On account of his careful notes on vegetation, whether it were grassland suitable for grazing or forests worthy of being milled, Alan Cunningham was the obvious choice when the Governor of New South Wales wanted a report on whether or not the region away to the north, now known as the State of Queensland, was suitable for development as "white man's country." At first much of this land was bare and inhospitable, and he was on the point of turning back, after having reduced the rations of man and horse, when, on breasting a rise for a last look, he found a pleasant valley opening to a great plain which was bounded on the far horizon by steep hills. Further exploration showed him a way through the encircling ranges to Moreton's Bay, where a broad highway now runs through Cunningham's Gap.

In the winter of 1830 he went to Norfolk Island and found a few interesting plants, including *Capparis nobilis*, a climber with handsome citron-yellow flowers, *Solanum Bauerianum*, worth growing for its fruits like bright-red, elongated Tomatoes, and *Lagunaria Patersonii*, a Hibiscus-like tree scattered over the grassy hillsides where it reached forty feet in height. In cultivation it is an elegant shrub for the warm greenhouse with whitish leaves and flowers of a very deep pink, fading to white, and about the size of a wineglass.

He arranged to visit the nearby Philip Island and spend the night there, but his trip was sadly interfered with by his attendants. The boat had been returned to headquarters at Norfolk Island, and in the night a number of convicts escaped, seized the boat and told the sentry they had been sent to fetch Mr. Cunningham. He was surprised while asleep and forced to give up chronometer, pistols, tent and provisions, and the convicts sailed away leaving him to shift for himself. The Government declined to compensate him for the loss of his instruments, and he was forced to replace them at his own expense.

Alan Cunningham returned to England the following summer and lived for some years in the quiet village, Strand-on-the-Green, across the Thames from Kew, and spent most of his time arranging and describing his botanical specimens and writing of his explorations. Six years later he returned to Australia as Colonial Botanist and Superintendent of the Sydney Botanic Garden, but relinquished the latter position within a few weeks of his arrival on learning that the dignified title merely concealed the post of vegetable grower for the military hierarchy who had thoughtfully assigned him fifty convicts for the purpose. There was nothing for it but to return to botanical exploration, but his health failed and in 1839 he died in a cottage in the Sydney Botanic Garden, "A martyr to geographical exploration and botanical science, in the forty-eighth year of his age." He was buried in a city cemetery, but in 1901 his remains were taken to the Botanic Garden, where the monument was erected in his memory.

Soon after his return to Kew in 1831 Alan had been offered the position in Sydney but had declined it in favour of his brother, Robert, at that time employed at Kew. Robert did a certain amount of plant-hunting in Australia and New Zealand before accompanying Colonel Mitchell on an expedition to investigate the complicated water systems of the Murray and Darling Rivers, in 1832.

When the explorers met to camp for the night of April 17th they were dismayed to find that Cunningham was not with any of them. Apparently he had been so intent on flower gathering that he had inadvertently become separated from the others and was unable to find his way back. A long and difficult search followed: two or three days later his tracks were lost and were not picked up again until about a week after he had gone amissing. His confused wanderings made the search much harder, but on the afternoon of the 23rd he was found to have been leading his horse aimlessly over the countryside. Later a handkerchief was found, and on May 2nd the horse was found, dead, with the saddle and bridle still on. Cunningham was never seen again, but his tracks were eventually traced to the bed of a dried-up river, and some aborigines informed the trackers that the white man had "gone west with the Myalls or wild men." When the mounted police came to investigate they found that about April 25th Robert Cunningham had been so exhausted by hunger and thirst that when he had stumbled upon an aborigines' camp they had taken pity on him and given him food and water. After the meal he had gone to sleep, but had become delirious in the night, and his strange behaviour had so alarmed the family that the chief had instructed that he be killed.

Although there are more than ten thousand species of wild-flowers and trees in Australia only a very few have achieved that degree of popularity that ensures a niche in the affections of the gardening public. Probably the best known of all is the Silky

Oak, *Grevillea robusta*, one of the glories of the Australian forests. In the land of its origin and other warm countries its graceful fern-like foliage and trusses of golden-yellow flowers are great favourites not only on account of their beauty but also because they can be relied upon to attract the honey-sucking birds. Although under such conditions it forms an elegant tree of eighty or a hundred feet in height, it is not in that state that it has achieved its greatest popularity, but as a graceful pot plant whose delicate leafage may be seen in lounges and ball-rooms throughout the world. Seeds of the Grevillea were sent to Kew by Alan Cunningham over a hundred and twenty years ago, but little notice was taken of it until towards the end of Queen Victoria's reign when sub-tropical bedding came into its own. Since that time its popularity has increased by leaps and bounds, until nowadays *Grevillea robusta* has come to be considered an indispensable foil to the hardy palms wherever decorative effects are desired.

The two brothers Cunningham are remembered in quite a number of the plants that grow wild among the forests, mountains, and riverbanks of Australia and New Zealand. From six thousand feet among the storm-swept rocks of the New Zealand Alps comes *Viola Cunninghamii*, whose pretty white flowers are pencilled with deep violet lines and emit a faint musky scent; from the forests of Queensland comes the dainty *Crotalaria Cunninghamii* with long trails of blossom like a glorified Laburnum, and there are many species of ferns that grace the moist forests with their delicate tracery.

The most attractive of the plants that commemorate these men is *Blandfordia Cunninghamii*, known in the southern hemisphere as Christmas Bells. This is one of the most famous wildflowers from the Blue Mountains. Many of the early explorers brought back tales of the wonderful flame-coloured lilies that spread great carpets of colour among the Wattle and

Gum trees and along the banks of many a mountain stream. When the far-famed Lilies reached Kew they were found to develop masses of bright green leaves growing about two feet high with the flower-stems rising a foot or more above and carrying sixteen or twenty bells. Each blossom is about two inches long and of the brightest coppery-red shading to a rich golden-yellow or glowing orange, so that *Blandfordia Cunninghamii* is one of the most beautiful flowers that may be grown under glass, and no plant hunter could look for a nobler species to bear his name.

"Forsyth's Plaister"

As soon as winter is gone the long arching sprays of Forsythia are arrayed from end to end with yellow blossom. The name Golden Bells is sometimes attached to these shrubs, but it does not seem to have come into general use and so the name of William Forsyth, at one time gardener to King George III, is remembered wherever they are grown. Probably the best loved of all spring-flowering shrubs, the Forsythias are too well known to require description, but they may be depended upon to lighten up the spring garden whether grown as single specimens or massed in the shrubbery.

William Forsyth was born near the small town of Old Meldrum, in the north of Scotland, in 1737, and is believed to have served for a number of years in the garden of Lord Aberdeen at Haddo House before going to London at the age of twenty-six. In 1771 he succeeded the famous Philip Miller as Curator of the Chelsea Physic Garden, where he carried out many alterations and improvements. Thirteen years later he was appointed Director of His Majesty's Gardens at Kensington Palace.

He was a prominent gardener in his day, but his main claim to our attention is on account of his having bluffed a Parliamentary Committee into granting an award of £1,500 for a mixture of sand and soap-suds. Much of the gardening literature of his time devoted a certain amount of space to "Forsyth's Plaister," a composition that he claimed was capable of healing wounds and re-conditioning decayed trees. The following is one version of his recipe. "Blend one bushel of fresh cow-dung with half a bushel of lime rubbish—that taken from the ceilings of rooms is best—with half a bushel of wood ashes and one-sixteenth of a bushel of river sand. The last three must be sifted fine and the whole reduced to the consistency of a thick plaster by mixing with a sufficient quantity of urine and soap-suds. Trim all the rough material from the wounds and apply to the thickness of about an eighth-of-an-inch all over the infected area."

The conclusion of the American War of Independence had left Britain alone and friendless against a hostile Europe with all the ships of the Dutch, Spanish and French navies harassing her merchantmen, and as the eighteenth century drew to its close the rise of Napoleon aggravated the position. As a result of this external pressure the necessity for a plentiful supply of good, sound oak timber, suitable for ship-building, impressed itself upon the nation as a matter of vital importance. Those were the days when retired naval men deplored the conditions and took up the practice of surreptitiously planting acorns in the hedgerows of many a country lane in the fond hope that some day they would grow into trees capable of providing "wooden walls" for the protection of the country.

The authorities who controlled the Royal Forests were not a little disturbed by the reports that showed a very high proportion of Oak trees under their charge were being rejected as unsuitable for the Navy. Having heard something of Forsyth's claims, the authorities consulted him on the position and he invited them to come and see for themselves the results of his experiments in the Palace Gardens at Kensington. No doubt some careful window dressing took place during that summer of 1789, the Inspection Committee was suitably impressed and in consequence a Parliamentary Committee was set up to investigate the full possibilities of Mr. Forsyth's treatment of semi-decayed trees. In due course another visit of inspection was made to the Kensington Gardens and all members were completely satisfied, not only that William Forsyth's claims were genuine, but also that he had made a discovery of inestimable value to the nation. It was agreed that he be given a grant of £1,500 in recognition of the debt of the nation and the promise of a further similar amount when his claims had been substantiated by concrete results. This grant to Forsyth shows something of the anxiety that haunted the people of Great Britain during the years that preceded the great victory of Trafalgar.

Having achieved such gratifying results Forsyth advertised the merits of his Plaister far and wide and continued his experiments with trees, hoping no doubt that he might stumble on a genuine discovery. His *Observations on Diseases* was published in 1801 and was followed by a *Treatise on Fruit Trees*, which included a revision of the *Observations* and ran into no fewer than seven editions, the last appearing in 1824, twenty years after his death. Strangely enough there seems to have been little or no criticism of Forsyth's remarkable claims until after the publication of his *Treatise*, but in those days plant morphology had made but little progress except in relation to fruits and seeds. In the second edition of his *Treatise on the Cultivation of the Apple and Pear*, published towards the end of 1801, Thomas Andrew Knight went so far as to make a blunt statement that he had no confidence in Forsyth's claims. This was the beginning of a long and bitter controversy that was carried on in the horticultural press for some two years after Forsyth's death in 1804.

There is no record that the second portion of the parliamentary grant was ever paid to William Forsyth or to his executors, and as the years went by "Forsyth's Plaister" and his primitive attempts at tree surgery gradually fell into disrepute. Johnson's *Gardeners' Dictionary*, published in 1846, mentions the composition, although it casts some doubt on Forsyth's right to claim it as his own discovery, but is careful to give no indication of its value or otherwise. The meticulous care exercised by our modern tree-surgeons shows the futility of the methods advocated by William Forsyth, and we may well imagine that many an earnest young gardener of the early part of the nineteenth century must have acquired a headache from the failure of his most painstaking efforts to recondition valuable specimen trees by means of "Forsyth's Plaister."

And so it is that in springtime when the Forsythias are in bloom we are reminded of that shrewd old Scotsman, William Forsyth, who capitalized on the wishful thinking of his time by selling as his own an idea that was common in garden practice long before he was born, so that the King's Commissioners persuaded a grateful nation to give him £1,500 for his trouble.

The Bitter Root

A RACE of hardy mountaineers from the alpine heights of the North-Western States, the Lewisias, have been hailed as America's greatest gift to the rock garden. They perpetuate the memory of Captain Meriwether Lewis who, during the first decade of last century, led an expedition sent out by the Government of the United States to explore on the vast, and at that time almost unknown, North-West Territory then in dispute between the British and American Governments. This expedition, the joint leader of which was Captain William Clark, for whom the Clarkias are named, took a great interest in the natural history of the region and brought back many new specimens of trees and plants.

One autumn day in 1805 the party had reached a range of hills lying on what has become the boundary between the States of Montana and Idaho, and being rather short of provisions sent Captain Lewis on ahead in search of game. Reaching the encampment of a small family of Indians, he dismounted and put down his gun. In a second the man pounced upon it and, jumping on a nearby horse, galloped off, followed by the remainder of the family. After a strenuous pursuit over some ten miles of broken country, the explorer overtook the thief and succeeded in retrieving his gun.

As he made his way back to his companions Captain Lewis again passed the Indian encampment and noticed some roots drying in the sun. Having been unable to find anything more promising as food, he acquired them, hoping that the friendly Indian guides might be able to explain their use. He was told that although the skin was ordinarily very bitter, during the flowering season it could be stripped off quite easily. He describes the starchy roots as "fibrous, parts were brittle, hard, the size of a quill, cylindric and as white as snow throughout." He goes on to explain that they were a favourite of the Indians when peeled and boiled, but he "found they became soft by boiling, but had a very bitter taste that was naucious to my pallate, and I transferred them to the Indians who ate them heartily."

In commemoration of that adventurous day the explorers called the surrounding ranges the Bitter Root Mountains, and the plant has been known ever since as the Bitter Root. When in due course it came to be classified, Pursch, the botanist, named it *Lewisia rediviva* in honour of the finder and on account of the fact that the original specimens flatly refused to become mere herbarium specimens but insisted on growing. He records that when planted in his garden they showed their gratitude by flowering next year.

Now acclaimed as the State Flower of Montana, *Lewisia rediviva* is both the joy and the despair of the ardent rock gardener until he has become familiar with its idiosyncrasies. In the springtime it sends up a crop of fat blue-green leaves, and as the summer advances they shrivel away to wisps of dry straw. When the distracted owner has at last resigned himself to its loss, his plant suddenly dons a robe of pink satin and quietly assumes its place as the reigning Queen of the Garden.

David Douglas

In the days when the Empress Josephine grew Mignonette in her drawing-room at Malmaison it was esteemed throughout Europe as the sweetest of all scented flowers, and pot-grown plants were in universal demand as the only suitable decoration for the salons of the rich. One of the main disadvantages of Mignonette was that, being an annual, replacements were necessary every few weeks and growers were constantly on the look-out for some more permanent type of scented plant that would not be so difficult to grow. The man who found it was David Douglas, the discoverer of the Douglas Fir, and one of the greatest of the many plant-hunters who scoured the vast American continent in search of new flowers for the gardens of Europe.

When the Kew collectors were withdrawn soon after the death of Sir Joseph Banks in 1820 the Royal Horticultural Society took up the task and one of its first plant-hunters was David Douglas. He began collecting in 1823, and made a number of very successful journeys from Hudson's Bay to California and, according to one authority, "no other collector has reaped such a harvest in America, or associated his name with so many useful plants."

Among his plants are the well-known *Clarkia elegans*, the lovely blue *Gilia capitata*, *Mimulus cardinalis*, a distinctive species in the herbaceous border where it is valued for the bright scarlet flowers whose recurving petals show a bright yellow throat, and the Flowering Currant, *Ribes sanguinea*. This, one of the most popular of all spring-flowering shrubs, had been discovered by Menzies at Nootka Sound, and Douglas considered it one of his best plants, noting his delight many times in his Journal at this "one of the finest and most interesting additions that had been made to our shrubberies for many years."

David Douglas received much assistance and encouragement from the Hudson Bay Company and its officers during his many excursions into country unknown to anyone but the trappers employed by the Company, and when he found a remarkable evergreen shrub or small tree in 1827 he paid Nicholas Garry, the secretary of the Hudson Bay Company, the compliment of naming the plant in his honour. No doubt the worthy secretary would never have been heard of except in the annals of the Company, but his name is well known to us on account of *Garrya elliptica* which festoons itself in winter and early spring with decorative catkins that may be up to twelve inches long and consist of silvery nile-green bowls strung one within the other.

One of the first of his plants to achieve popularity was what is now the State Flower of Alaska, *Mahonia Aquifolium*, which is probably better known as the Oregon Grape. He found it near Fort Vancouver in 1825 while camping there in a hut made of bark and sleeping in the open. At a time when the emphases were on evergreens it was hailed as one of his greatest discoveries. The shining foliage is a joy throughout the year, while the clusters of canary-yellow flowers followed in autumn by the masses of grape-like fruits give a plant of unusual beauty as they grow among the bronze-red foliage. For long the supply could not overtake the demand and plants were sold for £10 each, and it was not until 1837 that the price came down to 5s. per plant. David Douglas was one of the first white men to see the lovely blue flowers of *Camassia esculenta* covering the rich mountain valleys of the far north-west with such a profusion of blossom as to give the appearance of lakes of blue water. In all he collected some 340 new species of plants, including so many Conifers that he wrote to his friend William Hooker, "You will begin to think that I manufacture Pines at my pleasure."

In British Columbia he found the pretty little *Mimulus moschatus*, whose dainty yellow flowers had such a strong scent of musk that it very soon became known as the Musk Plant. Requiring practically no attention, it soon became a great favourite, and to some extent took the place of Mignonette, being grown as a room plant in cottage and castle throughout the Victorian era. Early in the present century someone noticed that his Musk plants did not appear to have any scent, and consulted the Kew authorities on the subject. Upon investigation it was found that all the Musk Plants grown in Britain had lost their scent, and this was followed by the astonishing discovery that even in its native land no one was able to find one fragrant specimen of the Musk Plant, although the older settlers of that part of British Columbia remembered the scent quite well. From time to time we hear claims of scented specimens having been found, but so far none of them has made its way to any of the great botanical institutions of the world. The simultaneous loss of scent in the descendants of the plants introduced into England by David Douglas and of all the wild plants in the land of their origin is one of the major botanical mysteries of the age, and so far no really satisfactory explanation has been arrived at.

Among other adventures, Douglas went down the Fraser River in a canoe and it was dashed to pieces on the Stony Islands, that have only recently been identified with the rocky islets in the Fort George Canyon. There he lost all his possessions, including scientific instruments, his Journal, and more than four hundred specimens of plants. Discouraged by the rigours and privations of exploration over the vast distances which he had to cover in North America, he left at the end of that year for Hawaii. The following summer, in 1834, while out botanizing among the mountains he fell into a pit that had been dug to catch wild cattle. Some days later a search party found his body there along with a young bull.

The name of David Douglas is perpetuated by many of the American trees and wildflowers that he introduced to the Royal Horticultural Society of Great Britain. Among them are *Iris Douglasii*, a pleasant violet-flowered species from the Rocky Mountains, the purple-flowered *Clematis Douglasii*, *Limnanthes Douglasii*, whose fragrant white and yellow buttercups are so attractive to bees, and many others. Probably the greatest compliment that was paid to this indefatigable plant-hunter was that given by Dr. John Lindley when he gave the name *Douglasia* to a small genus, brilliant cousins of the better-known Androsaces, that flourishes in the mountainous country to the far north-west of the United States. The only species that seems to have come down to our gardens is *Douglasia laevigata*, a true alpine beauty whose tight little hummocks of green foliage, studded with its charming pink flowers, never fails to attract attention in the rock garden.

The Oconee Bells

FAR away among the high hills of North Carolina grows one of the *élite* of that great floral company that makes its home in North America. Nowhere plentiful, the Oconee Bells prefer to ring out their fairy music among the great sheltering rocks where the sun rarely shines. There the masses of bronzy-green leaves form dense carpets above which dance the delicately fringed flowers. They are of a gleaming pearly texture that is sometimes of the purest white, but often suffused with delicate rose or flushed like the newly opened apple-blossom, and are a joy to behold during the first months of spring.

André Michaux, the French botanist who spent ten years in the Americas studying the flora, found it while botanizing among the Blue Ridge Mountains one December day in 1788. While examining a clump of the stately little *Galax aphylla*, he detected the seed-pods of a stranger, but search where he would he could not discover a trace of the flowers. This was all the more disappointing because he was sure that he had found something new to science, and as all plants are classified by the structure and arrangement of the floral parts, he was quite unable to diagnose the family connections of his foundling.

About two years earlier Michaux had inserted an advertisement in a local newspaper informing the people of New York that "Mr. Michaux, Botanist to His Most Christian Majesty Louis XVI of France," had come amongst them and was prepared to sell plants from his nursery which was established for the primary purpose of acclimatizing American wildflowers before they were shipped home to Europe. It was while on an expedition to search the territory lying between the Alleghany Mountains and the Bahamas that he found the first specimens of the Oconee Bells. They were packed away among his botanical material and narrowly escaped being lost when the ship that carried Michaux back to France was wrecked off the Dutch coast. It was rescued and lay forgotten and unknown for more than forty years, until Asa Gray, the famous American botanist, came across it while studying Michaux's specimens in a Paris herbarium in 1839.

He saw at a glance that he had chanced upon a new plant, something quite different from any American wildflower known in those days. Thinking that his old friend Dr. Charles W. Short of Kentucky should be given the honour of having the new plant named for him, in recognition of his extensive knowledge of, and enthusiasm for, American plants, Asa Gray got into touch with the various botanists working on the American flora and told them of the project, and thus it came about that the new plant was given the provisional name of *Shortia*, and in due course it came to be known as *Shortia galacifolia*, in recognition of its resemblance to the foliage of *Galax*.

When news of Gray's discovery reached the eastern States all who had any interest in the wildflowers of the region went out in search of it. All were disappointed. A year or two later Asa Gray took up the task of finding the Shortia, but without any success, although he visited the Blue Ridge Mountains and searched most diligently in the locality whence Michaux's original specimens had been found. Many years passed by and nothing more was seen of this elusive species until gradually its very existence was forgotten by all but the interested few.

One May morning in 1877 a young school-teacher, George M. Hyams, found a colony of pretty little crimpled bells growing on the mossy banks of the Catawba River in North Carolina. He showed some of them to his father, who in turn sent them to a friend, so that ultimately they reached Asa Gray. He instantly recognized the leaves as being the same as those he had found in Paris forty years before.

The following year he visited the locality, but although he saw the plants growing in their native habitat he was too late to see any flowers. The colony of Shortia was a small one and the story of its discovery, the end of forty years' search, was noised abroad and it was not long before the last of the plants had disappeared from that locality. In those days the necessity for protecting wildflowers had not yet been appreciated.

The American botanists did not despair, however, because they believed this to be only an outlying station and that sooner or later the Oconee Bells would be found away back among the high mountains. This surmise proved correct when several years later, almost a century after its original discovery, the original location was re-discovered. As the years passed by it was gradually established that the Shortia is not such an uncommon plant after all, more and more stations were located but the plant was never found in abundance. So far as can be ascertained these favoured spots do not appear to offer any special conditions that are not to be found elsewhere, and no reason can be given for the limited distribution of the species. At one time the genus must have been much more widespread because there is a very closely allied form, that is very well known in gardens, which has made its home in the moist woodlands of northern Japan.

The Story of the Poppies

ALTHOUGH the Poppies are a beautiful family as a whole, so many of them are annuals or biennials and are so anxious to have done with the care-free days of blossom-time in order to get on with the more serious business of seed-making that they are not of very much value for landscape effect. Some of the more permanent species, however, are among the brightest and gayest of all our hardy flowers, and best of all is the Eastern Poppy, *Papaver orientale*, which comes from the remote valleys where Persia meets Afghanistan. With an easy-going nature that responds to the simplest of cultural methods, this fine Poppy is one of the most effective plants for the herbaceous border, and few are so useful when grown by lake-side or river-bank, whether singly or massed for effect. Under such conditions the Oriental Poppy carries an atmosphere of exotic splendour that forms a delightful foil to sweeps of green lawn and reaches of placid water.

With the approach of high summer the Oriental Poppy is one of the most striking plants in the garden, with its bold clumps of luxurious foliage surmounted by great orange-scarlet flowers whose beauty is enhanced by the blotches of maroon at the base of the petals. This old favourite has been grown since the beginning of the eighteenth century, rather more than a hundred years before the blood-red variety *bracteatum* came from Siberia in 1817. The latter, which gets its varietal name from the bracts that appear at the base of the petals, is probably the better garden plant of the two, because the flowers open rather earlier and last a little longer than the type form.

The two forms remained quite distinct until less than fifty years ago, when an English nurseryman, Mr. Amos Perry, of The Hardy Plant Farm at Enfield, began experimenting with a view to raising new and better varieties. It is fully forty years since he achieved an Award of Merit from the Royal Horticultural Society for the variety "Miss Marsh," which was described at the time as "a fine flower with a showy blending of scarlet and white." Within the next few years he produced a number of plants of varying shades of pink, and several of them gained a like distinction. The best was, and still is, the well-known "Mrs. Perry," which still keeps a place in the nurserymen's lists by reason of its erect and sturdy habit and the pleasant effect of its handsome apricot-pink flowers.

In 1912 the International Flower Show was held at Chelsea, and there Mr. Perry made history by gaining an award for the first white-flowered variety "Silver Queen," which was a seedling from his pink "Queen Alexandra." The Silver Queen was soon forced to abdicate her throne, however. Soon after the Show one of Mr. Perry's customers wrote to him that she had seen the winning exhibit and that she had raised some seedlings from Mrs. Perry, and one of them was a far better plant than the prize-winner, the blooms being "borne upon rigid stems and of a beautiful shade of satiny-white with a conspicuous eye." Mr. Perry went to see the plant, bought it, and put it on the market in 1914 as "Perry's White," and although more than thirty years have passed since then this fine variety is still considered to be the best of the white-flowered Oriental Poppies.

Although *Papaver orientale* and its many varieties are second to none as plants for the open garden they are of little value as cut flowers, and we have to turn to the Iceland Poppies when we want flowers for indoor decoration. These lovely flowers, with their satiny sheen and wonderful range of gay colours, will last for days if picked in the early morning, just as they are about to shed their sepals, and the stems dipped into boiling water for a few seconds. As their common name implies they come from Iceland and the far north, the farthest margins of Canada and Siberia, where their flowers fluttering under the midnight sun are the glory of the sub-arctic moorlands. In the wild state the colour is usually yellow, but under cultivation many delightful tints have been developed. The first to be marketed were the Sunbeam Poppies, a strain with orange and tangerine flowers, sent out by a British nursery firm a good many years ago. Some years they were augmented by the Moonbeam strain, which consisted of amber shades, and about fifteen or twenty years ago they were supplemented by the Coonara pinks. The latter were hailed with delight at the time but have long since been taken for granted as just another shade of the Iceland Poppy, and the very name Coonara is all but forgotten.

A very different story is to be told of the Shirley Poppies, which have taken the name of a small English village to every part of the world. These charming flowers were all derived from a specimen of the common red Corn Poppy that was found growing by the edge of his vicarage garden by the Rev. W. Wilks of Shirley in Surrey. In the summer of 1880 Mr. Wilks noticed that one flower in a mass of Corn Poppies,

Papaver Rheos, differed from all the others in having the margins of the petals lined with white. He marked the plant and carefully collected all its seeds, so that next season he had several hundreds of seedlings of which only a few showed any noticeable difference from the ordinary Corn Poppies of the fields.

Year by year Mr. Wilks selected all seedlings that showed any marked sign of variation, and in course of time developed the well-known strain as a definite type that can be depended upon to come true from seed. In addition to the airy grace of the wild type, the Shirley Poppy, with its silky petals of an infinite range of colour from crimson and orange-scarlet through various tints of rose and salmon pink to that peculiar smoky-blue so rarely seen in flowers, although usually lacking the characteristic black blotch of the common British wildflower, has long been one of the most popular of our garden annuals.

Most aristocratic of the annual species is the haughty Opium Poppy, *P. somniferum*, notable alike for its pleasing architectural form and the splendour of its blooms that may be had in the purest white or in shades of scarlet, pink or mauve, while there is a deep maroon-coloured form that is often grown as the Black Poppy. A native of the Mediterranean region, the Opium Poppy, has been grown since the dawn of history, as has been shown by the discovery of its seeds, which were probably used as food, on the site of ancient lake-dwellings in Switzerland. The white form, which is believed to be the source of the most potent sort of opium, has long been grown all through the Levant and North Africa to the farthest limits of eastern Asia.

The drug is derived from the milky latex that appears when any part of the plant is scratched, and seems to have been known for many thousands of years. For centuries its manufacture was a secret confined to the Middle East, but gradually it spread eastwards until to-day the opium habit is generally assumed to be a characteristic of the Far East. By all accounts the Indian opium has long been the most popular brand, and the story of how it was smuggled into China about a century ago is still one of the romances of the sea. Only the fastest sailing ships were used, and theirs was a particularly dangerous task, sailing along an uncharted coast with the possibility of a typhoon always in the background, and pirates a menace to be reckoned with at every windfall. Such ships were always a juicy morsel for raiders; on the outward voyage they had the cargo of opium, and when homeward bound were laden with the riches their trading had brought. Contrary to general opinion opium seems to have been almost unknown in the Chinese Empire before that time. Even so late as 1842 we are told of a crew of a British ship that had been wrecked on the Island of Formosa being taken to Peking. There they were treated very badly and repeatedly questioned about the Opium Poppy, how it was grown and the best methods of obtaining the drug.

There are many garden varieties of the Opium Poppy; the double Carnation-flowered and Pæony-flowered forms are no new development, as Gerard, writing in 1597, says, "There are divers varieties of double poppies and their colours are commonly either white, red, darke purple, scarlet, or mixt of some of these." The double varieties are of most use in the garden, as they last for several days longer than the single forms, and when the petals drop the shapely seed-pods stand aloft and for a time there is a pleasant assemblage of flowers and pods as the later blooms come on. At the end of the season the upstanding capsules may be harvested and used for winter decoration.

Pansies and Violas

"THE Hearts-ease or Pansie hath many round leaves at the first coming up; afterward they grow somwhat larger, slightly cut above the edges, trailing or creeping upon the ground; the stalkes are weake and tender, whereupon grow floures in form and figure like the Violet, and for the most part of the same bignesse, of three sundry colours, whereof it took the syrname *Tricolor*, that is to say purple, yellow and white or blew; by reason of the beauty and bravery of which colours they be very pleasing to the eye, for smel they have little or none at all."

Gerard's description of the Pansies of Queen Elizabeth's day tells us that they were grown in gardens, but showed little or no difference from the little English wildflower that grew by the heath or hedgerow. In those days the flower had quite a number of common names, but even then the best known was Pansy, supposed to be a corruption of the French, *pensée*, "that's for thoughts," as sad Ophelia explained.

The difference between a Pansy and a Viola is a question that puzzles many a garden-lover who is not enlightened by the statement that while all Pansies are really Violas, not all Violas are suitable for classification as Pansies. The explanation is that all our modern Pansies are developed from two British wild violets, the *Viola tricolor* mentioned by Gerard, and the golden-flowered *Viola lutea*, which another old English writer called the "flammea or great yellow pansie" which he "increased by slips for I could never observe that it bore seeds."

The development of the Pansy as a garden flower goes back to the early part of the nineteenth century, when a small group of keen gardeners living in the south of England began to collect all the different wild varieties and grow them in their gardens. The best yellow variety is said to have been brought from Malmaison soon after the fall of Napoleon, and the finest blue is said to have been of Russian origin. Lord Gambier, who had been discharged from the British Navy under somewhat trying circumstances and took up gardening to help forget his troubles, is often credited with being the first Pansy fancier, but Mr. Thomson, his gardener at Ivor in Buckinghamshire, was really the pioneer. Thomson found the first black-eyed variety growing as a chance seedling in a clump of Heaths, and it was widely distributed under the name "Lady Gambier," although a later critic assures us that it was more like a child's windmill than one of the Show Pansies of his day.

Thomson became one of the recognized leaders in the development of the flower, and a near neighbour, Mr. Hales, gave both encouragement and assistance. Although both these men distributed a number of named varieties, their work was overshadowed by Charles Turner, the nurseryman of Slough, who is still remembered by the fine old Ivy Geranium "Charles Turner"—a lovely plant with geranium-lake flowers—while John Downie, the Edinburgh nurseryman whose name is familiar on account of his namesake the Crab Apple, was one of the foremost growers in Scotland.

Throughout the first half of the Victorian era the growers made the Show Pansy their ideal with flowers such as may never be seen again with their circular outline and perfect symmetry in both form and markings. The gardening books of the day show lovely illustrations of the variously coloured sections such as glossy black, blue or primrose self-coloured varieties, and others with either a white or a yellow ground in which the colours of the lower petals were perfectly symmetrical. About 1860 the Fancy or Belgian Pansies made their appearance, differing from the accepted form in the absence of edgings to the petals while the colours showed nothing of the symmetry that had been the ideal for so long, but were "blotched or otherwise fantastically marked in many beautiful shades with eccentric markings, quite novel in the Pansy." The foreigners soon became very popular and the rules had to be altered to include them, and so all other forms that could not be included within the confines of the Show Pansy came to be classified as Fancy Pansies.

In those days the most precise rules were laid down to cover all merits and faults, but there seems to have been no ruling authority and in consequence there was much confusion in the duplication of names, and it was next to impossible to be sure that the same name was not being used by several raisers. When the vogue was at its height many lovely strains were available in which the colouring and marking were so remarkable that if any of the flowers illustrated in the gardening magazines of the time were shown in a modern flower show, they would fill the gardening world with amazement and delight. The blooms that were set out on the show table were enormous, but they made a poor showing in the garden, and when a younger generation began to grow flowers for garden effect a different type became desirable.

The new taste demanded plants suitable for bedding, with a dwarf spreading habit and masses of bloom over a lengthy period, the individual flowers not necessarily large so long as they were shapely and of good colour. Towards the end of the century a Dr. Stuart of Edinburgh raised a race of what he termed Tufted Pansies on account of their upright habit of growth. This name did not take on, however, and it was gradually displaced in favour of Viola. Dr. Stuart did not approve of this at all and protested in vain that "botanically violets, pansies, and heartsease are all the same, they are the true *Violas*. Tufted Pansies come from garden pansies and *Viola cornuta*, the latter being the seed-bearer." The Viola has come to stay, and may best be described as a flower with a light centre, edged or suffused with a darker colour. The centre should never be darker than the rest of the flower, whereas the Pansy should always have a dark patch in the centre of each of the three lower petals. This dark blotch may be of any colour so long as it gives the typical pansy face. There are no hard or fast rules about colours, but for exhibition purposes the most acceptable flowers are those which have the marginal colour, if any, of the same width and shade all round the bloom.

There is now such a vast range of colour among Pansies and Violas that some of the old distinctions are no longer of first importance. As a general rule Violas are smaller than Pansies, but they are more persistent and can be depended upon to give a greater show of colour over a longer period. The centre of the bloom is still of great importance whether it be the dense dark patch of the Pansy or the soft flawless tints of the Viola. Both are the result of many years' breeding, selection, and development. One of the most difficult tasks in the long story of achievement that has given us the lovely flowers of the modern garden from the tiny wildflowers of the English countryside has been the elimination of the rays or honey guides which still spoil many an otherwise perfect flower, from the exhibition point of view. Those delicate pencillings which we condemn as faults are all that remain of the well-marked honey guides that are to be seen in the wild species from all parts of the world. They are difficult to eliminate because the Viola family has evolved them at great pains, through aeons of time, and carried them in all its wanderings through the temperate regions of the earth, over mountain, plain and swamp so that insect visitors may be guided to the secret store of nectar which has been laid out for the enjoyment of all who are prepared to assist in the supreme task of seed production.

Sweet Violets

WE may trace the story of the Violet through two thousand years of history from the shady Olive groves of ancient Greece to the flowershop around the corner, and during all that time men have been charmed by its quiet and retiring disposition no less than by its fragrant beauty. In Athens Carnations and Violets were the best beloved of all flowers and were worn as garlands at weddings and other ceremonial occasions, and when the main features of the Greek culture were transplanted to Rome these flowers were included. Even in those far-off days the Violet had already made a place for itself among the medicinal herbs, a compress of Violets, Strawberry leaves and Poppy seeds being one of the popular remedies for sick headaches and sleeplessness.

In the monastery gardens of the Middle Ages it was listed among the plants that were "powerful against evil spirits," but by the time Gerard came to write his *Herball* he was able to give his readers a clearer view of the virtues of the Violet. "The floures are good for all inflammations, especially of the sides and lungs; they take away the hoarseness of the chest, the ruggednesse of the windepipe and jaws, and take away thirst."

About a thousand years before Gerard began to plant Violets in his London garden Queen Radegonde of France was growing them at Poitiers. She had founded a nunnery there, and helped to lay out the garden with her own hands. Bishop Fortunatus sent a present of Violets and other scented plants with the message, "Of all fragrant herbes none I send can compare with the nobleness of the purple violet; they shine in royal purple, and perfume and beauty unite in their petals. May you show forth in your life the peace they represent."

Violets are still the "choise floures of delight" in early springtime, and because of our modern methods of hybridization the Violets that we grow to-day are much finer than any that were known in the old days. All these lovely varieties, "Princess of Wales," the finest deep purple, "Rosina," the best rose-coloured variety, the popular "Czar White" and the giant "Double Russian," are believed to have been developed from *Viola odorata*, the fragrant wild species that is equally at home among the hedgerows of England, the shady gorges of the Mediterranean region, and cool banks of Siberia or the far Himalayas.

Little seems to be known of the far-famed Sweet Violets of Parma. Some authorities believe they may have originated in the Moorish gardens of old Spain, while others think they came from Turkey by way of Italy. It seems to be established, however, that when the Empress Josephine began to build up the famous plant collections at Malmaison she sent to Parma for the best-known varieties of Violets. Napoleon's love of Violets, flowers that have always been looked upon as the emblem of modesty, was made manifest when he attempted to grow them in his garden at St. Helena, but they had been recognized as his favourite flowers many years before.

Josephine wore Violets on her wedding day, and his habit of presenting her with a bouquet of fragrant Violets to mark the anniversary gave considerable impetus to their cultivation in France. But it was his banishment to Elba that really set all France thinking in terms of Violets. As he was being taken away his last words to his friends were, "I shall return with the violets in spring." The flower was immediately adopted as a symbol of loyalty by friends and adherents and as a means of identification at their secret meetings, while the terms "Le Père Violette" and "Caporal Violette" were much in evidence as passwords among the initiated.

When the news reached Paris that Napoleon had broken loose again Violets were in great demand; ladies wore violet dresses, and a wonderful display of his favourite flowers greeted him at the Tuileries, but we may imagine that he had little time to admire them. After the crash of all his dreams at Waterloo he went to Josephine's grave and picked a few Violets, which were found in a locket on his breast when he died. With the return of the Bourbons Violets disappeared from the streets of Paris, and one famous actress was hissed off the stage for wearing them, but they returned to favour with the rise of Napoleon III.

He is said to have met his future wife while touring his new

Empire and to have asked the way to her bedroom. Eugenie answered, "Through the chapel door," and appeared at the Court Ball that night wearing a violet gown and Violets in her hair, and this tribute to the "Great Ancestor" won the day. Of course, she had to wear Violets at her wedding and was duly presented with bouquets of them on the anniversaries. Thus it came about that a small boy's affection for the scented Violets that grew in the cool glades of Corsica caused France to take these flowers to her heart and excel in their cultivation and development for a century after his death.

From the cultivation of the Sweet Violet and its varieties is but a step to growing some of the delightful wild species that grow in all parts of the world. The Viola family must be an old one because its three hundred species have gone forth and colonized every temperate clime in both north and southern hemispheres. From the bleak coast of Greenland comes *Viola Selkirkii*, with prettily scalloped leaves and drifts of soft lilac flowers, while the shady nooks among the sunbaked cliffs of Australia have given us *V. hederacea*, remarkable for its starry purple flowers that flutter bravely above a carpet of neat green leaves. From the storm-scarred uplands of the European Alps there comes a gay company of which the gem is probably *V. calcarata*, that spreads its mantle of violet and gold over many a shingly ridge and moist rocky bank. No less enchanting are scores of others from Alaska, the Straits of Magellan, the cool woods of eastern America and the mossy mountain sides of western China.

An old garden variety whose origin is unknown is known as Viola Jackanapes; for generations it was only to be propagated by cuttings, and despite its hardy constitution was gradually dying out. About ten years ago a Swiss nurseryman managed to set a few seeds and nowadays it has taken a new lease of life, although not always quite true to type. The enchanting little flowers are an arresting combination of rich mahogany red above and bright golden yellow below, and has been described as "profusely flowering cushions that resemble a party of small pert imps, the numerous saucy flowers being borne on strong stems."

Benedict Roezl

THE allure of searching for strange new flowers took many an adventurous young man into the wildest and most remote corners of the earth during the middle years of the nineteenth century, when the great rain-forests that clothe the tropics of both hemispheres were combed so thoroughly that later travellers have complained that many of the rarer species have been all but exterminated. These plant-hunters had some very remarkable adventures, but few had such good fortune as befell the Czech collector Benedict Roezl, who had a rare plant come and look for him. This happened in 1871 as he was returning from an expedition into the mountainous interior of New Granada. He was coming down the turbulent Rio Dagua, one of the swiftly flowing rivers that take the nearest course from the mountains to the sea, and was almost within sight of the Pacific when he noticed that he was being accompanied by a huge tree. This old giant had been torn up by the storm of the day before and was a veritable botanic garden with its myriads of perching plants, mosses, ferns, and orchids. Growing among this vegetation was a mass of carmine-purple flowers such as he had never seen before. He sent his servant to collect the plants, a feat that on account of the swiftly flowing current was not easily· accomplished, and when they were hoisted aboard he found it to be a pleasing shrub of two feet high with hairy leaves and numerous terminal panicles of flowers.

On arrival in Europe its history was told and the new plant was named *Roezlia granadensis*, but it was later found out that the foundling was a close relation of the pink-flowered *Monochaetum Bonplandii* and was altered to *M. quadrangularis*. A change would have been necessary in any case because the same name had already been given to the yucca-like plant we now know as *Furcraea Roezlii*, a plant which is well known in gardens under a multitude of names.

Benedict Roezl was born near Prague about 1824 and served as a gardener at the famous gardens of Tetschen for a number of years before he became a professional plant-hunter. He spent the best years of his life in all sorts of out-of-the-way places, from the mountains of California to the hinterlands of Patagonia, but his name is scarcely known to the modern generation of gardeners. In the course of his travels he was robbed no fewer than seventeen times, and one of his most remarkable escapes took place in the broad sunlit plains of Mexico. He was going peacefully on his way when suddenly he found himself surrounded by a band of robbers. Eagerly they searched his baggage in search of gold, and deep was their chagrin when they found nothing but bundles of dead flowers. Some of the more bloodthirsty were anxious to kill him on the principle that dead men tell no tales, but the leader would not hear of this, being of the opinion that should any harm come to this poor harmless creature ill luck would follow them. His argument was that the fellow was only a simpleton roaming over the countryside picking flowers, and as all such are under the special protection of God it would indeed be tempting providence to meddle with him. Roezl was accordingly allowed to go free and was able to continue introducing new plants to the gardens of Europe. One of the best known of all his plants is the lovely *Lilium Roezlii*, a close relative of the well-known Panther Lily of California, but even more desirable on account of its orange or blood-red flowers dotted with purple spots. Among the other lilies he introduced are *L. parvum* and *L. washingtonianum*.

One of his most hair-raising adventures was among the trackless forests that clothe the high mountains of Colombo. He happened to be working late one evening checking over notes and the specimens collected during the day. Suddenly he became aware that a great spotted jaguar was watching every movement through the open doorway. The only reaction was to remain perfectly still while the creature explored the tent and quietly rubbed the side of its head against the rough edge of the table and purred as gently as a domestic pussy. With a sudden movement Roezl snatched up the kerosene lamp and threw it at the intruder and dropped to the floor, hoping for the best. Great was his relief when the jaguar vanished into the night with a snarl of fear, and by the time the porters arrived upon the scene to find out what all the commotion was about, the creature had gone and the only evidence of its visit was the broken lamp and some footprints on the soft clay floor.

He returned to Europe and settled at Prague, where he died in 1885, and a statue has since been raised there in his honour. Although an outstanding plant hunter he seems to have lacked the discrimination necessary for the successful botanist. In 1857 he published a catalogue of the Mexican Conifers he had growing in a nursery he had established in that country so that they could be acclimatized for introduction into Europe. There he listed no fewer than eighty-two new species of Pinus, but these were soon found to be none other than varieties of six or seven species that had been described by earlier botanists.

He introduced a vast number of plants into European gardens, including several species of Agaves and other succulents from the dry uplands of Mexico, a pale orange-red Hippeastrum from Bolivia, the curious *Anthurium Roezlii* with its quaint white spathes from the Andes of Santa Martha and, finest of all, the dwarf variety of *Aphelandra aurantiaca* that bears his name. This distinguished pot plant for the tropical glasshouse is probably the best of all his introductions, with its spikes of deep orange-scarlet blossoms and curiously twisted leaves which have a silvery sheen between the veins.

Benedict Roezl will always be remembered as an Orchid collector, and few men knew so much as he did about the whereabouts of all the more aristocratic members of the family that make their home in the forests of the American continent. His name is commemorated in numerous species and varieties of Cattleya, Selenipedium, and, in fact, most of the Orchid genera from Mexico or South America. Among the best known are *Masdevallia Roezlii*, whose quaint flowers of indian-purple are among the most striking forms of the fantastic Chimerae group; another is the yellow and brown Stanhopea from Nicaragua, and among the most useful is *Miltonia Roezlii*, which under good cultivation may be depended upon to bloom twice a year, during the cool periods of spring and autumn. The large, flat, white blooms always attract attention, with their purple bands at the base of the petals and the stain of tangerine at the labellum.

A Family of Aristocrats

ORCHIDS are the crown and glory of the plant world, and members of this aristocratic family are to be met with wherever wild-flowers grow, from the chilly bogs lying within the Arctic Circle to the teeming jungles that swelter under the tropical sun. Although there are about ten thousand species of wild Orchids the only member of the family that has ever been of any economic importance to man is the Vanilla, a climber from the tropics of Mexico. Vanilla was used by the Aztecs to flavour chocolate long before Columbus discovered America, and the old way of obtaining it was to dry the semi-ripe seed-pods in the sun so as to cause them to secrete it on the outside in the form of crystals. Nowadays, however, Vanilla flavouring can be produced synthetically at a fraction of the cost of the natural product, and in consequence the commercial cultivation of the Vanilla Orchid is no longer profitable.

Many of the European ground Orchids were well known to the old herbalists, although they were probably never cultivated in gardens, and it was not until 1731 that the first exotic species—a pink-flowered Bletia from the Bahamas—arrived in Britain. During the next century or so many species from both the temperate and tropical forests of the world found their way into the gardens of Europe, but their needs were so little understood that few of them survived for any length of time. This great family has colonized every part of the world, but the largest-flowered and most desirable types grow only where they can find warmth and moisture in abundance, in the great rain-forests of eastern Asia and South America.

Most of these are perching plants, preferring the tops of the loftiest trees or outcrops of moss-covered rock to the over-crowded conditions of the forest floor, and to achieve this end they have developed a very special kind of root which is capable of absorbing moisture from the air. This peculiarity, together with the need for a suitably humid atmosphere, baffled the early growers and even within the past century it was still considered a matter for congratulation if some of these perching plants could be persuaded to produce a few flowers before dying. Thus the whole Orchid family got a reputation of having flowers whose distinctive beauty was excelled only by their fragility.

The gorgeous blooms were so difficult to grow and so expensive to buy that the cult of the Orchid revealed itself as the rich man's hobby, and even the fantastic sums spent on Tulips, in the days when all the Netherlands went crazy about them, paled into insignificance in comparison with what was spent by the rich merchant princes of the Victorian era at the height of the orchid fashion. Some varieties became so rare as to be almost priceless, and achieved a position among the treasures of men comparable only with the masterpieces of sculpture and art.

The forests of eastern Asia have given us some of our most popular Orchids: the charming Coelogynes, of which the virginal *C. cristata* is an abiding favourite; the gay Dendrobiums, among whom the bright maroon-eyed *D. nobile* has for centuries been a popular medicinal plant among the Chinese; and the scented Vandas with their blossoms of many shades and colours, of which the most delightful of all is the famous Blue Orchid, *Vanda coerulea*. The Blue Orchid was first seen by Dr. William Griffith in the Khasia Hills of Assam in 1837. It was brought to England, flowered and lost, and was not seen again for many years. About the middle of the century it was re-introduced and was long regarded as a great treasure, the hosts of soft blue butterflies placing it high among the ranks of cultivated plants.

Sir Joseph Hooker, who visited the Khasia Hills about 1850, tells in his *Journal* of his meeting with the Blue Orchid. "Near the village of Larnac oak woods are passed in which *Vanda coerulea* grows in profusion, waving its panicles of azure flowers in the wind. As this beautiful orchid is at present attracting great attention from its high price, beauty and difficulty of cultivation, I shall point out how totally at variance with its native habits is the cultivation thought necessary for it in England. The dry, grassy hills which it inhabits are elevated 3,000 to 4,000 feet, the trees are small, gnarled, and very sparingly leafy so that the Vanda which grows on their limbs is fully exposed to sun, rain and wind. There is no moss or lichen on the branches with the Vanda, whose roots sprawl over the dry rough bark." He goes on to describe the climate at considerable length and proceeds—"now this winter's cold, summer's heat and autumn's drought, and above all this constant free exposure to fresh air and the winds of heaven, are all things which we avoid exposing our orchids to in England. It is under these conditions that all the finer Indian Orchidacea grow. We collected seven men's loads of this superb plant for the Royal Gardens at Kew, but owing to unavoidable accidents and difficulties few specimens reached England alive. A gentleman, who sent his gardener with us to be shown the locality, was more successful. He sent one man's load to England on commission and, although it arrived in a very poor state, sold for £300, the individual plants fetching prices varying from £3 to £10. Had all arrived alive they would have cleared £1,000. An active collector, with the facilities I possessed might easily clear from £2,000 to £3,000 in one season by the sale of Khasia orchids. On the following day we turned out our Vandas to dress the specimens for travelling and to preserve the flowers for botanical purposes. Of the latter we had three hundred and sixty panicles, each composed of from six to twenty-one broad pale blue tasselated flowers, three and a half to four inches across, and they formed three piles on the verandah floor, each a yard high. What would we not have given to have been able to transport a single panicle to an English fete?"

In course of time Hooker's remarks reached India, and the Calcutta businessmen took up the export of Blue Orchids from the Manipur district of Assam. The exploitation of these plants reached such dimensions that the Government of Assam in conjunction with that of Burma had to prohibit the export of Orchids in order to prevent the complete denudation of the forests. In this way the lovely Blue Orchid came to be one of the first wildflowers to be protected by legislation.

The Moth Orchids, Phalaenopsis, have been termed the grandest of the family, and their queen is the enchanting *Phalaenopsis Aphrodite*, whose lovely white flowers are handsomely marked with scarlet and gold. On its arrival from the Philippines in 1836 it was immediately acquired by the Duke of Devonshire for one hundred guineas, and in consequence was still extremely rare when Robert Fortune visited Manila nine years later with the object of procuring it in quantity.

Being particularly anxious to get some fine specimens of *Phalaenopsis Aphrodite* he offered one dollar, a large sum of money in those days, for the best specimen. He camped in the neighbourhood of a lake and held a sort of daily market for the

purchase of plants, and it was not long before each day saw the
front of his hut strewn with Orchids just as they had been removed
from the trees, many still smothered with blossoms. Some days
after he had offered the reward for the best Moth Orchid he was
delighted to see two native boys approaching with a plant of
extraordinary size, "having ten or twelve branching flower-
stalks upon it, and upwards of a hundred flowers in full bloom.
'There,' they cried in triumph, 'is not that worth a dollar?' I
acknowledged that they were well entitled to the reward and
took immediate possession of my prize." In due course it
arrived in England, and as the finest specimen of *Phalaenopsis
Aphrodite* in cultivation, was for many years the pride of the
Royal Horticultural Society's garden at Chiswick.

The great rain-forests of Brazil and Central America have
given us many Orchids that have become horticultural treasures
of great value: the graceful Oncidiums, with their clouds of
dainty moth-like blossoms marked with bars or spots of bronze
and gold; the quaint Masdevallias, with their oddly shaped
flowers and gay colours; and the giants of the family, the reed-
like Sobralias, which form thickets up to twenty feet in height
and surmount them with waves of purple blossom.

But most variable and best beloved of all are the glorious
Cattleya, considered by most orchid growers as the noblest
members of the family. When one fancier attempted to raise the
exquisite *Cattleya Thayeriana* from seed he obtained eighty
seedlings, none of which matched each other exactly, and some
were so very different from each other and from the parent that
it seemed incredible that they should all be the offspring of the
same plant. The blooms, varying from six to eight inches across,
ranged from white and pale pink to the most entrancing shades
of lilac and crimson, while the orange and carmine markings of
the lip had background tonings of blush pink and old rose.

In 1818 there arrived in England a very pleasing variety that became known as *Cattleya labiata vera* so that it might be distinguished from the various forms of *Cattleya labiata* already in cultivation. In later years the plants of *vera* seem to have lost their constitution and it became very rare, the last specimen being lost when a mansion in the south of England was burned down, destroying the conservatory. When it was desired to replace this variety the grower found that not only was the plant lost to cultivation, but even its original home had long been forgotten. Many years afterwards the discovery was made that the original plant had arrived as a stowaway among the packing around a consignment of lichens and mosses that had been sent from the Organ Mountains in the south of Brazil.

For nearly seventy years this lovely flower was the Holy Grail of the Orchid-hunters, and all efforts to locate it in its wild state were in vain. One day in the summer of 1889 a rumour reached London that the elusive beauty had been seen disporting itself in a fashionable part of Paris. An expert was sent posthaste to confirm the good news and if possible find out where the long-lost treasure had been found, and in this way *Cattleya labiata vera* returned from the forests of Brazil to bewitch a new generation of Orchid lovers.

Three-quarters of a century ago Orchid-hunting was not quite such a romantic business as it might appear to-day, because the background of keen commercial competition compelled each and every one of the explorers to keep secret the plans he had made and the places where the finest and most desirable species were to be found. To-day we have become so accustomed to plant-hunters being sent out more or less by public subscription, and such men as Reginald Farrer and Captain Kingdon Ward sending progress reports from the most remote places, that the rivalry of the commercial plant-hunters tends to be forgotten.

The modern plant-hunter gives us books and maps which

show the country and its vegetation with so much thoroughness and detail that the studious reader may become almost as well-informed about the flora of north-western Kansu or the Mishmi Hills as the explorer himself. The old-time Orchid-hunters had a very different outlook. Each and every one of them observed the slogan "Guard your stations," knowing only too well that not only success but livelihood itself depended to a great extent on keeping all activities secret. We are told that many of them used maps in which no names of any sort appeared, although their own secret hieroglyphics marked rivers, valleys, mountain passes, and the locations where good plants had been found or were suspected of growing. Some collectors even went so far as to give false stations to their friends and employers, "for prudential business reasons."

A very good example of this commercial outlook is given in the story of *Cypripedium Spicerianum*, a charming little Slipper Orchid with blooms of ivory, violet, and green, that comes from the hills of Assam. Originally found by a Tea-planter named Spicer, it was sold to a German professional plant-hunter who, with the thoroughness typical of his race, took great pains to exterminate it in its only known locality so as to be able to introduce a rare species into Europe in 1870.

The secrecy of the collectors in the field and the faulty methods of cultivation at home meant that quite a number of highly desirable Orchids were grown and flowered and then lost to cultivation. Little or nothing was known of their native habitat, and in some cases many years passed before they were seen again. Such a one was *Cypripedium Fairrieanum*, whose colouring is a symphony of purple, violet, yellow, and brown, with the petals beautifully fringed with long, silky hairs. It was discovered in the Himalayas in 1855 and sent home to England, and bears the name of a Mr. Fairrie of Liverpool, who obtained it at a sale of Assam plants. It flowered three years later and was shown at the Royal Horticultural Society's show, where the handsomely marked flowers, each about three-and-a-half inches across and arising from woolly sheathing bracts, aroused a good deal of interest. It was lost soon afterwards, however, and the forests of northern India were ransacked without result. For nearly fifty years it was known as the "Lost Orchid," and a reward of £1,000 was offered for its capture and return to civilization. *C. Fairrieanum* was not seen again until 1904, when a party of surveyors came across it in an inaccessible valley where the mountains of Bhutan meet those of the adjacent Sikkim. Unfortunately, they seem to have bungled the introduction of the plant into cultivation, and reaped but little reward for their discovery.

Among the flowers that have been loved and lost few have had such a strange history as *Cypripedium Curtisii*, which was first sent home from the Botanic Garden of Penang by Charles Curtis, who was a collector for the famous firm of Veitch of Chelsea. That was in 1883, and apparently the plant was soon afterwards lost. Nothing was known of its origin, but as it had come from Penang it was assumed to be a native of the Malayan uplands, and quite a number of collectors went out there to look for it. Not one of them was successful, and as the years rolled silently by it joined the ranks of the "lost Orchids" and its existence began to be no more than a vague memory. About the turn of the century a young Swede named Ericson happened to be plant-hunting among the mountains of Sumatra, and was forced to seek a night's shelter in a small hut. There on the walls he found the portrait of a dainty purple and white spotted Slipper Orchid, and underneath ran the legend, "C.C.'s contribution to the adornment of the house."

Realizing that he had been fortunate enough to have stumbled across the home of Curtis's Slipper Orchid, Ericson made up his mind to stay on in the locality until he had found it. For three weeks he searched every likely and unlikely habitat but without success and, unable to spare any more time, he was on the point of giving up in despair when he sat down to rest and admire the view from a rocky eminence. He happened to look down and there he found the lost Slipper Orchid growing in great plenty in the shady crevices of the rock.

Gone are the days when men were happy to spend vast sums of money on Orchid plants, but a new interest is arising in this amazingly versatile family. Gardeners the world over are beginning to scrape an acquaintance with the vast number of beautiful hardy species growing wild in all parts of the temperate region. These ground Orchids, desirable for the extraordinary variety of their flowers, may be grown in any ordinary garden and require no more detailed attention than is usually bestowed on any other specialized group of flowers. And as they become better known it may be that a new race of fanciers is being born to worship at the feet of this aristocratic family.

Robert Fortune

At the beginning of Queen Victoria's reign there was little beyond evergreens to provide some colour and interest in the garden between the fall of the leaf and the appearance of the first snowdrop, but a century ago Robert Fortune went to China at the request of the Royal Horticultural Society and sent home a number of plants that may be depended upon to flower during the dull period. In addition to the Chinese Leadwort, Japanese Anemones and Chrysanthemums of autumn, he sent the winter Honeysuckles, *Lonicera fragrantissima* and *L. Standishii*, whose fragrance compensates for their pale flowers, and the indispensable yellow Jasmine so familiar throughout the long months of winter on account of its yellow stars that gleam on many a sheltered wall. Spring is ushered in by his Golden-Bell, *Forsythia Fortunei*, and the graceful Bleeding Heart, *Dicentra spectabilis*, which was hailed as the finest hardy plant of the century and is still met with in many an old-fashioned garden.

Although he reached Hong Kong about the middle of 1843, it was not until about the middle of the following year that the full tide of his plants began to arrive in London. Among the first was *Chirita sinensis*, a fine plant with erect spikes of a most pleasing shade of lavender, found under the dripping rocks of a ravine where ferns and small shrubs grew in abundance. Within a few weeks he was off to Amoy, whence came some "very pretty roses producing small double flowers of great neatness and beauty."

Among the tombs on the ramparts of the old part of the city of Shanghai he found the stately *Anemone japonica*, now so well known for its profusion of pure white, shell pink or red flowers that last well through the autumn. From the same place came the Chinese Leadwort, *Ceratostigma plumbaginoides*, whose starry clusters of gentian blue phlox-like flowers are followed by the most brilliant autumn tints we have among herbaceous plants. Most of the early specimens distributed by the Royal Horticultural Society failed to survive their first English winter. In 1847 Lady Larpent exhibited some of the flowers at a London show, and an enterprising firm of nurserymen adopted the plant as a "novelty," so that within a year or two it was being distributed throughout the land as *Plumbago Larpentae*, a name by which it is still listed by some old-fashioned nurserymen.

The Chinese, who had right on their side, had been defeated and unjustly compelled to pay a large indemnity, felt so hostile to foreigners that it was practically impossible for Robert Fortune to venture far beyond the Treaty Ports of Amoy, Canton, Foochow, Ningpo, and Shanghai. While in Shanghai he heard so much about the great nurseries of the interior that he took the risk of visiting them in the guise of an itinerant Chinese beggar. This journey proved a big disappointment and almost ended in disaster, but he was able to bring back a few plants, including his lovely yellow Tea Rose and the white form of *Wistaria sinensis*.

From the environs of Canton came the pretty Blue Spiraea, *Caryopteris Mastacanthus*, but it, too, was lost within a few years, and the aromatic leaves surmounted by trusses of Hyacinth-blue flowers were not seen again until 1880. From Ningpo Fortune made a series of journeys into the nearby hills to study the cultivation and manufacture of Tea, being the first European to do so. While there several new plants were found along with the attractive *Rhododendron Fortunei*, notable for its peculiar spicy scent, but the most striking find was probably the large-flowered *Clematis languinosa*, to which we are indebted as one of the parents of the gaily-coloured tribe of Clematis whose flowers of crimson, violet, purple, and blue have so long been among the indispensables.

He took the opportunity of exploring the island of Chusan while it was still under British control, and thought it one of the pleasantest places on earth. There for the first time he saw wild plants of *Wistaria sinensis* climbing through the hedges and trees with long festoons of blossom decorating the narrow mountain tracks. Among his captures were the Chusan Palm, one of the hardiest members of a vast tropical family, the pretty *Azalea ovatum*, the Chusan Daisy that later became the progenitor of the Pompon Chrysanthemums that became so popular a generation later. He visited the island several times and spent many happy days rambling over the hills admiring the myriads of wildflowers. Early in spring he found them covered with *Daphne Genkwa*, whose long, slender wands of lilac-coloured blossom presented a memorable sight. It was in a mandarin's garden on Chusan that he first met *Diervillea florida*, which is really a native of north China, and thought it one of the most beautiful of all shrubs when the leaves were hidden beneath a mantle of pink brocade.

It is recorded somewhere that when Robert Fortune was making his arrangements to leave for the China coast he asked the Committee for permission to buy a gun, and one of the members suggested that his energies would be better employed in learning to speak Chinese. He took a double-barrelled gun, and it is as well that he did so, otherwise he might not have returned. The only European on board a Chinese junk, he was in bed with fever when the captain announced that they were about to be attacked by pirates. At first he ridiculed the idea, but one glance was enough to send him into action. Ahead were four or five junks acting in a most suspicious manner, while all around was bustle and confusion as the crew and native passengers hastened to hide their valuables among the ballast. Only when everything was put out of sight were some stones brought up from the hold. These were intended to be hurled at the enemy, but while he was still a long way off all the natives lost heart and disappeared below. The only exceptions were the two helmsmen, who were kept at their post by Fortune's guns. He allowed the pirates to fire several broadsides before taking the offensive. " 'Now, Mandarin, now! They are quite close enough!' cried my companions who did not wish another broadside like the last. I, being of the same opinion, raised myself above the high stern of the junk; and while the pirates were not twenty yards from us, hooting and yelling, I raked their decks fore and aft with ball and shot from my double-barrelled gun. Had a thunderbolt fallen among them they could not have been more surprised. Doubtless many were wounded and probably some were killed. At all events the whole crew, no fewer than forty or fifty men, who a moment before crowded the deck, disappeared in a marvellous manner, sheltering themselves behind the bulwarks or lying flat on their faces. They were so completely taken by surprise that their junk was left without a helmsman; her sails flapped in the wind; and as we were still carrying all sail and keeping on our right course, they were soon left a considerable way astern."

Another pirate bore down on them and the same tactics were employed, the helmsman was killed and it too was left with sails flapping helplessly in the wind. The others, seeing what had happened, prudently withdrew, and the doughty crew came forth and began to pass rude remarks about the pirates they had recently found so terrifying. Two days later another pirate fleet intercepted them, only to be driven off by the same methods, and when Chusan was reached the crew was so impressed with Fortune's ability to deal with pirates that he was not allowed to land until he had again demonstrated the persuasive qualities of the double-barrelled gun.

Fortune had been appointed at a salary of £100 per annum and expenses, and when, after a year's experience of the trials and difficulties of life in China, he wrote home asking that it might be increased he was coldly informed that "the mere pecuniary returns of your mission ought to be but a secondary consideration to you." Although he spent nearly twenty years plant-hunting in the Orient, it is not altogether surprising that his late ventures were made under the auspices of more generous employers.

More than a hundred years have passed since Robert Fortune began to look for wildflowers along the fringes of the "Flowery Land," and although the conditions at that time made it impossible for him to amass the vast numbers collected by later travellers, he made a very important contribution to our garden flora. Some of his plants became instant favourites and before long invaded every cottage garden in the country, while others gave rise to garden varieties of great merit and, so popular have many of these plants become, there is scarcely a garden that does not owe something of its charm and beauty to the work of Robert Fortune.

The Story of the Daffodil

"The Narcissus wondrously glittering, a noble sight for all, whether immortal Gods, or mortal men; from whose root an hundred heads spring forth, and at the fragrant odour thereof all the broad heaven above, and all the earth laughed, and the salt-wave of the Sea."

Thus Homer sang the praises of the Daffodil in his *Hymn to Demeter* away back in the very dawn of history. None of our garden plants has enjoyed such constant favour as the Daffodil, because even in those old years it was greatly prized as a decorative flower in connection with the ancient rites of death and burial. In addition to the hundreds of garden forms, the family as at present recognized consists of about fifty species and well-defined varieties of wildflowers from Spain and Morocco through the Mediterranean region and northern Europe to the western boundaries of the old Chinese Empire. All are of easy cultivation, they require only to be left alone and will pay an annual tribute of scent and beauty that increases with the passing of the years. One of the first to bloom is the splendid *N. maximus*, and every week brings other and more graceful flowers from the Hoop-petticoats, the many-flowered Tazettas, the sweet Jonquils until the season ends with the fragrant Poets' Narcissus, one of the loveliest of all flowers.

In all probability Homer paid tribute to the scented *N. Tazetta* which grows wild in all its many well-known forms from the Canary Islands to the open woodlands of China. The form from the Far East, known in gardens as the Sacred Lily of China, has been adopted by the Chinese as the emblem of spring from time immemorial. They have a legend which tells of a rich merchant who gave all his money to the poor, leaving only a few barren acres to his son, Sung Li. The young man went off to see the world and somewhere on the borders of Persia was set upon, robbed, and left for dead. A lonely hermit nursed him back to health, and when spring came the banks of a nearby creek were covered with masses of the most beautiful flowers Sung Li had ever seen. He dug up a few roots and set off for home. Although poor and dispirited he set to work and cultivated the few stony acres, and as the years passed he was able to sell bulbs of the lovely flower he had found in his wanderings. It reached Europe about the middle of the eighteenth century, and soon became well known as the Chinese Sacred Lily. The flower was known to the Chinese as the Flower of the Gods and, grown in shallow vessels of sand and water, became the emblem of spring.

In Europe the yellow trumpet Daffodil is the most popular member of the family, although why Linnaeus should have called it *Narcissus pseudo-Narcissus*, the "false Narcissus," does not seem clear when it bears so triumphantly "the rising stalks with yellow blossoms crowned" that were found by the nymphs who sought to bury the body of the beautiful Narcissus. Every flower-lover knows the myth of the youth who was doomed to admire his own beauty until Nemesis took pity and changed him into a flower. This ancient Greek legend was evidently well known in medieval times, and the rare old herbal *Ortus Sanitatis*, published in 1491, has a remarkable figure that may well represent the comely youth in the process of being transformed.

The wildflower from which most of our Daffodils have sprung is recognized as the form with the yellow trumpet and citron perianth that grows on the banks of streams or in open woodlands along the fringes of the European continent from Scandinavia to Spain and through the cool moist woodlands of the south to the edge of the Balkans. The common name, a corruption of Asphodel, the lovely flower that grew in the Elysian Fields, became Daffodil by capping itself with a letter it has worn with dignity and grace for wellnigh four hundred years through much the same process of alliteration as gave us Hollyhock, Beauty Bush, and many others.

The first description of the Daffodil to be published in English was written by William Turner, who had a famous garden near the present site of Kew Gardens, early in the sixteenth century. At that time only about two dozen different sorts were known, but when John Parkinson, Apothecarie to James I, took up the task in 1629 the number of species and varieties in cultivation had increased to nearly a hundred. He is the first to mention the "greate Nonesuch Daffodil, or Incomparable Daffodil—the cup doth very well resemble the chalice that in former dayes with us, and beyond the Seas is still used to hold the Sacramental Wine, that is with a narrower bottome and a wide mouth."

One of the most widely known members of the *Large-cupped* section of the daffodil family is "Sir Watkin," on account of its rich primrose colour and cup of golden yellow, that is known to be a very old variety long known in gardens as the "Big

Welshman" before it was taken up by the nurseryman, William Brockbank, over sixty years ago. Some lovers of old-fashioned flowers like to think that it may actually date back to the days of John Parkinson, but unfortunately there is no reliable evidence to support the contention.

John Rea, who published his *Flora Culturum* in 1665, did not make any attempt to describe all the numerous varieties grown in his time, but was the first Daffodil grower to discuss the problem of raising new forms from seed. "If any desire to sow seeds of Daffodils in the hope to raise some new varieties, those of the Nonpariel, the great Spanish Yellow, the Spanish whites, and the Jonquilla are the aptest to bring good seeds and the likeliest to yield diversities; they may be sowed in September and not removed of three yeares, and then in June taken up, and presently set again in good ground at wider distances, where they may stand until you may see what flowers they will bear, and disposed of as they deserve." These remarks show that the production and selection of seedlings had already begun, but little progress seems to have been made by British gardeners. When Philip Miller wrote his *Gardeners' Dictionary* three-quarters of a century later he lamented that most of the newer varieties were being imported. After discussing some of the more popular sorts he goes on to say, "There are several other varieties of these flowers that are annually brought over from Holland and Flanders where gardeners are very industrious in raising these and other bulbous-rooted flowers from seeds, whereby they continually procure some new varieties which recompenses them for their trouble and expense; but in England there are very few persons who have the patience to propagate any of these flowers that way, it being commonly five years before they can expect to see the fruits of their labour," and points out that this dependence on the Dutch growers has kept up the price "on account of the great demand for 'em in England."

The next half-century saw the rise of Kew and the great English nurseries which specialized in new and rare plants, so that it was not until about a hundred years ago that a keen interest in Daffodils was revived. One of the first fanciers was William Herbert, Dean of Manchester Cathedral, who in 1837 published a book on the *Amaryllidaceae*, the family to which the Narcissi belong. While in the process of gathering the material for his book he found that about 1799 a clockmaker named Johnson, who lived at Prescot in the north of England, had crossed two distinct species of Amaryllis and had obtained the plant that is still grown as *A. Johnsonii*. This, incidentally, is the first recorded example of a plant being raised by artificial pollination between two distinct species. Noting that the *Incomparabilis*, or chalice-cupped, group appeared to be midway between the trumpet Daffodils and the Poets' Narcissi he made a number of crosses to see whether or not these plants should be classified as true species or as natural hybrids. The new varieites which were named and described in his work showed the remarkable possibilities of plant-breeding among the Narcissi, and did much to create an interest in the raising of hybrids.

One of the best known of the early hybrids is *N. Horsfieldii*, whose broad white perianth and rich yellow trumpet keep a place in the modern lists, which was raised about 1845 by John Horsfield, a cottage weaver of Prestwick, who crossed the best flower in his garden with one of the wild Daffodils that grew on the banks of a nearby stream. He gave a few bulbs to a neighbouring nurseryman, who named them "Mrs. Harrison Weir," but about twenty years later the variety fell into the hands of Peter Barr, who distributed it under the name it still bears. The next to take up the cult of the Daffodil was Edward Leeds, a stockbroker of Manchester, who owned a large garden and orchard on the banks of the Stretford Canal, some miles from the city. He raised many varieties between 1835 and his death in 1877, but none of them seems to have had sufficient merit to live until the present time.

It is to Peter Barr more than any other man that we are indebted for the modern Daffodils that flutter and dance their way through the spring sunshine. In 1863, along with a friend, he founded the firm of Barr and Sugden, and within a short time began to specialize in Daffodils. When William Backhouse, the raiser of the well-known "Emperor" and "Empress," and many others, died in 1869, the firm acquired his collection. When Leeds died the bulk of his material was also acquired, and many of the flowers were such a distinct advance on anything that the firm had grown hitherto that they were kept separate as "Leeds' Seedlings," and ultimately became the nucleus of the Leedsii or White Star, section as it used to be known.

Six years later the firm of Peter Barr and Sons was founded, and the first of their seedlings appeared the following season. From then until his death in 1909 Peter Barr led the world in growing, selecting, crossing, and improving the Daffodil. He travelled all over the Iberian Peninsula and other parts of southern Europe where Narcissi grow wild, and came to have the finest collection of wild species and varieties in existence. He was one of the sponsors of the first Daffodil Conference held at the Royal Horticultural Society's garden at Chiswick in 1884, and from about that time began to be known as the Daffodil King. Many new varieties were placed on the market by Peter Barr and Sons, and their work was commemorated in the Barrii, or Star, section of the Narcissus family. Undoubtedly their greatest triumph was the introduction of the White Trumpet variety, "Peter Barr," which gained all possible Daffodil awards in the years following its appearance in the spring of 1902. It was put on the market at the, then, fabulous price of £50 per bulb, and even to-day is still worthy of a place in the garden.

Peter Barr's greatest thrill as a collector was the discovery of the charming *N. cyclamineus* growing in boggy places in the mountain valley of Vallonga, not far from Oporto, in 1887. This lovely flower, with its reflexed perianth and straight tube-like yellow trumpet, had been known in England more than two hundred and fifty years before, having been figured in the *Theatrum Florae* published in 1633. It had long been lost to cultivation, and Dean Herbert would not even accept it as a true species, but dismissed it as "an absurdity which will never be found to exist."

Probably the most interesting event in the long story of the Daffodil took place in 1911 at the Investiture of Edward, Prince of Wales, when the flower was officially adopted as the National Flower of Wales. This takes us back to the middle of the fifteenth century when Henry Tudor was making a bid for the English Crown. He was only a poor Welsh gentleman, whose grand-mother, Catherine d'Valois of France, married Henry V of England, and who two years after the king's death married his ancestor Owen Tudor in 1425. Owen was a nobody, according to the standards of the day, and his family adopted the d'Valois colours of green and white.

Ever since Wales had been overrun by the English the bards had been prophesying that one day one of the Cymry brother-hood would rule the land. Henry Tudor, taking advantage of his Welsh ancestry, landed secretly in South Wales in 1485 and quietly set about encouraging them to bring the old prophecy up to date, so that the ancient dream of liberation from the hated English would help his cause. His colours, green and white, became the password among the patriots of the day. When they met no words were necessary, one or other picked a Leek or Daffodil, or indeed any other plant that happened to be handy so long as it had a green stem springing from a white root. There is plenty of evidence that in those days the Leek was one of the commonest plants in cultivation: one authority on medieval customs states that "Laec tun" was a vernacular term for kitchen garden used in the same way as "Cabbage patch" is used to-day. During the succeeding centuries there has been a long rivalry between the humble Leek and the aristocratic Daffodil for the honour of representing Wales in the floral world. Now that the matter has been officially settled it is good to know that "Sir Watkin" and his kindred belong to a family that knows something of ancient dignity.

"Sweet-scented Peas"

FEW chance seedlings have been accorded the homage paid to a Sweet Pea that made its appearance during the first year of the present century, just one season after the great show held in the Crystal Palace, London, to celebrate the bi-centenary of the introduction of the flower. Sweet Peas are all descendants of a weedy little Vetch that grows wild in Sicily, but has been grown in England since the days of Queen Anne when Father Fran-

cisco Cupani, a devout Italian monk, sent seeds from his garden
at Palermo to Dr. Uvedale, master of the Grammar School at
Enfield and famous as "a curious collector and introducer of
many rare exoticks, plants and flowers." The small flowers with
their purple standards and sky-blue wings, about the size and
shape of the ordinary garden Peas, attracted but little attention.
Within a quarter of a century "Sweet-scented Peas" were on
sale in London, and some years later we hear of the appearance
of the first named variety, "The Painted Lady," a bicolour with
white or blush-pink wings and rose-coloured standards. This
variety was still being grown at the beginning of the present
century when it was superseded by the improved form "Blanche
Ferry."

Gradually the flowers found favour, and in 1793 seeds of
black, scarlet, and white forms, in addition to The Painted Lady,
were offered by John Mason of the Orange Tree in Fleet Street,
London, but another eighty years were to pass before there was
very much improvement. Captivated by the grace and lightness
of the flowers, combined with their free flowering and easy
cultivation, Henry Eckford began experimenting with them at
a time when it is doubtful if there were more than fifteen distinct
varieties in existence. He, more than anyone, made possible the
Sweet Peas as we know them to-day. He developed flowers that
were more pleasing to the eye and greatly increased the colour
range without sacrificing the fragrance that has always been the
flower's greatest asset. So successful was he that at the great
Bi-Centennial Show held at the Crystal Palace in London, in
1900, no fewer than 115 of the 264 varieties listed up to that
time had originated at Henry Eckford's nursery at Wem in
Shropshire.

The Sweet-pea fanciers gathered at that great show from all
parts of the world had no idea that they were on the eve of the
most remarkable improvement that has ever taken place in the

development of a garden flower, and that the varieties they all admired so much would be considered old-fashioned within a few short years.

The following summer Silas Cole, gardener to the Earl Spencer at Althorp Park near Northampton, showed a variety that had appeared among his Sweet Peas, a variety that completely revolutionized the popular conception of Sweet Peas at that time. It created a sensation, nothing had been seen to compare with it. Its beautifully waved and frilled flowers, increased size, and attractive colour captivated the hearts of Sweet-pea lovers everywhere. So great was the enthusiasm that the *Daily Mail* newspaper offered a £1,000 prize for the best bowl of Sweet Peas shown at the Crystal Palace. Inquiries were made as to its origin and the fact was established that it arose as a variety from Eckford's "Prima Donna," one of the beauties of the day whose lovely pink colouring had been bequeathed to its offspring along with the ability to produce four flowers to the stem.

Silas Cole was pestered for seeds, and eventually the new variety was distributed under the name of "Countess Spencer" in honour of the wife of his employer. The fact that this new form, whose blooms were so light and graceful and the wings so wonderfully waved and frilled, this, the very latest thing in twentieth-century modernity, was almost completely lacking in scent was quite overlooked, and from then on Sweet Peas began to lose much of their greatest charm—their fragrance. The new varieties began to be known as "Waved Spencers" to distinguish them from Henry Eckford's "Grandiflora" type, and as the years rolled silently by the frilled kinds slowly but surely gained ascendancy over the older plain-edged varieties. Nowadays the term "Waved Spencer" has practically disappeared. Modern seed catalogues may devote six or eight pages to Sweet Peas, and every year sees more and more new varieties, but two or three lines suffice for the old-fashioned (non-frilled) varieties. There is a certain lack of fragrance in our modern Sweet Peas, although many varieties are delicately scented, but we have to go back to the old Grandiflora type for the rich perfume that compensates for their relatively dowdy appearance.

The New Zealand Tea Plant

Few wildflowers from the Antipodes are hardy enough to find a place in the gardens of Europe and America, but chief among that small number is *Leptospermum scoparium*, which is known in the lands of its origin by the Maori name, Manuka. During his first visit to New Zealand Captain Cook brewed a sort of tea from the aromatic leaves. This proved to be both a pleasant drink and a good protection against scurvy and in consequence the New Zealand Tea Plant became one of the most famous species of the South Seas during the early exploration of the Pacific. When Bligh of the *Bounty* reached Tasmania he noted in his log that, "What is called the New Zealand Tea plant grew here in great abundance; so that it was not only gathered and dried to use as tea, but made excellent brooms. It bears a small pointed leaf, of a pleasant smell, and its seed is contained in a berry about the size of a pea, notched into five equal parts on the top."

This elegant shrub or small tree covers thousands of acres of rough hill-country and forms the southern counterpart of the moorland plants of the northern hemisphere. Apiarists say it is one of the richest nectar-bearing plants of Australia and New Zealand, producing a honey second only to the famous Heather honey of Scotland. Like many another species of wide distribution the Manuka shows considerable variety in its habit of growth and in the size and colour of its fragrant flowers. Some of the best of these wild varieties have been grown in gardens for many years. One of the first was found by Judge Chapman on the hills above the city of Dunedin in 1895. Known as *L. s. Chapmanii*, the original plant is still growing in the Judge's old garden, although cuttings and seedlings have made the scented rose-pink flowers familiar to gardeners in all parts of the world.

The brightest member of the family is well known for its purplish-red foliage and its deep crimson flowers, which are borne in such abundance that it is advisable to remove the seed-pods to allow the plant to make satisfactory growth. Hailed as one of the most beautiful of all flowering shrubs, *Leptospermum scoparium var. Nichollsii* was first grown and distributed by Mr. Robert Nairn, a nurseryman of Christchurch, who was very proud of the part he had played in introducing this world favourite into our gardens, and equally fond of telling the story of its origin.

In the summer of 1904 Mr. W. Nicholls, one of the leading wool-buyers of the city, came into Mr. Nairn's nursery with a spray of the crimson Manuka in his button-hole. On being asked where he had found it the wool-buyer declined to give any information until Robert Nairn, hoping to touch his vanity, suggested that if a few cuttings were to come his way Mr. Nicholls, as the finder, would be immortalized by having the plant named for him. This was agreed to, and a few days later Mr. Nicholls turned up with a branch, but it was a very scrubby one and useless for cuttings. Fortunately it bore a few seed-pods, which on being sown produced one hundred and ten plants. Of these only seven were of a good crimson colour, the others being either white or various shades of pink. When the seedlings flowered Mr. Nicholls was invited to the nursery to select the best form which should bear his name. Some years later rooted cuttings were taken to England and in 1912 one of them was shown at the Chelsea Show, where it was awarded the First Class Certificate of the Royal Horticultural Society as the best new plant of the show.

It was not until some years later when the plant became well known in New Zealand that Mr. Nairn discovered the full story of its origin. Mr. W. P. Spencer of "Sandilands" told him that it was he who had originally found it about 1898. Growing in thick scrub, on the banks of the Styx, not far from Kaipoi, he had found it as a boy while mustering sheep. He and a friend had turned up at the homestead wearing sprays in their hats, but on being sent back next morning failed to locate it, although they searched the greater part of the day.

It was Mr. Spencer who had given the original material to Nicholls and, although somewhat surprised at his subsequent interest, had thought nothing of the matter as its possibilities as a garden plant had not occurred to him. Under the circumstances he felt that the plant should bear either his name or that of his sheep-run "Sandilands." Mr. Spencer was disappointed to hear that the plant had been named by the authorities at Kew and it was too late to make any alteration, and we are left with the reflection that although William Nicholls has been immortalized for his part in the introduction of the Red Manuka, it may not be in quite the light he would have wished.

From time to time other beautiful forms of the Manukas have been found and brought into cultivation, until we have a number of varieties varying from single whites and pinks to the lovely double pink Rose Manuka. Like most of its relatives it does not grow very big, rarely exceeding five feet, and the plumes of dainty finely cut foliage are garnished in spring with quantities of pink blooms which look rather like small Cecile Brunner Roses and are about the same size. The best of the double whites is that form whose long arching branchlets studded with rosettes give something of the impression of a miniature snowstorm. It is known under the varietal name of "Sir George Fenwick," in memory of a great lover of New Zealand plants. This variety was found by a rescue party on the lonely Waiapapa Point when going to the assistance of passengers stranded there by the wreck of the S.S. *Manuka*.

Most of the Manukas flower in spring and early summer, but the exception is *L. s. Keatleyi*, which has unusually large flowers of a soft carmine rose and bears the name of its finder, Captain E. J. Keatley of Auckland. On being asked about its origin he says, "I found it at Te Haupua, within one and a half miles of North Cape, the most northerly point of New Zealand, in 1917, while I was Master of the S.S. *Rimu*. I was taking home some Maori soldiers who had just returned from the Great War, and, the Sunday being fine, I spent it ashore, following my usual practice of wandering over the hills searching for new native shrubs, especially manukas. I suddenly dropped across one small tree with very large flowers; it was the only plant so I took cuttings of it, wrapped them in damp moss and posted them to my old friend, the late F. J. Walker of Wanganui. He managed to strike one of them. It was from this plant that Mr. Kingsbeer, a nurseryman of Palmerston North, took cuttings and raised a number of plants, of which he sent me one. I might say that I have found quite a number of varieties of Manuka including both double pink and double white, away up in North Auckland. Kingsbeer named Keatleyi against my will. I have never found any other, or heard of any, with such large flowers. That is all there is to it."

Captain Keatley's Manuka is a handsome plant at any time, with its upright habit and long twigs of dark evergreen foliage covered during the greater part of the year, with the soft carmine flowers shading to an attractive tone of bengal rose in the centre. The individual blossoms are about one-and-a-half inches across and nearly double the size of the other varieties of *Leptospermum scoparium*. They are very pleasing, with the five rounded petals set well apart so that a triangular portion of the maroon-coloured calyx shows at the base of the corolla, and their value in the garden is greatly enhanced by the fact that in mild climates they are produced throughout the winter.

The Story of the Lily

THE dignified grace and beauty of the Lilies distinguish them above all other flowers and confer on all members of the family an air of refinement that stamps them as kin despite the diversity of their size and colour. Among the very oldest inhabitants of gardens, they are also among the best beloved, and it is a matter of common knowledge that many people who have little or no interest in flowers and gardens have a deep and lasting regard for Lilies. A group of fragrant Lilies scenting the air in the cool of a summer's evening is one of the greatest joys of the garden.

The quiet charm of the family has not been without its appeal to the botanists who have described the various species, and they have vied with one another in bestowing the most complimentary names they could think of, including *regale*, *speciosum*, *pulchellum* and *superbum*. In all there are about one hundred species and well-defined varieties of Liliums to be found wild among the grassy ridges, the banks of mountain streams and in sheltered glens in all the more temperate parts of the northern hemisphere. It is only in the Philippines and the Island of Formosa that they venture into the warmer parts of the world, and there they prefer the cool upland valleys high above the shady forests.

Only about one-fifth of these Lilies make their home in Europe, all the others come from Asia or the North American continent. In Europe pride of place has always been given to the Madonna Lily, *Lilium candidum*, and the scarlet Turks' Cap, *L. chalcedonicum*, both of which have been grown for their beauty longer than any other species. While the beauty of Lilies has long been recognized in both art and poetry, there is no doubt that they were first grown for their real or supposed medicinal value. One of the old herbalists tells us that the Madonna Lily bulbs "stamped with hony gleweth together sinues that be cut in sunder," while the small Red Lily, *L. croceum*, is of great value for drawing out "by siege unprofitable blood."

No one is now certain of the wild home of the Madonna Lily although it has been found in one or two stations among the Balkan mountains. The possibility that it may be one of the Balkan wildflowers is strengthened by the fact that the variety *Salonikae*, which comes so readily from seed, and is comparatively free from disease, was originally found in the winter of 1916–17 growing among some light thorny scrub some thirty miles from Salonika. The Lily has been found apparently wild in all sorts of places from the north of France to the far fringes of the Syrian hills, an area that was all within the confines of the old Roman Empire, and this may be of considerable importance when we consider that many of these colonies seem to be more or less incapable of setting fertile seed. The suggestion has been made that at least some of these colonies may be the remnants of plantations made long, long ago. In those old years the Madonna Lily held a high reputation for healing wounds and curing internal disorders, and it may be that the Roman equivalent of our medical orderlies planted a few bulbs near some of the more permanent camps so as to provide a supply of a medicament so valuable in keeping the army fit.

In Banckes's *Herbal* of 1525, the first plant book to be written in English, more than half a page is devoted to the virtues of Lilium, but no indication of its appearance is given. But by the time another hundred years had passed the art of recognizing differences in plants had developed to such an extent that Parkinson, in 1629, was able to describe twelve Lilies so clearly that we have no difficulty in recognizing them. It is rather surprising to find that he grew *L. chalcedonicum var. maculatum*, which is now so uncommon that a well-grown group in all the glory of its fine scarlet flowers, lightly spotted with black, never fails to arrest attention, even in a garden of rarities.

Parkinson also mentions the Canada Lily, the first American species to cross the Atlantic, which had been grown in Paris nine years earlier. The next American Lily to be grown in Europe was *L. philadelphicum*, which had been taken home to France from the French colony of Acadie about 1675, but was soon lost and not seen again until John Bartram sent some bulbs to the Chelsea Physic Garden in 1737. Next year some of his bulbs of *L. superbum* flowered in Peter Collinson's London garden, and he was so thrilled by their splendour that he determined to specialize in American plants and lived to be the leading authority on their cultivation in Britain.

By the end of the eighteenth century the plant-hunters were searching the far places of the world for new flowers, and Thunberg made known several of the Japanese Lilies, but it was not until the arrival of the Tiger Lily, *L. tigrinum*, that British gardeners took any interest in them. The bulbs were among some plants sent home in 1804 by William Kerr, a collector who had been sent out from Kew, and when the new Lily flowered the gay colour of its handsome cinnabar-red flowers and its hardy constitution were an assurance of both admiration and success. This is probably the oldest Lily in cultivation, as it has been grown all over China, Korea, and Japan in great quantities as a field crop for more than a thousand years. The name is derived from the Latin *tigris*, a tiger, presumably on account of the colour, but can scarcely be described as appropriate, and one writer observes "red tigers ornate with purple spots cannot often be seen even in Cathay."

Many of those who were employed by the great trading concerns in the Far East took a keen interest in the wildflowers and garden plants and sent many of them back to the homeland. One of the most important of these was Dr. F. P. von Siebold, who spent six years in Japan and is commemorated in several Japanese plants, including the Plantain Lily, *Funkia Sieboldii*, so valuable for grouping for landscape effect. When he returned to Europe in 1829 he took a number of Japanese garden plants with a number of Lilies, including *L. elegans* and several forms of *L. speciosum*.

When Mr. C. M. Hovey, one of the leading nurserymen of Boston and the President of the Massachusetts Horticultural Society, visited Britain in 1844 he was so bewitched by *L. speciosum* and its varieties that he decided to make them known in American gardens. He took home *rubrum*, notable for its pink and carmine shadings against a white background, *punctatum*, whose beautifully formed blooms are suffused and spotted with tonings of crimson, and the lovely white *album*, most fragrant of them all. Next year he crossed them with every available Lily, including *candidum*, *chalcedonicum*, *superbum*, *tigrinum,* and *canadense*, which had been specially grown in pots so as to flower at the same time. As was to be expected, Mr. Hovey raised a heterogeneous collection of seedlings, and during the three years between seed-sowing and flowering allowed the wooden labels to rot away so that he had no idea of the parentage of most of them.

Mr. Hovey gave several accounts of his work in *The Garden*, telling how the seedlings succeeded, but was apparently unable to see that his swans were only geese. "I had twelve packets of seeds, the results of fertilization, from which I raised the finest lilies of the type yet produced, including the variety Melpomene, each petal of which is completely covered with blood-red, excepting a clear white border on every petal, and the papillae which are of crimson-black." He named nine of the best of them after the Muses of Greek mythology, and was so uncertain of the origin of Melpomene that he even hazarded the suggestion that it may have been the offspring of *L. speciosum var. rubrum* crossed by either *L. chalcedonicum* or perhaps *L. tigrinum*!

All Mr. Hovey's efforts to give a new Lily to the world were frustrated, as there is not one of his named hybrids in commerce to-day. His Melpomene made something of a name for itself, however, and when the story of its origin had been forgotten the Japanese growers capitalized on the American demand and named their own broad-leaved variety "Maruha" as Melpomene; this, one of the best forms of *L. speciosum*, is masquerading under that name in all parts of the world where Lilies are grown.

The next great event in the story of the Lily was the appearance of *L. auratum* at a London Flower Show in 1862. Dr. von Siebold had attempted to introduce it nearly forty years before, but it was to J. G. Veitch of the famous Chelsea firm of nurserymen that was given the honour of introducing it to Europe, although Robert Fortune sent a consignment of bulbs to the rival firm of Standish and Noble about the same time. If the Japanese thought of the plant at all they regarded it merely as we regard wild mushrooms, a delicacy to be collected and eaten. With their own ideals of beauty they were quite indifferent to the flowers which were hailed in England as "The most splendid creation of the temperate zone, unrivalled in pure distinction, aristocrat in every line, and when the day comes that the House of Veitch must pass, it may well leave its laurels with the 'Golden Lily of Japan.' "

As a result of the great demand for this and other species the Japanese thought nothing of despoiling their countryside by tearing up Lily bulbs by the cart-load for export. The wild plants could not stand up to the excessive demand, and nowadays wild Lilies are only to be seen in the most inaccessible parts of the country. The only way to keep up stocks was to grow the bulbs under nursery conditions, and the growers were not long in finding out that tiny seedlings planted in the rich moist lands by the sea grew into nice, big, marketable bulbs within a year or so. When the demand was at its height, in 1912, the Yokohama Nursery Company alone exported fifteen millions of *L. auratum* bulbs to America and Europe. The big soft bulbs produced in such quantities soon fell prey to mosaic disease, and one European dealer estimated that less than $2\frac{1}{2}$ per cent of them produced flowers in the western hemisphere. While this was all very good for the Japanese nurserymen, gardeners soon began to tire of trying to grow *L. auratum*, and many lost interest in Lilies because they were "too difficult."

A new era in Lily growing began with the advent of the Regal Lily in 1911, and it played very much the same part in reviving interest in the family as had been done by the Tiger Lily at the beginning of the nineteenth century. These two lovely Lilies are so easy to grow that through them gardeners began to pay more attention to the other members of the family. This increased popularity has brought them under the notice of the hybridists, with the result that within the past quarter of a century many fine new Lilies have appeared. The old saying that "no hybrid Lily is half so good as its parents" has certainly been proved false by some of our modern strains, and one of the crosses, the lovely

L. "Maxwill" has the distinction of being the only Lily to win the Royal Horticultural Society's Cory Cup for the best new flower of the year.

The home of the Regal Lily, *L. regale*, is in the lonely Min Valley in that little-known tract of country where western China meets Tibet, and the story of its discovery is a tale of adventure in our own time. The finder was the late E. H. Wilson, Keeper of the Arnold Arboretum in Massachusetts, better known to his own generation as "Chinese Wilson" because of his many successful explorations in the old Chinese Empire, and the vast number of new Chinese plants which he made known to the gardeners of the western hemisphere.

The Regal Lily may be termed a Wilson Lily, as he named and introduced it, and in his books, *The Lilies of Eastern Asia* and *Plant Hunting*, he tells how he set out in 1910 to find the beautiful Lily he had found some years previously, but had not been successful in introducing.

In the Min Valley only, he found it in abundance, flourishing among the scrub and coarse grass which clothe the dry cliffs of that semi-arid country. So plentiful is it that for a few weeks its delicious fragrance scents the air, and the whole of that desolate countryside is transformed into a vision of beauty. About the middle of May the first flowers appear along the banks of the turbulent Min River, some 2,500 feet above sea-level, and as the season advances, the tide of blossom creeps up the mountain sides so that by the end of July it reaches its maximum altitude of 6,000 feet, and the show is over for another year. *L. regale* seems to be confined to this one valley because it is unable to cross the encircling mass of snowy peaks that hem it in.

Although one of the main trade routes through China and Tibet traverses the Min Valley, it is always a dangerous road for travellers. It meanders through interminable gorges, on the rocky walls of which warnings have been carved in Chinese characters telling of the constant danger from rock avalanches, and pointing out that it is advisable to rest only under the shelter of high cliffs. The road carries a considerable traffic, chiefly coolies and mule trains coming down with the pastoral produce of Tibet to the crowded cities of China, and returning with manufactured goods such as cotton and brick tea.

Wilson was hurrying down the valley in the late summer of 1910, satisfied with the arrangements he had just made for a consignment of seven thousand bulbs of the Regal Lily to be lifted in the autumn and encased in clay before being packed in charcoal for despatch to America. He travelled in a sedan chair, because in those days the natives were impressed by it. A sedan chair was thought to give an air of respectability, if not of authority, to any party, and was of the utmost importance in winning the confidence and goodwill of the populace.

Suddenly a small stone struck the road in front of him, another struck the chair and, before he reached the shelter of the cliffs, a third boulder struck him and broke a leg in two places. Fortunately he was not knocked unconscious. Had that happened it is probable that his men would have deserted him and yet another plant-hunter would have met his death in the wilds. Even so, things were decidedly unpleasant, he was alone with a few Chinese coolies, and several days' march from the nearest medical assistance. The leg was in the process of being bandaged, using a camera tripod for splints, when a train of almost fifty mules came upon the party. The place was too dangerous for the mule train to stop—another rock avalanche might fall at any moment —and as there was not sufficient space for it to turn back, it had to go on. The only course was to lay the patient on his back across the road and allow the animals to step over him. He breathed a sigh of relief when the last of them had passed over without mishap.

After a forced march he reached the nearest missionary post

in three days. He received instant attention, but unfortunately infection had set in and the necessity for amputation was urged upon him. This he would not allow, and it was many months before he reached home. On account of the infection the leg was considerably shorter than the other, and he had a limp for the rest of his life, but despite all he had gone through Wilson always thought that the Regal Lily had been worth it.

A few days after his return to America the bulbs arrived. They were found to be in excellent condition, were planted the following spring and some of them flowered that first year and actually succeeded in setting fertile seed. All the millions of Regal Lilies that grace the gardens of the world are the descendants of that consignment, and now, more than thirty years later, the paeans of praise that greeted their arrival are still being added to. The Regal Lily is still the Queen of her patrician race.

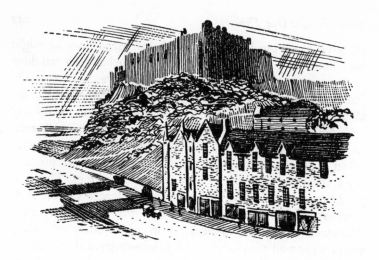

George Forrest

THE first naturalists to give the western world an inkling of the myriads of wildflowers growing in the hinterland of China were the French missionaries who served there during the eighteenth century, but their work has been completely eclipsed during the past forty years by such men as E. H. Wilson, Reginald Farrer, and George Forrest, who systematically botanized vast tracks of that extensive territory. Forrest was the last of a long line of Scotsmen that began with Francis Masson and included such names as David Douglas and Robert Fortune, collectors who searched the uttermost ends of the earth for plants worthy of the gardens at home. He began life as a chemist in a quiet Scottish town, and his early studies of *materia medica* were the foundation on which he built an extensive knowledge of plants. In the course of seven expeditions he came to know more than any other man about the flora of that mountainous region where the outskirts of Burma and China merge into the fringes of Tibet.

George Forrest did not write very much about his plants or

his adventures, but had he survived that last journey he might have found time to tell something of what he had seen and done in that strange, inaccessible country. But it was not to be. On January 5, 1932, he died of a heart attack at Tengyueh. He had all but finished packing his seed harvest and was out for the day with his gun when he collapsed and died almost immediately. In 1935 the Scottish Rock Garden Club of Edinburgh published a slender volume containing a sketch of his life and work, including some of his more important writings. This is of great interest to all of us who have not ready access to the back numbers of *The Gardeners' Chronicle*, the *Royal Geographic Magazine*, and other periodicals in which they originally appeared, and all plant-lovers will acknowledge a deep debt of gratitude to the Club for its timely tribute to a great plant-hunter.

Forrest is said to have found his true vocation as a result of sheltering from a shower of rain in the south of Scotland. From his shelter he noticed the end of an old stone coffin emerging from a shingly bank, and on investigation found that it contained a pre-historic skeleton. His search for information about his find brought him into contact with Professor Bailey Balfour, Regius Keeper of the Edinburgh Botanic Garden, and began an association unique in the history of botanical exploration. These two men collaborated for nearly twenty years with great benefit to each other and to botanical science. The botanist found an absorbing interest for the last years of an active life, and the collector received that instant appreciation and technical recognition so necessary to the man in the field, but for which most plant-hunters have had to be content to hope.

On arrival at his destination Forrest found himself beset with difficulties. Not only was he handicapped by having no experience of the professional collectors' methods, but he had little or no knowledge of the Chinese language, the terrain was extremely difficult and inaccessible with high mountain ranges cut by deep gorges, and the local authorities, both Tibetan and Chinese, were definitely hostile. During the early years he met either passive resistance or active antagonism at almost every turn, but his kindly treatment of native porters and collectors won him respect and friendship over the whole district, so that the later years were not nearly so difficult, although conditions generally were much less peaceful, as brigandage became common after the fall of the Chinese Empire.

During that first summer of 1905 he had some dreadful experiences and barely escaped with his life. Trouble had arisen between the Tibetans and Chinese, and the Lamas took the opportunity to attack the Christian Mission of Tzekou, which he had made his headquarters. The Christians made an effort to escape but were cut off and over sixty persons, including two aged French priests, lost their lives. Forrest had several narrow escapes as he hid for nine days in the hills, his only food being a handful of parched Peas and a few ears of Wheat dropped by one of the natives.

On one occasion he was so hemmed in that he had almost given up all hope of escape and was on the point of selling his life dearly in a last stand, when something attracted his attention. "It seemed to be the figure of Père Dubernard (who had been in charge of the Tzekou Mission), farther up the hill-side waving him to proceed down stream. This he did and escaped detection for that time, but the wonder was that the Reverend Father had been slaughtered three days before." He had to discard his boots on account of tale-tell footprints, and some days later stepped on a sharpened bamboo spike that went right through his foot, protruding two inches from the top surface. He ultimately reached a friendly village, and nearly three weeks later arrived at the Chinese city of Talifu, more dead than alive and minus all his personal belongings and the results of his labours, including photographs, over two thousand herbarium specimens, and seeds of more than eighty species of plants.

As his harvest through the years Forrest introduced many plants whose garden value is of the highest order, wildflowers that had grown among those mountains and passes since the beginning of time, but had never before been seen by appreciative eyes. He found the lemon-pale *Meconopsis integrifolia* growing in such abundance that he noted somewhere, "Can we ever get away from it?" Among the plants he sent home was the aptly named *Iris chrysographes*, whose dark, velvety-blue flowers are delicately pencilled with gold; the glorious *Anemone glaucifolia*, whose best forms are covered with soft silvery down and produce flowers of the clearest blue measuring nearly three inches across; the lovely *Nomocharis pardanthina*, whose widespread lily-like blooms are lightly spotted with purple; quaint *Roscoea cautleoides* with soft aurelian yellow blooms over a long period; *Gentiana sino-ornata*, departing from the accepted code of the family and spreading its mats of sky-blue blossom in autumn; *Osmanthus Delavayi*, so near the gardener's ideal and lacking only colour, and *Gaultheria Forrestii*, whose feature is its singular porcelain-blue berries. In all he collected no fewer than 31,015 different consignments of seeds, and it would be a simple matter to find dozens, nay scores, of plants as good as, or even better than those we have mentioned.

But the real wealth of his territory was in its Rhododendrons, and soon he made those his favourites, discovering such hosts of new species as to alter all the old accepted views of the family. At one time it was thought that the evergreen members, whose flowers are all provided with the full quota of ten stamens, were the true Rhododendrons and quite distinct from the somewhat similar group of Azaleas, which were distinguished by having only five stamens and dropping their leaves in winter. Among the hundreds of new species discovered by Forrest there were all sorts of forms that completely bridged the gap between the two groups, with the result that all are now classified as Rhododendrons. So that some kind of order might be brought out of the chaos the vast genus of Rhododendrons had become, Professor Bailey Balfour segregated them into about forty groups, or "series," and gardeners have found that their old favourites are easily identified as the "Azalea Series."

Among those new species were all manner of plants from *R. gigantea*, a moss-clad giant reaching eighty feet in height, which must be a wonderful sight when its forty-foot spread of branches is decorated with trusses of rose-pink flowers, to the tiny creeping *R. repens* that spreads a delightful carpet of blood-red bells over the surface of the ground. There is almost as much diversity in the foliage as there is in the habit of the plants, with all the variations of shape and size from the small *R. radicans*, whose leaves are scarcely more than a quarter of an inch long, to those of *R. sino-grande* at the other end of the scale, which are some twenty inches long and rather more than half that in breadth.

Although the older species in cultivation were mostly handsome evergreen shrubs, it is now possible to get Rhododendrons to please all tastes from trees of thirty feet or so, such as *R. croceum*, whose soft yellow flowers cast a moonlight radiance over the garden during the dull days of late spring, or *R. fulvum*, whose rose and crimson flowers are quite ordinary but is highly desirable on account of the leathery leaves being covered on the under side with bright cinnamon-brown felt. Among the medium-sized shrubs are the charming *R. chasmanthum*, rather unusual in the combination of its lavender-coloured flowers being spotted with olive-green, but even more attractive are the drought-resistant *R. Griersonianum*, striking on account of its fragrant geranium-scarlet, almost flame-coloured, blooms, and the

true *R. lacteum*, with huge trusses of beautiful canary-yellow
bells.

Most worthy of all are the low-growing species that rarely
reach more than ten or twenty inches, some of the best of which
are *Rr. haematodes, impeditum, muliense*, and *hippophaeoides*,
which, planted in heath-like masses, will cover themseves with a
sea of blossom that surges over rocky outcrops to form unfor-
gettable pictures of scarlet, golden-yellow, lilac, and even blue,
such as can rarely be obtained by any other means. While as
specimen clumps in the rock garden no other group of small
shrubs is so valuable for the small garden where space forbids
the inclusion of the stronger-growing species.

No account of Forrest's plants would be complete without
some mention of the species that bears his name, *R. Forrestii*,
which is one of the smallest of the alpine gems, besides being
one of the most pleasing. It is unusual among Rhododendrons
in being able to climb up perpendicular cliffs and moist rocks by
means of ivy-like roots on the undersurface of the stem. The
bell flowers of a deep crimson shade are produced singly but in
great abundance.

If Rhododendrons were Forrest's favourites, Primulas were a
close second, and he introduced many species that have long
been acknowledged as the choicest denizens of bog or water
garden. Some of the finest of his introductions are *Primula
aurantiaca*, with flowers of a rich coppery gold, the tall spikes of
P. sino-plantaginea, grown for their nodding purple bells, the
snowy *P. chionantha*, whose large snow-white flowers are
deliciously fragrant, and the clear yellow heads of *P. helodoxa*,
whose florets rise in rings one above the other for weeks on end.
From his first expedition he sent back some of the best of any
that he found, including the reddish-purple tiers of *P. Beesiana*,
named for his sponsors, the famous seed firm Bees, Ltd., of
Liverpool, and the lovely orange-coloured *P. Bulleyana* that

commemorates their managing director, Mr. A. K. Bulley. At the same time he found the fairy-like *P. malacoides*, whose airy panicles of scented heliotrope and lavender flowers are among the indispensables for the winter conservatory. The most remarkable departure from the conventions of a beautiful family are the elfin *P. muscarioides*, so exactly like an exquisite little Grape Hyacinth, and the incomparable *P. Littoniana*, named in honour of his friend G. L. Litton, British Consul at Tengyueh.

Litton was able to give the collector much valuable information on local customs, tracks, and bridges, and reliable men who could be trained as collectors and porters. On one occasion the two friends went on an exploratory trip over the Salween-Irrawady Divide which forms the Yunnan-Burmese boundary, and through the territory of the Black Lissoos into a region where even the Chinese officials dared not penetrate without the protection of an armed guard. They had a very adventurous time, and their dealings with the people of Lo-mi-da is typical. They had arranged with the villagers to have their baggage taken across a rope bridge. The people on the other side of the river wanted the job and resulting fees and were prepared to fight for them.

Their leader shot off a poisoned arrow to show that he meant business, and the two explorers had to take a hand. Forrest "fired several shots over his head at a boulder on the other side of the river. The effect of seeing the bullets smash against the stone at such a distance was immediate and then, through interpreters, we told the man and his friends that if they made a show of stringing their bows again, the next bullet would find a resting place in one of their carcases." The explorers were allowed to proceed on their way, but the grateful people of Lo-mi-da were so anxious to show that they were civilized, and harped so much on the low type living across the way, that the explorers had to make a forced march to shake them off.

They soon found themselves in the midst of a local war, but this time it seemed to be little more than a game. The two groups met with all the pomp, pride, and circumstance of war, including blackened faces, deer horns, bows, arrows, swords, and shields, on the steep hillside, but "neither side got farther than swearing and stringing bows until the time arrived for the afternoon meal, when the combatants dispersed to their respective homes, from which we judged that their wars resembled those of Tweedledum and Tweedledee 'who felt that they must fight for half an hour, and then have tea.'"

It is the memory of such adventures that *P. Littoniana* brings back to us, and Forrest could not have paid his friend a higher compliment than by dedicating this beautiful wildflower to his memory. It has been described by Reginald Farrer, another wanderer among the high hills of Asia, as "a tuft of upstanding oval foliage, ribbed and downy and soft; and then up shoots a tall powdered stem, terminated by a spike often six inches in length, of brilliant scarlet bracts, from which, as the stem grows taller, unfold the innumerable pendant little packed flowers of lavender-lilac or deep violet, till in mid-bloom the spikes seem tapering ghost-flames of blue aspiring to their long tips of crimsoned fire, making an unparalleled effect as they hold up their millions of tall steady candle-lights in the lush grasses of the Yunnanese alps."

"Of Garden Origin"

WHEN we are told that such and such a plant is "of garden origin" it may mean that it is either the result of careful cross-fertilization and wise selection or simply a chance seedling that "appeared" in some garden or nursery where its merits and possibilities were quickly realized. The present fashion is to name many of these garden hybrids from the parents, as, for example, Lilium "Maxwill," which is the result of crossing *L. Maximowiczii* with *L. Willmottiae*, but for long it has been the rule to commemorate in the foundling the person who first discovered it or the place where it originated. Such a one is *Cytisus kewensis*, one of the most pleasing of the smaller Brooms, although we may not altogether agree with the enthusiast who tells us, "Had Kew no other claim to fame than the production of this one shrub, it would be enough to perpetuate her memory for so long as there are gardens and gardeners. Foaming sunshine is the only metaphor to indicate its beauty when in flower. Only a matter of twelve inches high, it will cover an area of twenty-five feet or so, but it is much more superbly displayed on a bold rock or dry wall."

C. kewensis was first noticed in 1891 along with two other hybrid Brooms, and at the Tree and Shrub Conference held in London in 1938 the story of their origin was told by Mr. W. Dallimore of Kew. He said the young plants were transferred to the nursery until sufficient stock had been obtained, and while one was named *C. kewensis*, another was called *C. Beanii* for Mr. W. J. Bean, who later became a world authority on trees and shrubs. One day Mr. Bean remarked that he wondered why the Curator had given his name to "that poor washy thing. I wouldn't have minded if it had been this one," pointing to the third hybrid, an upstanding little tuffet of a foot or so adorned with numerous glowing yellow florets. The offender disappeared and its name was transferred to the plant that for more than half a century has been acknowledged as one of the best of its kind.

From the gardens of old Persia came Pissart's Rose, a delicate pink form of the well-known *Rosa moschata*, but a stronger and more arresting plant that will reach twenty-five or even thirty feet under favourable conditions. It is to the true *R. moschata* that we are indebted for the Noisette clan, of which "Souvenir de la Malmaison" and the lovely old "Maréchal Niel" are among the most fragrant of childhood's memories. There is something of a mystery about the origin of the first Noisette Rose. Many writers are content to say that it was originally raised in America by Philippe Noisette and sent home to his brother Louis in Paris about 1817, while others assure us that it was raised by John Champney of Charleston, South Carolina, probably as a chance seedling, and was known as Champney's Pink Cluster long before it reached France. The truth appears to be that Champney did raise a Rose that was supposed to be a cross between the old Blush China and *R. moschata*, and that Philippe grew a number of seedlings from the original and sent one of the best to his brother in Paris. The new Rose soon became very popular in France, where it became widely known as Noisette's Rose, *R. Noisettiana*.

M. Rene Pissart, a Frenchman who went to Teheran as gardener to the Shah of Persia in 1880, sent home a number of garden varieties to France. One of the most widely grown of them is the bronze-leaved Flowering Plum that bears his name, *Prunus Pissartii*. At the end of the nineteenth century M. Edouard André, who is commemorated in the bronze and gold *Cytisus scoparius Andreanus*, which he found growing wild in Normandy, noticed a bronze-leaved seedling growing among some *Prunus Mume* in his nursery at La Croix, near the village of Blire. It flowered for the first time in 1901 and was identified as a natural hybrid between *P. Pissartii* and *P. Mume*. When it was put on the market four years later as *P. Blireiana* it was accepted as one the best of the coloured leaved Flowering Plums on account of the freedom with which it produced its fragrant, semi-double blossom in early spring.

It is quite surprising how many of our most popular garden plants are chance seedlings. Among them are *Erica darleyensis* from the Darley Dale nurseries in England, and *Geum*, "Mrs. J. Bradshaw," which came up among some plants of *Geum coccinea* in Mrs. Bradshaw's garden in the south of England. *Viola florairensis* is a neat little lilac Pansy that came up in M. Henri Correvon's famous nursery near Geneva in 1910. It has been diagnosed as a natural hybrid between *V. cornuta* and the Rouen Violet, while the latter is itself a chance seedling that originated in the Rouen Botanic Garden in 1781. From the same source came the Rouen Lilac, famous for its splendid panicles of blossom. Contrary to general belief, *Potentilla Menziesii*, which forms a bush three feet high and covers itself with flowers buff without and crimson within, does not commemorate the famous doctor who sailed with Captain Vancouver. It is a chance seedling found in the gardens of Hope House in Yorkshire, over a hundred years ago, and was named by a local nurseryman in honour of the gardener who found it. Something of the same sort happened in the case of *P. Hopwoodiana*, which was found growing in a bed of *P. nepalensis* and is believed to be a self-sown hybrid between that rosy purple species and the sulphur-yellow variety of *P. recta*. It was first reported about 1848.

Among ornamental trees and shrubs there are several natural hybrids which are of outstanding value in the garden; chief among them are *Crataegus Leeana*, *Berberis stenophylla*, and *Magnolia Soulangeana*. The Crataegus is one of the most handsome of the Thorn trees with dark, more or less hairy, leaves, and small clusters of fine white flowers that are followed in due season by red fruits. A charming tree at all times, it has something of the beauty of both *C. tanacetifolia* and *C. punctata*, the reputed parents, during flowering and fruiting periods, but nothing has been preserved about its origin. At the time it was named it was believed to have been raised at Lee and Kennedy's famous Vineyard Nursery near London, but even that is doubtful. No such doubts exist about *Berberis stenophylla*, the loveliest of all the flowering Barberries and almost equally attractive in autumn when draped with its tiny grape-like fruits. This is a self-sown seedling that came up in a nursery in the north of England about eighty years ago, and when it produces its long slender wands of golden blossom it will give an air of distinction to any garden.

It is about one hundred and twenty years ago since *Magnolia Soulangeana* flowered for the first time in the garden of M. Soulange-Bodin at Fromont, near Paris. It was a chance seedling that grew near a clump of the chaste white *M. conspicua*, and competent gardeners soon realized that it must be a cross between that species and the wine-purple *M. liliflora* that grew close by. With all the traditional "hybrid vigour," *M. Soulangeana* soon made a place for itself by its strong constitution and the freedom with which it produced its great white goblets of flowers, each petal of which is stained at the base with the coloured blood of its pollen parent. As the years went by a number of seedlings were raised from it and one of the most popular of them all is *M. Lennei*, which was found in Lombardy by a German nursery-man, Herr Kurt Topf. He took it to Erfurt in 1850 and soon afterwards named it for Herr Lenne, who was in charge of the Royal Gardens at Berlin.

It must be a quarter of a century ago since a passing remark led to the discovery of yet another plant "of garden origin." A Dutch nurseryman, passing through his nursery on the way to the office, came across a boy weeding an extensive bed of the violet-coloured *Anemone Pulsatilla*, that had been raised from seed. In passing he made the remark, "Bring along a pink one to the office and I will give you a florin." Within a few days the lad had obeyed orders and collected his reward. He had found the lovely pink blooms that have since become universal favourites ever since the plant was first distributed under the name of the nurseryman's wife, as *A. Pulsatilla* "Mrs. Van der Elst."

From that selfsame nursery, now under different management, came one of the most important additions to the herbaceous border to be introduced in the years just prior to the war, the elegant rose-pink *Delphinium Ruysii* "Pink Sensation." Growing up to about four feet or so, it resembles the Belladonna type in both general appearance, in foliage, and in the size of the individual blooms, while the many graceful lateral growths give a delightfully misty effect. About forty-five years ago Mr. B. Ruys of Dedemsvaart, Holland, set his heart on raising a good red Delphinium. At that time he engaged a scientist to transform his dream into a reality, but all his attempts to cross some of the cultivated Delphiniums with the low-growing *D. nudicaule*, whose orange-scarlet flowers may be found wild along the mountain streams of northern California, were so disappoint-ing that they had to be abandoned. Some years later another attempt was made on scientific lines, but that too had to be given up.

Although he had found it necessary to give up his systematic experiments Mr. Ruys did not lose sight of his dream-plant, and thus when a stray seedling appeared among some young plants of *D. nudicaule,* his optimistic faith in the laws of Mendelism led him to success, if not yet to his heart's desire. It had all the appearance of being a cross between *D. nudicaule* and the tall European species, *D. elatum.* The parentage was right, but the poor dingy colour was not at all attractive, and it was only through careful self-fertilization and diligent selection that the good colour of the one parent and the habit of the other gave "Pink Sensation," which we are told has been "weighed in the balance of colour, habit of growth, and constitution and been found well-nigh blameless."

It was entirely a matter of chance that an English nurseryman, on holiday in a remote part of western Ireland, came across a drift of pink flowers in the village doctor's garden. There they were, lighting up the late autumn with masses of pink spikes such as he had never seen before. He instantly realized that he had stumbled across something new and straightaway bought the lot for £50. The doctor's wife welcomed the windfall, provided she could keep a few roots, and that is how the pink Kaffir Lily, *Schizostylis coccinea* "Mrs. Blanche Hegarty" came to our gardens. After the flowers had been shown in London the following year, 1921, and given the coveted prize of the Royal Horticultural Society, the Award of Merit, the name of that village doctor's wife became known all over the world.

A few years later a somewhat similar happening occurred in California when another observant eye spotted another World's Darling growing in a cottage garden. Mr. J. C. Bodger of El Monte first saw the famous "Golden Gleam" Nasturtiums in a small garden, and all his efforts to find out where they came from were without avail. He was told that the seeds had originally come from Mexico and spent three weeks in that country searching for it, but was unable to find any trace either in the wild state or in cultivation, and had to return home because no one knew anything about it. He then went back to the cottage garden and acquired all available seeds, and when sufficient stock had been raised sent test packets to some of the world's leading seedsmen. In both Europe and America the new flower was guaranteed an instant success, and these glowing reports confirmed his belief that he had spotted a winner.

Sure enough, a little judicious advertising, and the "Golden Gleam" became almost a household word overnight. At the Chelsea Show of 1931 it was given the Award of Merit, the hallmark of success in the floral world, and the following year even Mr. Bodger's ten tons of seeds did not fill the demand for small packets of "Golden Gleam" Nasturtium.

The latest example of careful plant-breeding combined with a gift from the gods in the form of a few stray seedlings is to be seen in the story of the Marigolds, both African and French, which within the past ten years or so have stepped out of the garden and brought their wealth of colour, maroon, bronze, lemon, and gold, to the forefront of the cut-flower trade. Despite their common names both these flowers are derived from a pair of species of Mexican wildflowers whose seeds were smuggled back to Europe in the days when the treasure-laden Spanish galleons had to run the gauntlet of the Atlantic as they carried the treasures of the New World across the seas.

The flowers soon became very popular in the south of Europe, where they became known as the "Rose of the Indies," and within a comparatively few years the more robust species, *Tagetes erecta*, had made itself so much at home along the coast of North Africa that it was accepted as one of the wildflowers of the region. It is said to have been taken to England by some of the corsairs who helped to free Tangier from the Moors, and thus became known as the African Marigold. The brown and gold *T. patula* flowered for the first time in Britain in the summer of 1573 from seeds brought out of France by the Huguenot refugees, who sought sanctuary there after the dreadful Massacre of St. Bartholomew's Day in August 1572. They were mostly weavers of silk, cotton, and wool, and their great love of flowers and new methods of cultivation had considerable influence on the art of gardening in Britain for the next hundred years.

The two types of Marigolds remained quite distinct right up to the present day, and the first great improvement was the rise of a strain in which the distinctive odour of the leaves and stems was eliminated. This characteristic aroma, although quite pleasant in the garden, became rank and disagreeable when the plants were rubbed or bruised and spoilt their use for indoor decoration. It is said that some twenty years ago an anthropologist, digging up the remains of the ancient Mayan city of Minanha in Central Amercia, sent his wife in New York some seeds of a wild Marigold he found growing among the ruins. The resultant plants were rather weedy and insignificant, with one exception. Seeds of the best plant were saved and ultimately fell into the hands of a seedsman who, hearing its history, thought that if such a Cinderella could be found among the ugly sisters there was a possibility that a Marigold with odourless foliage would be found among the ordinary French or African varieties. Many hundreds of plants had to be tested before it was found, but it was found, and within a few years the first of the odourless foliaged varieties was on the market.

The next step was the development of brighter and better combinations of colour, and while that was being attempted one plant-breeder was successful in crossing the French and African types, a task that had baffled many growers for more than three centuries. Nowadays we may grow Marigolds of many shapes and sizes with the short and sturdy growth-form that is so suitable for bedding or the long-stemmed forms that are most useful for indoor decoration. In addition to this we have colour combinations through pale primrose yellow and coppery bronze through various flame and tangerine shadings to the richest mahogany-red and garnet-brown, so that during late summer and autumn we may plan colour schemes that rival even the sunset in the gorgeous splendour of these lovely flowers.

Patience and Perseverance

THIS is the story of a kind-hearted old Englishman who parted with his greatest treasure, the result of a quarter of a century's care and devotion, to give a youth the opportunity to do some of the things that he himself had been unable to do when young.

The advent of the Russell Lupins was one of the many attractions planned to delight the numerous visitors who flocked to England in the summer of 1937 to celebrate the Coronation of King George VI and Queen Elizabeth. Exhibited at the June show held in London by the Royal Horticultural Society, the enthusiasm they aroused was even greater than their sponsors, Messrs. Baker of Wolverhampton, had dared to hope for. Everyone who saw them was thrilled, and over seventy thousand people visited Baker's Floral Farm at Boningdale to see the Russell Lupins growing in the fields. By the time the first catalogue was published over half the sixty or so named varieties had been sold out.

Everyone wanted to know the story of their origin, and an interesting one they found it. A tale of a quiet, persevering old Englishman, sixty years of age, who followed a vision through the whole of a King's reign, and at the beginning of another accomplished a success far beyond his wildest dreams. The seed of this new race of garden flowers was sown in the mind of George Russell at a gala held in the ancient city of York, to celebrate the Coronation of King George V, in June 1911. As he gazed upon those old-fashioned blue and white Lupins he thought how wonderful they would be if only some more colour could be infused into them. There and then he decided to do the job himself.

He set to work at once buying specimens of every available variety, and sending to all parts of the world for seed. As time went on he crossed and re-crossed his seedlings, keeping only the very best and ruthlessly eliminating all the others. Many a businessman who retires at the age of sixty longs for something to occupy his mind, but George Russell continued to earn his living as a jobbing gardener and tended his Lupins in his spare time.

He lived on from one June to the next to see the results of his work, and it was not for ten or fifteen years that he began to see some improvement, something for all the time and trouble he had spent on the project. With the results came offers from some of the chief trade growers in the country, and as the years slipped by the offers became more and ever more tempting. On one occasion he was offered five dollars by an enthusiastic American for "just a thimbleful of seed," and other visitors offered as much as £50 for one plant, but George Russell was not yet satisfied with his achievements, and anyway he had no wish to sell, and all such proposals were turned down.

When eventually he was persuaded to sell his interest in the new race of Lupins he had invented, financial reward was still but a secondary consideration. He wanted to turn his plants to account in his desire to build up a career for a boy who had helped him with his flowers for a number of years. One of the main conditions of the transaction was that this lad be given the opportunity to continue the work that he, too, had learnt to love.

Even when the excitement about his Lupins was at its height George Russell was still the quiet, unassuming old man, just a gardener ready to do any job of work wherever he was required. Now well over eighty years of age, he had worked for nearly half a lifetime to make those flowers what they are and could rest content that he had made a very notable contribution to the beauty of gardens throughout the world.

Perhaps the best tribute to his work was given by D. W. Simmons, a member of the Royal Horticultural Society's Floral Committee. He wrote in *My Garden* as follows:—

"My first impression was indescribable, never before have I seen such marvellous colouring, or been thrilled by such exotic blendings, and I can safely claim to have seen every worthwhile plant or race of plants introduced during the past forty years; I have praised some and condemned many, but with the exception of the Spencer Sweet Peas I have seen nothing to come within a mile of the new Russell Lupins as staged at the Royal Horticultural Society's show by Messrs. Baker in scores of shades and colours; self-colours in rich pink, orange-yellow strawberry-red; bicolours of royal purple and gold, apricot and sky-blue, rose-pink and amethyst, and dozens of intermediate shades and combinations, on hundreds of massive spikes. The highest possible Royal Horticultural Society's award, the Gold Medal, was never more richly deserved."

Our Debt to the Missionaries

MOST of the Spanish missionaries who followed in the wake of Columbus were far too intent on the serious business of saving souls to take more than a passing interest in the strange wild-flowers of the New World. The Canna was a rare exception, but the seeds were sent to Spain early in the sixteenth century on account of their being used as rosary beads rather than to show the people at home the beauty of their gaily coloured flowers.

By the middle of the following century Protestant England began to send out her own missionaries, and one of the first of them was John Banister, who travelled widely, botanizing wherever he went. He is remembered in the elegant silvery-leaved climber *Banisteria argyrophylla* that he brought back from Brazil. Later he settled down as a parson in Virginia and about 1678 compiled the first known catalogue of Virginian plants and sent it home to Henry Compton, Bishop of London, who saw it through the publishers. After his tragic death in 1692—he was killed by falling from a rocky precipice while plant-collecting in Virginia—all his notes and specimens were sent to the Bishop who had encouraged him so much to collect plants and seeds.

Bishop Compton is commemorated by the old-fashioned *Comptonia asplenifolia*, a small American shrub with scented fern-like leaves, that is rarely seen nowadays. He had a very famous garden at Fulham Palace containing over one thousand species and varieties of tropical plants and about half that number of hardy trees and shrubs, the greatest collection grown in any garden in England at that time. Among them were the Black Virginian Walnut, the fragrant pink *Azalea viscosa*, the Fringe Tree, *Chionanthus virginica*—so well known by its quaint tassels of scented bloom—and the Swamp Bay, *Magnolia glacua*, whose perfumed chalices are among the *élite* of the spring flowers.

About this time an interest began to develop about the Far East, and after several unsuccessful attempts had been made to establish Christianity there the Jesuit Fathers adopted the principle of being more than mere missionaries and trained their personnel in some of the arts and crafts likely to prove useful in Asia. By this means the entry was forced into China, but Japan remained aloof for another century and a half.

These Jesuit Fathers sent home the fullest accounts of all the strange things with which they came into contact, and as was to be expected their first interest in plants was largely economic. This bias is seen in the work of Joseph George Kamel, whose name is perpetuated in Camellia, who spent a number of years in the Philippine Islands and made over ninety drawings of plants which included no fewer than seventeen varieties of orange. Another of this early band was Michel Boym, whose *Flora Sinensis*, published in 1656, gave descriptions of several Chinese herbal remedies and created an appetite for the floral treasures of the East. *Cobaea scandens*, sometimes called the Cup and Saucer Vine, with pink, white or purple flowers that are not unlike those of the Canterbury Bells except that they are borne singly, is a rampant climber from Central America which was named after Father Cobo, a Spanish Jesuit of the seventeenth century who lived in America for a number of years and studied natural history.

The most famous of those pioneers was Pierre d'Incarville, who arrived in China in 1740 and is credited with being the first naturalist to explore the woodlands, streams, and hill tracks of North China. A pupil of Bernard de Jussieu of the Jardin des Plantes in Paris, he sent home many seeds, plants, and dried specimens. The Chinese plants that made their appearance in Europe before his time were mostly garden varieties from the palace and temple gardens of the south. He collected assiduously for about seventeen years, and some writers say he was the first to send home seeds of the China Asters.

Probably he did send seeds of this Chinese wildflower to Europe, but the records state that it was originally introduced in 1728. It is doubtful if any credence should be given to the story that it was the sight of a mass of these flowers in the Jardin des Plantes that fired the young d'Incarville with a determination to see for himself the wildflowers of China. Among the seeds he sent to Paris were those of the Tree of Heaven, *Ailanthus altissima*, and the graceful *Sophora japonica*, while his dried specimens included many plants which did not reach our gardens until the beginning of the present century, such as *Viburnum fragrans* and *Syringa villosa*. His work is kept before us in the well-known Incarvilleas, whose variously coloured trumpets have the reputation of being the finest herbaceous plants that ever came out of the Flowery Land.

Another French Jesuit was Paul Perney, who was sent out to China about the middle of the nineteenth century. He worked for ten years in the Province of Kiuchu, which he is said to have originally entered in the guise of a Chinese beggar, with pigtail and begging bowl complete. During his leisure hours he botanized far into the hinterland, and his contribution to our knowledge of the Chinese flora is commemorated in a small evergreen tree, *Ilex Perneyi*. One of the most refined of the hollies, its young twigs are a bright mahogany-red in early spring, and all through the year the leaves, spiny and almost rectangular, crowd along the twigs after the fashion of a dwarf ivy. During late summer and autumn they are studded with pretty little scarlet berries.

About this time Armand David reached Pekin, and during the next ten years made a series of journeys that will live forever in the annals of plant exploration. Those expeditions took him up the Yangtze River to Chungking, across Szechuan to the mountains of Shensi and southern Mongolia, where he found wild silkworms living on wild mulberry trees. He collected over fifteen hundred specimens, of which no fewer than one-sixth were new to science. We are reminded of him when we admire the lovely *Lilium Davidii*, *Clematis Armandii*, with its clusters of white or pink flowers, the delphinium-blue bells of *C. Davidiana* and the lovely pink buds of *Prunus Davidiana* that do not wait for the last of the winter's frosts to disappear before they come to tell us that spring is on the way.

The most extraordinary of all his finds is *Davidia Vilmoriniana* from the wilds of West Szechuan. He found it in 1869 growing to a height of sixty feet, and in early summer hanging out great white bracts, like ladies' handkerchiefs, on long stalks, so that they could sway gently with every passing breeze. In due course they are followed by purplish walnut-like fruits with seeds embedded in the hard core. When Paul Farges sent the first seeds to the French nurseryman whose name it bears in 1897 they failed to germinate, and after two years were cast out. In June 1899 a plant somewhat resembling a young lime was noticed growing in the rubbish heap, was rescued, and lived to be the only specimen of Davidia in cultivation.

By 1873 the Abbé's health began to fail and he returned to France, where he inspired Jean Marie Delavay to go out to China and continue his work. Delavay collected for ten years in the Yunnan territory between the great Tali Lake and the Likiang Ranges, later in Szechuan and Hupeh. He contracted plague in 1888, became partly paralysed, but continued collecting until his death seven years later. He is said to have actually discovered more plants, suitable for gardens in temperate lands, than any other collector, having amassed over twenty thousand specimens comprising some four thousand species. It is rather surprising to find that he discovered many of the "new" plants that have only come into general cultivation within fairly recent years, among them the famous Blue Poppy, the graceful lavender-flowered *Primula malacoides*, and *Nomocharis pardanthina*, described as "This charming Liliaceous plant, which one may hope to see in cultivation one day, is an ornament of the pastures of calcareous soil of Mount Koua-la-po in the district of Tali, where it grows amongst herbs after the fashion of a lily."

It is quite impossible to mention all the missionaries who have sent home plants from far countries, but a brief survey of the wild roses of China does give some indication of the contribution these wanderers have made to our gardens. From the sacred Mount Omei in Szechuan comes *Rosa omiensis*, conspicuous because of its fine fern-like foliage and bright red hips that appear soon after midsummer. It was introduced by the

Rev. Ernest Faber, who found it in 1886. From the highlands of the Tibetan frontier comes *R. Moyesii* with blood-red flowers, commemorating its finder, the Rev. J. Moyes, while its greatest rival, the buttercup-yellow *R. Hugonis*, bears the name of Fr. Hugo, who sent the seeds to Kew about the turn of last century. Other Catholic missionaries are commemorated in this way by *R. Fargesii*, with bright pink flowers, and the paler *R. Davidii*, whose floral beauty is excelled only by the clusters of elegant red hips. Few plants are more successful in keeping trespassers at bay than the spreading *R. Soulieana*, whose characteristic grey-green leafage is surmounted by dainty panicles of blossom.

Flowers from all parts of the world tell us of men who have gone into the lonely places of the earth and found solace in the study of wildflowers. There is the charming little *Careya herbacea* from India to remind us of William Carey, founder of the Baptist Missionary Society, who lived in India for forty years and translated the New Testament into Bengali. From Australia comes the Blackfellow's Lancewood, with festoons of white blossom, bearing the name *Backhousia myrtifolia*, in recognition of James Backhouse who went to the Antipodes in 1832 and worked in the mission fields and among the convicts for six years, "for the purpose of discharging a religious duty."

One of the most striking plants from Madagascar is the White Orchid, *Angraecum sesquipedale*, whose flowers are distinguished by having a long tail, which may be fourteen inches in length. The first three plants to be seen in cultivation were sent to England by a missionary, Mr. Ellis, who said he found them, in the hottest part of the island, growing "most frequently on the driest parts of the trunks and branches of the thinly-leaved trees. With leaves neither numerous nor large in its native state the plant frequently presented a starved appearance and straggling habit. In this state the flowers were abundant and deeper in creamy colour than those growing in shade. The roots were not matted nor succulent, but few in number, long and wiry, frequently running down the trunk on which it grew twelve or eighteen feet or more."

The first naturalist to botanize the high mountains of New Zealand was the Rev. W. Colenso, who arrived in the country in 1834. The following year he was fortunate in meeting Charles Darwin, then on the "Voyage of the Beagle," who advised him to study the wild life of the country. As a result Colenso began an association with Kew that lasted for over sixty years, during which time he sent Hooker sufficient material to enable the production of his *Flora of New Zealand* at second hand. In 1845 he climbed the Ruahine Mountains accompanied by a few Maoris, and his delight in seeing a new flora spread before him tells us something of the joy experienced by all the plant-hunters who have searched for new plants for our gardens.

"When we emerged from the forest and the tangled shrubbery at its outskirts, on the open dell-like land just before we gained the summit, the lovely appearance of so many varied beautiful and novel wild plants and flowers richly repaid me the toil of the journey and the ascent, for never did I behold at one time in New Zealand such a profusion of Flora's stores. In one word I was overwhelmed with astonishment, and stood looking with all my eyes, greedily devouring and drinking in the enchanting scene before me. Here were plants of all the well-known genera of the Bluebells and Buttercups, Gowans and Daisies, Eyebrights and Speedwells of one's native land, closely intermixed with the Gentians of the European Alps and the rarer southern and little-known novelties—*Drapetes, Ourisia, Cyathodes, Abrotanella* and *Raoulia*. But how was I to carry off specimens of these precious prizes, and had I time to gather them? These mental pictures completely staggered me, for I realized my position well. We had left our encampment that morning, taking nothing with us, so we were all empty handed. However as I had no time to lose, I first pulled off my jacket, a light travelling coat, and made a bag of that, and then driven by necessity, I added thereto my shirt, and by tying the neck, etc., got an excellent bag, whilst some specimens I also stowed in the crown of my hat."

INDEX

Abelia, 74
Acacia, 144, 161
Acacia armata, 160
Acacia caleyi, 160
Acacia podalyriaefolia, 160
Acdcia verticillata, 145, 160
Acer macrophylla, 157
Achillea ageratum, 56
Aconitum delphinifolium, 145
Actinotus helianthi, 98
Agaves, 202
Ailanthus altissima, 262
Aiton, William, 87, 126, 128, 168
Alexander the Great, 14
Aloe, 165
Aloe dichotoma, 131
Aloe suscotrina, 132
Altar of Roses, 36, 37
Amaryllidaceae, 221
Amaryllis, 221
Amaryllis johnsonii, 221
Anderson, Johannes, 12
Anderson, William, 143, 145
André, M. Edouard, 251
Andrieux-Vilmorin, 26
Andromeda, 77, 78
Androsaces, 182
Anemone, 15, 101, 102

Anemone coronaria, 100
Anemone, French, 100, 101, 102
Anemone glaucifolia, 244
Anemone, Japanese, 212
Anemone japonica, 213
Anemone pulsatilla, 253
Anemone pulsatilla "Mrs. Van der Elst", 253
Angraecum sesquipedale, 265
Anne, Queen, 224
Anthemis, 136
Anthurium roezlii, 202
Aphelandra aurantiaca, 202
Apricocke, Algiers, 48
Araucaria imbricata, 158
Arbutus menziesii, 157
Arundo conspicua, 141
Ashmole, Elias, 49
Ashmolean Museum, 49
Asparagus, 164
Asphodel, 219
Aster, China, 262
Aster tradescantii, 56
Augustus, Philip, 150
Auriculas, 56
Avicenna, Dr., 37
Azalea, 244, 245
Azalea ovatum, 214

Azalea viscosa, 261

Bachelieu, Maitrê, 102
Bachelor's Buttons, 99
Backhouse, William, 222, 265
Backhousia myrtifolia, 265
Bacon, Francis, 29, 42
Balfour, Bailey, 242, 245
Banckes, Richard, 22, 234
Banister, John, 260
Banisteria argyrophylla, 261
Banks, Sir Joseph, 12, 98, 124–130,
     128, 129, 131, 133, 139, 142, 143,
     146, 153, 154, 155, 158, 160, 161,
     162, 163, 165
Banksia, 129, 161
Banksia ericifolia, 129, 130
Banksia integrifolia, 129, 130
Banksia menziesii, 155
Barberry, 252
Baret, Jean, "Jeanne", 91–94
Barr, Peter, 221, 222
Bartram, John, 81–83, 234
Bartram, William, 83
Bateson, General, 114
Baudin, Commodore Nicholas, 106
Baxter, W., 87
Bay, Loblolly, 83
Bay, Swamp, 261
Bean, W. J., 250
Beauty Bush, 219
Bee Balm, 46
Beeflower, 28
Belon, Pierre, 122
Beluze, Jean, 108
Berberis empetrifolia, 92
Berberis stenophylla, 92, 252
Berg, J. T. van der, 111
Bergamot, 46
Bertrand, Madame, 114
Billardiera, 99
Billardiera longiflora, 99
Billbergia pyramidalis, 168
Bitter Root, 177, 178

Blackcurrant, 149
Bladder Senna, 73
Blaikie, Thomas, 105
Blanchard, Captain, 136
Blanche of Castile, 14
Blandfordia cunninghamii, 172, 173
Bleeding Heart, 212
Bligh, Captain William, 96, 146, 147,
     148, 149, 162, 163, 227
"Blood drops of Christ", 101
Bloody Warrior, 28
Bluebells, 266
Blue Gum, 98
Boccone, Paul, 152
Bodger, J. C., 254, 255
Bonapartea gracilis, 107
Boswellia, 13
Bougainville, Countess de, 110
Bougainville, Louis Antoine de, 91,
     92, 93, 94, 96, 139
Bougainvillea, 90–94
Bougainvillea glabra, 90, 91
Bougainvillea mirabilis, 92
Bougainvillea, "Mrs. Butt", 91
Bougainvillea sanderiana, 91
Bougainvillea spectabilis, 90, 91
Bowie, James, 164, 165, 168
Bowiea volubilis, 164
Boyd, Christopher, 120
Boym, Michel, 261
Bread-fruit tree, 72, 146, 147
Bromeliaceous, 168
Broom, 249, 250
Broom, Canary Island, 132
Browall, John, Bishop of Åbo, 79
Browallia, 79
Browallia alienata, 80
Browallia demissa, 79
Browallia elata, 79
Brown, Robert, 163
Brown, William, 146, 149
Brunsvigia josephinae, 103, 104
Buckingham, Duke of, 48
Bulley, A. K., 247

Bulrush, 145
Buphana disticha, 131
Burleigh, Lord, 42
Burton, David, 128
Burtonia scabra, 128
de Busbecq, O. G., 57
Buttercup, 144, 266

Cactus, 107, 151
Caesar, Augustus, 78
Caleana, 163
Caley, George, 160–163, 169
Camassia esculenta, 181
Camellia, 106, 261
Camomile, 22
Canna, 261
Canterbury Bells, 262
Capparis nobilis, 169
Carey, William, 265
Careya herbacea, 265
Carnation, 16–19, 108, 134, 195
Carnation, "Anne Boleyn", 18
Carnation, "Fiancée", 19
Carnation, "Mrs. W. T. Lawson", 19
Carnation, Perpetual-flowering, 18, 19
Carnation, "Souvenir de la Malmaison", 108
Caryopteris mastacanthus, 213
Castor Oil Plant, 72
Cattleya labiata vera, 208
Cattleya thayeriana, 207
Cattleya vera, 168
Cavanilles, Abbé, 109
Cedar, Marengo, 107
Cedar of Lebanon, 121–124
Celandine, 15
Celsius, 75, 79
Ceratostigma plumbaginoides, 213
Cereus leeanus, 88
Cereus speciosissima, 112
Cervantes, Vincente, 109
Champney, John, 250
Chapman, Judge, 228
Charles I, 48

Cheiranthus cheiri, 27
Cheiry, 28
Cherisaunce, 28
Cherry blossom, 134
Cherye, Boore's, 47
Chicory, 14
Chimerae, 202
Chionanthus virginica, 261
Chirita sinensis, 212
Chorizema, 97
Chorizema ilicifolia, 95
Christian, Fletcher, 149
Christmas Bells, 172
Chrysanthemum, 49, 112, 134, 135, 136, 137, 212
Chrysanthemum, "Hairy Japanese", 137
Chrysanthemum, "Mrs. Alpheus Hardie", 138
Chrysanthemum, "Old Purple", 136
Chrysanthemum, Pompon, 137
Chrysanthemum erubescens, 52
Chrysanthemum frutescens, 50
Chrysanthemum leucanthemum, 50
Chrysanthemum maximum, 50
Chrysanthemum sinense, 137
Cie, Messieur, 26
Cinerarias, 132
Clark, William, 177
Clarkia, 177
Clarkia elegans, 180
Clematis, 214
Clematis armandii, 263
Clematis davidiana, 263
Clematis douglasii, 182
Clematis indivisa, 142
Clematis languinosa, 214
Clianthus dampieri, 73
Clianthus puniceus, 12
Clifford, George, 76
Clifford, Rosamund, 33
Clivia nobilis, 165
Clove Carnation, 16, 17
Clove Gillofloures, 17

Clove Pink, 16
Clovis, king of the Franks, 24
Clusius, 37
Cobaea scandens, 262
Cobo, Father, 262
Coelogyne cristata, 204
Cole, Silas, 226
Colenso, Rev. William, 12, 266
Collection of Roses from Nature (Mary Lawrance), 39
Collinson, Peter, 76, 81, 82, 113, 234
Columbine, Canadian, 46
Columbus, Christopher, 153
Colutea arborescens, 73
Commelin brothers, 79
Commelina, 79
Commerson, Philibert de, 91, 92, 93, 94, 96
Compte de Brie, 21
Compton, Bishop Henry, 261
Comptonia asplenifolia, 261
Coneflower, 46, 75
Cook, Captain, 12, 126, 131, 139, 140, 141, 143, 144, 145, 146, 148, 154, 155, 159
Cooper, Lieutenant, 140
Cordyline australis, 145
Coriaria ruscifolia, 141
Cornflower, 46
Coronae, 16
Cotterau, Nicholas, 56
Cow-parsnip, 145
Crab Apple, 193
Cranberry, Banks's, 127
Cranberry, Red, 127
Cranberry, White, 127
Craspedia richei, 99
Crataegus, 252
Crataegus leeana, 252
Crataegus monogyna reginae, 119
Crataegus, "Paul's Scarlet", 120
Crataegus punctata, 252
Crataegus tanacetifolia, 252
Creeper, Virginia, 46

Crocus, 100
Crocus, Autumn, 20
Crocus sativus, 21
Crotalaria cunninghamii, 172
Cunningham, Alan, 73, 163, 165, 167–173
Cunningham, Robert, 171
Cupani, Father Francisco, 225
Cupressus nootkatensis, 157
Currant, Flowering, 180
Curtis, Charles, 210
Cyathodes, 266
Cypress, Swamp, 46
Cypripedium curtisii, 210
Cypripedium fairrieanum, 209, 210
Cypripedium spicerianum, 209
Cytisus beanii, 250
Cytisus canariensis, 132
Cytisus kewensis, 249, 250
Cytisus scoparius andreanus, 251

Daffodil, 217–224
Daffodil, "Big Welshman", 219
Daffodil, "Emperor", 222
Daffodil, "Empress", 222
Daffodil, *Incomparabilis*, 221
Daffodil, Incomparable, 219
Daffodil, Jonquilla, 220
Daffodil, Large-cupped, 219
Daffodil, Leedsii, 222
Daffodil, "Mrs. Harrison Weir", 221
Daffodil, Nonesuch, 219
Daffodil, Nonpariel, 220
Daffodil, "Sir Watkin", 219
Daffodil, Spanish white, 220
Daffodil, Spanish yellow, 220
Daffodil, White Star, 222
Daffodil, Wilmer's Double, 55
Dahl, Dr. Andreas, 109, 110
Dahlia, 107, 109, 110, 111, 112
Dahlia, Cactus, 109, 111, 112
Dahlia, Collarette, 109
Dahlia jaurezii, 111, 112
Daisy, 136, 137, 266

Daisy, Chusan, 137, 214
Daisy, "Early Giant", 51
Daisy, "Esther Read", 52
Daisy, "G. H. Sage", 52
Daisy, Memorial, 50
Daisy, Michaelmas, 46, 51, 81
Daisy, Moon, 49, 50, 51
Daisy, "Mrs. C. Lothian Bell", 52
Daisy, Ox-eye, 49, 50
Daisy, Paris, 49, 50, 51, 52
Daisy, "Shasta", 51
Daisy, White Swan, 50
Dallimore, W., 250
Dampier, Captain William, 70, 72, 146
Daphne genkwa, 214
Dauphin of France, 34
David, Armand, 263
Davidia vilmoriniana, 263
De Arboris Coniferis (Pierre Belon), 122
Dead Man's Fingers, 151
Delavay, Jean Marie, 264
Dendrobium nobile, 205
Delphinium, 253
Delphinium elatum, 254
Delphinium nudicaule, 253, 254
Delphinium ruysii "Pink Sensation", 253, 254
Dianthus, the Divine Flower, 16
Dianthus caryophyllus, 16
Dicentra spectabilis, 212
Diervillea florida, 214
Dillenius, 76
Dodonaeus, 43
Dorloff, T. H., 149
Double Sweet Rocket, 55
Douglas, David, 179–182, 241
Douglasia, 182
Douglasia laevigata, 182
Downie, John, 192
Dracophyllum menziesii, 155
Drapetes, 266
Drimys winteri, 127, 141

Drosera menziesii, 155
Dykes, W. R., 26, 27

Earl of March, 28, 29
Echium, 132
Eckford, Henry, 225, 226
Edmund, 31
Edward I, 31
Eidelweiss, 99
Elderberry, 74
Eleanor of Aquitaine, 33
Eleanor of Provence, 31
Elizabeth, Maid of Neidpath, 28, 29
Elizabeth, Queen, 17, 18, 42, 47, 191
"Elruge", 56
Embothrium coccineum, 141
English Flower Garden (William Robinson), 41
D'Entrecasteaux, Bruni, 96
Epacris purpurascens, 161
Epilobium angustifolium, 145
Erica, 126
Erica concinna, 131
Erica darleyensis, 251
Erica marifolia, 131
Erica massonii, 132
Ericson, 210
Erythraea massonii, 130
Erythrina caffra, 131
Eskimo Potato, 146
Eucalypt, 144, 161
Eucalyptus, 106
Eucalpyptus globulus, 98
Eugenie, Empress, 198
Euphorbia, 77, 78, 165
Evelyn, 70
Eyebrights, 260

Faber, Rev. Ernest, 265
Fair Maids of France, 55
Fairrie, Mr., 209
Farges, Paul, 264
Farrer, Reginald, 208, 241, 248
Ferdinand I, Emperor, 57

Fern, 200
Fir, Douglas, 179
Fire Bush, Chilean, 141
Firth, Captain, 87
Flannel Flower, 98
Flax, New Zealand, 142, 145
Fleur-de-Louis, 24
Fleur-de-lys, 15, 23–27, 96
Flora Culturum, 220
Flora of New Zealand, 266
Flora sinensis, 262
Flower of the Gods, 218
Forrest, George, 241
Forster, Johann Georg, 138, 140, 159
Forster, Johann Reinhold, 138, 139, 140, 141, 159
Forstera, 138
Forstera sedifolia, 138
Forsyth, William, 173, 174, 175, 176
Forsythia, 173
Forsythia fortunei, 212
"Forsyth's Plaister", 173–176
Fortune, Robert, 136, 206, 212–216, 236, 241
Foster, Sir Michael, 25, 26
Foxgloves, 15
Fragaria vesca var. *hispida*, 48
Frangipani, 150–153
Frangipani, Count Mercuteo, 152
"Frankincense", 13
Franklin, Benjamin, 83
Franklinia altamaha, 80, 83, 84
Frederick the Great, 141
Fringe Tree, 261
Fritillaria kamtschatkensis, 146
Fuchsia, 85, 86, 87
Fuchsia, Californian, 156
Fuchsia coccinea, 86, 87
Fuchsia macrostemma, 87
Fuchsia triphylla, 85, 86, 87, 156
Fuchsia triphylla coccinea, 85
Funkia sieboldii, 235
Furcraea roezlii, 200

Galax aphylla, 183, 184
Gambier, Lord, 192
The Gardeners' Chronicle, 242
Gardeners' Dictionary (Johnson), 176
Gardeners' Dictionary (Miller), 220
Garry, Nicholas, 180
Garrya elliptica, 180
Gastrell, Rev. Mr., 118
Gaultheria forrestii, 244
Gentian, 14, 81, 130, 266
Gentiana sino-ornata, 244
George III, 81, 125, 166, 173
George V, 258
George VI, 257
Geranium, 106, 107
Geranium, Ivy, "Charles Turner", 192
Geranium erianthum, 145
Gerard, John, 17, 21, 41–44, 56, 65, 125, 190, 191, 192, 196
Gerardia purpurea, 41
Gesner, Conrad, 58
Geum, "Mrs. J. Bradshaw", 251
Geum coccinea, 251
Gilia capitata, 180
Gilliflower, 17, 47
Ginkgo, 115, 116
Ginkgo biloba, 115
Gladioli, 165
"Glory Pea", 12
Golden Bells, 173, 176, 212
Good, Peter, 128
Goodia lotifolia, 128
"Goose or Barnacle-Tree", 43
Gooseberry, 149
Gordon, James, 83, 116
Gordonia pubescens, 83
Gorse, Common, 76
Gourle, 56
Gowan, 266
Grape-fruit, 147
Grape, Oregon, 180
Gray, Asa, 184, 185
Grevillea, 161, 172
Grevillea caleyi, 163

Grevillea robusta, 172
Griffith, Dr. William, 205
Gum Tree, 173

Hakluyt, 21
Hammer, Sir Thomas, 58
Hardie, Captain Alpheus, 137
Harris, W. K., 69
Hartlib, Samuel, 53
Harvey, Dr., 164
Hatshepset, Queen, 13
Hawthorn, Common, 119, 120
Heart, Tradescant's, 47
Hearts-ease, 191
Heath, 107, 116, 157, 192
Heath, Australian, 161
Heath, South African, 131
Heather, 228
Hebe elliptica, 141
Hebe menziesii, 155
Helebras albus, 47
Helianthemum, 155
Hemoley of Kew, 86
Henderson & Sons, Messrs., 86
Henry III, 31
Henry V, 223
Henry VI, 50
Henry VIII, 22
Henry of Navarre, 51
Herbal (Richard Banckes), 22, 234
Herball, or Generall Historie of Plantes
   (Gerard), 42, 125, 196
Herbert, William, 221, 223
Herte's Ease, 28
Hertott, 22
Hibiscus, 106, 170
Hippeastrum, 202
Hogg, Thomas, 86
Hollyhock, 55, 219
Holy Thorn, 119, 120
Homer, 217
Honesty, 55
Honeycombs, 109
Honey-flower, 155

Honeysuckle, 74, 212
Hooker, Sir Joseph, 205, 206
Horsfield, John, 221
Hortus kewensis (Aiton), 168
Hovey, C. M., 235, 236
Howea forsteriana, 142
Hsu, Empress, 135
Hugo, Fr., 265
Hyacinth, 58, 107
Hyams, George M., 185
Hydrocleis commersonii, 92
Hydrocleis nymphoides, 92
Hymn to Demeter (Homer), 217

Ilex perneyi, 263
Incarville, Pierre d', 262
Incarvilleas, 263
Ipomoea batatas, 12
Iris, 23, 24, 25, 26
Iris, Alcazar, 26
Iris, "Ambassadeur", 26
Iris, Amber, 27
Iris, Bearded, 24, 26
Iris, "Dominion", 26
Iris, Florentine, 26
Iris, German, 24
Iris, "Jacquesiana", 25
Iris, "Madame Cherau", 25
Iris, "Susan Bliss", 26
Iris, "W. R. Dykes", 27
Iris, Water, 23
Iris albicans, 26
Iris aphylla, 25
Iris chrysographes, 244
Iris douglasii, 182
Iris florentina, 26
Iris germanica, 24, 25
Iris kochii, 25
Iris pallida, 25
Iris pseudacorus, 23
Iris setosa, 145
Ivy, Kenilworth, 77
Ixia, Green, 131
Ixia viridiflora, 131

Jackson, B. D., 80
James I, King, 117, 118, 219
Jardin de la Malmaison (Ventenat), 106
Jasmine, 14, 151, 212
Jasminum sambac, 65
"Jerusalem Cross", 14
Jessamine, 14
Johnson, 176, 221
Josephine, Empress, 38, 88, 103–108, 110, 111, 179, 197
Jussieu, Bernard de, 123, 124

Kalmia, 126
Kalmia glauca, 126
Kamel, Joseph George, 261
Keatley, Captain E. J., 230, 231
Kennedy, Lewis, 38, 88, 105, 106
Kennedya coccinea, 106
Kentia, 142
Kerr, William, 128, 234
Kerria japonica, 128
Knight, Thomas Andrew, 175
Kniphofia aloides, 67
Kowhai, Red, 12
Krokos, 20
Kumara, 12, 13

Labillardiere, Citizen, 95, 96, 97, 98, 99
Laburnum, 172
Lagunaria patersonii, 170
Laine, M. J., 108
Lancewood, Blackfellow's, 265
Lapageria, 104
Lapageria rosea, 103
Lapeyrousia corymbosa, 96
Lavender, 14
Lawrance, Mary, 39
Leadwort, Chinese, 212, 213
Lee, James, 86, 87, 88
Lee and Kennedy of Hammersmith, 38, 105, 106, 116
Leeds, Edward, 221

Leek, 223
Lemoine of Nancy, Messrs., 64
Lemon, M., 25
Lenne, Herr, 253
Leptospermum scoparium, 144, 227, 231
Leptospermum scoparium chapmanii, 228
Leptospermum scoparium keatleyi, 230
Leptospermum scoparium var. nichollsii, 228
Les Liliacées (Redouté), 106
Lete, Nicholas, 17
Leucanthemum, 136
Leucopogon richei, 97
Lewis, Meriwether, 177
Lewisia, 177
Lewisia rediviva, 178
Lilac, 63–66
Lilac, Common, 63, 64
Lilac, "Lucie Baltet", 64
Lilac, "Mrs. August Belmont", 64
Lilac, Persian, 63
Lilac, Rouen, 64, 251
Liliaceous, 264
The Lilies of Eastern Asia (Wilson), 238
Lilium album, 235
Lilium auratum, 236
Lilium canadense, 235
Lilium candidum, 233, 235
Lilium chalcedonium, 233, 235
Lilium chalcedonicum var. maculatum, 234
Lilium croceum, 233
Lilium davidii, 263
Lilium davuricum, 146
Lilium elegans, 235
Lilium harrisii, 69
Lilium longiflorum eximium, 69
Lilium maximoiviczii, 249
Lilium "Maxwill", 238, 249
Lilium parvum, 201
Lilium philadelphicum, 81, 234

Lilium pulchellum, 232
Lilium punctatum, 235
Lilium regale, 232, 238
Lilium roezlii, 201
Lilium rubrum, 235
Lilium salonikae, 233
Lilium speciosum, 232, 235
Lilium superbum, 81, 232, 234
Lilium tigrinum, 234
Lilium washingtonianum, 201
Lilium willmottiae, 249
Lily, 58, 66–69, 104, 173, 232–240
Lily, American, 234
Lily, Bermuda, 69
Lily, Canada, 234
Lily, Chinese Sacred, 218
Lily, "Chinese Wilson", 238
Lily, Easter, 69
Lily, Golden, of Japan, 237
Lily, Guernsey, 68
Lily, Josephine's, 103
Lily, Kaffir, 254
Lily, Madonna, 15, 233
Lily, "Maruha", 236
Lily, Melpomene, 236
Lily, Panther, 201
Lily, Plantain, 235
Lily, Red, 233
Lily, Regal, 238, 239, 240
Lily, St. Joseph, 69
Lily, Scarborough, 68
Lily, Tiger, 234
Lily, Turks' Cap, 233
Lily, Wilson, 238
Lily, Zephyr, 92
Lily-of-the-valley, 127
Limnanthes douglasii, 182
Linaria cymbalaria, 76
Lindley, Dr. John, 115, 182
Linnaea borealis, 74
Linnaeus, 24, 65, 74–80, 110, 113, 129,
    131, 218
Linne, Carl von (Linnaeus), 75
Litton, G. L., 247

L'Obel, 33
Lobelia cardinalis, 46
Lobelia gibbosa, 98
Loddiges, Conrad, 116
Lonicera fragrantissima, 212
Lonicera standishii, 212
Louis VII of France, 24
Louis IX, 14
Louis XVI, 96, 184
Lupin, 46, 258, 259
Lupin, Tree, 156
Lupins, Russell, 257, 258, 259
Lupinus arboreus, 156
Lychnis chalcedonica, 14

Macquarie's Cabbage, 144
Madronna, 157
Magnol, Pierre, 79
Magnolia, 78, 81
Magnolia conspicua, 252
Magnolia glacua, 261
Magnolia grandiflora, 107
Magnolia lennei, 252
Magnolia liliflora, 252
Magnolia soulangeana, 252
Mahonia aquifolium, 180
Maidenhair Tree, 115, 116
Mallows, 15
Manuka, 227, 228, 229, 230, 231
Manuka, Captain Keatley's, 231
Manuka, Red, 230
Manuka, Rose, 230
Manuka, "Sir George Fenwick",
    230
Maple, Oregon, 157
Maple, Red, 46
Maple, Sugar, 81
Marguerite, 49–52
Marguerite, "Anna Hay", 52
Marguerite, "Brown Eyes", 52
Marguerite, "Comte de Chambord",
    52
Marguerite, "Étoile d'Or", 52
Marguerite, "Mother's Favourite", 52

Marguerite, Pink, 52
Marguerite de Valois, Queen of Navarre, 50, 52
Marguerite of Anjou, 50
Marie Antoinette, 105
Marigold, 255, 256
Marigold, African, 256
Marsden, Samuel, 162
Marshall, Dr. M., 83
Mary, Queen of Scots, 34, 119
Masdevallia roezlii, 202
Mason, John, 225
Masson, Francis, 68, 128, 130, 131, 132, 133, 241
Massonia latifolia, 127
May, Common, 119
Meconopsis integrifolia, 244
Melaleuca squarrosa, 144
Menzies, Archibald, 96, 154, 156, 157, 158, 159, 180
Menziesia ferruginea, 157
Michaux, André, 183, 184
Mignonette, 107, 179, 181
Miller, Philip, 79, 88, 125, 128, 220
Millera, 79
Miltonia roezlii, 202
Mimosa, Nelson's, 145
Mimulus cardinalis, 180
Mimulus moschatus, 181
Mitchell, Colonel, 171
Mock Orange, 65
Monardez, 32
Monkey Puzzle, 158
Monochaetum bonplandii, 200
Monochaetum quadrangularis, 200
Morus alba, 118
Morus nigra, 118
Moss, 200
Mother of Thousands, 77
Mulberry, 117
Mulberry, Black, 118
Mulberry, White, 118
Musa, Antonius, 78
Musk, 152

Musk Plant, 181
My Garden (Simmons), 259
Myrtle, 107
Myrtus nummularia, 92

Nairn, Robert, 228, 229
Napoleon, 105, 107, 114, 192, 197
Napoleon's Bell, 103
Narcissus, 58, 217, 218, 222
Narcissus, barrii, 222
Narcissus, Hoop-petticoat, 218
Narcissus, Jonquil, 218
Narcissus, "Peter Barr", 222
Narcissus, Poets', 218, 221
Narcissus, Star, 222
Narcissus, Tazetta, 218
Narcissus, White Trumpet, 222
Narcissus cyclamineus, 223
Narcissus horsfieldii, 221
Narcissus maximus, 218
Narcissus pseudo-narcissus, 218
Narcissus tazetta, 218
Nasturtium, "Golden Gleam", 254, 255
Nectarine, 56
Nelson, David, 96, 143, 144, 145, 146, 147, 148
Nelsonia campestris, 144
Nepenthes, 77
Nerine sarniensis, 68
Nicholls, Mr. William, 228, 229
Niven, Joseph, 106
Nivenias, 106
Noisette, Philippe, 250
Nomocharis pardanthina, 244, 264
Norton, John, 13
Nova Plantarum Americanarum Genera (Plumier), 152
Numidia, King of, 18
Nunn, Kit, 18

Oak, Silky, 172
Oak Tree, 175
Obrotanella, 266

Observations on Diseases (Forsyth), 175
Oconee Bells, 183–185
Oleander, 14
"On Gardens" (Bacon), 29, 42
Orchid, 164, 200, 202, 203–211
Orchid, Bletia, 204
Orchid, Blue, 205, 206
Orchid, Cattleya, 202, 207
Orchid, Coelogyne, 204
Orchid, Dendrobium, 204
Orchid, ground, 145
Orchid, "Lost", 210
Orchid, Masdevallia, 207
Orchid, Moth, 206, 207
Orchid, Oncidium, 207
Orchid, Perching, 151
Orchid, Phalaenopsis, 206
Orchid, Slipper, 209, 210, 211
Orchid, Sobralia, 207
Orchid, Vanda, 205
Orchid, Vanilla, 203
Orchid, White, 265
Orchidacea, Indian, 205
Orris Root, 25, 152
Ortus sanitatis, 219
Osivega Tea, 46
Osmanthus delavayi, 244
Ourisia, 266
Ourisia antarctica, 92
Oxheart, 47
Oxylobium ellipticum, 144

Paeonias, 15
Palm, Chusan, 214
Pampas Grass, 141
Pansies, 191–195
Pansy, 191, 192, 251
Pansy, Fancy or Belgian, 193
Pansy, "Lady Gambier", 192
Pansy, Show, 192, 193
Pansy, Tufted, 194
Papaver bracteatum, 187
Papaver orientale, 186, 188

Papaver rheos, 189
Papaver somniferum, 189
Paradisus (Parkinson), 33
Parkinson, John, 18, 33, 46, 55, 219, 220, 235
Paul, William, 39, 120
Pea-flower, 106
Pear, Brazilian Prickly, 168
Pearson, Joseph, 148
Pelargonium, 106
Pelargonium, Cape, 132
Pentstemon, 41
Pentstemon menziesii, 157
Peony, 14
Pernettya mucronata, 127
Perney, Paul, 263
Perouse, Comte de la, 95, 96, 98
Perry, Amos, 187
Petigny, Monsieur R., 116
Petunia, 90
Phalaenopsis aphrodite, 206, 207
Philadelphus, 65
Philadelphus coronarius, 65
Philesia buxifolia, 93
Phlox, 46, 106
Phormium tenax, 142
"Physic nut", 72
Piccolimini, Aeneas Silvius, 43
Picea sitchensis, 157
Pigeon Bush, 97
Pine, Banks', 158
Pink Cluster, Champney's, 250
Pinus, 202
Pipe Tree, Arabian, 65
Pipe Tree, Blue, 65
Pipe Tree, White, 65
Pissart, M. Rene, 251
Pitcher plant, 77
Plant Hunting (Wilson), 238
Pliny, 36
Plum, Flowering, 251
Plumbago larpentae, 213
Plumier, Father Charles, 85, 86, 152
Plumiera, 150, 151, 152, 153

Plumiera acutifolia, 151
Plumiera fragrantissimum, 151
Pococke, Edward, 123
Podalyria sericea, 144
Poivre, Pierre, 39
Pomegranate, 14
Pope, Alexander, 114
Poplar, Lombardy, 14
Poppy, 14, 186–190, 196
Poppy, Black, 189
Poppy, Blue, 264
Poppy, Coonara, 188
Poppy, Corn, 188
Poppy, Iceland, 188
Poppy, "Miss Marsh", 187
Poppy, Moonbeam, 188
Poppy, "Mrs. Perry", 187
Poppy, Opium, 15, 189, 190
Poppy, Opium, Carnation-flowered, 190
Poppy, Opium, Pæony-flowered, 190
Poppy, Oriental, 186, 187, 188
Poppy, "Perry's White", 188
Poppy, Shirley, 188, 189
Poppy, Silver Queen, 187
Poppy, Sunbeam, 188
Poppy, Water, 92
Potentilla menziesii, 251
Preston, Isabelle, 64
Priest, Dr., 43
Primrose, Cape, 164–167
Primula, 246, 247
Primula aurantiaca, 246
Primula beesiana, 246
Primula bulleyana, 246
Primula chionantha, 246
Primula helodoxa, 246
Primula littoniana, 247, 248
Primula malacoides, 247, 264
Primula muscarioides, 247
Primula sino-plantaginea, 246
Prostanthera caleyi, 163
Proteaceous plants, 129

Proteas, 131
Prunus blireiana, 251
Prunus davidiana, 263
Prunus hopwoodiana, 252
Prunus mume, 251
Prunus nepalensis, 252
Prunus pissartii, 251
Prunus recta, 252
Pursch, 178
Pyrethrum, 136

Queen's Tree, 119

Ranunculus, 14
Ranunculus aconitifolius, 55
Ranunculus asiaticus, 14
Ranunculus nelsoni, 144
Rauolia, 266
Rea, John, 220
Red Hot Poker, 67
Redouté, Pierre-Joseph, 106
Reeves, John, 136
Remembrances for Master S. (Hakluyt), 21
Rex, George, 165
Rhododendron, 107, 141, 244, 245, 246
Rhododendron chasmanthum, 245
Rhododendron croceum, 245
Rhododendron forrestii, 246
Rhododendron fortunei, 214
Rhododendron fulvum, 245
Rhododendron gigantea, 245
Rhododendron griersonianum, 245
Rhododendron haematodes, 246
Rhododendron hippophaeoides, 246
Rhododendron impeditum, 246
Rhododendron lacteum, 246
Rhododendron nuliense, 246
Rhododendron radicans, 245
Rhododendron repens, 245
Rhododendron sino-grande, 245
Rhodora, 126
Rhubarb, 54

Ribes sanguinea, 180
Ribes speciosum, 156
Richard, Duke of York, 31
Riche, C. A., 97
Rivers, Thomas, 38
Robert III, 28
Roberts, Rev. Mr., Rector of Radnor, 69
Robinson, William, 41
Roezl, Benedict, 199–202
Roezlia granadensis, 200
Rosa alba, 30, 34
Rosa centifolia, 36
Rosa davidii, 265
Rosa fargesii, 265
Rosa hugonis, 265
Rosa lawrenceana, 39
Rosa moschata, 250
Rosa moyesii, 265
Rosa mundi, 32, 33
Rosa noisettiana, 250
Rosa omiensis, 264
Rosa roulettii, 40
Rosa soulieana, 265
Rosa ultramarina, 54
Roscoea cautleoides, 244
Rose, 15, 30–40, 104, 105, 107, 134
Rose, Austrian Briar, 37
Rose, Austrian Copper, 37
Rose, Ayrshire, 104
Rose, Blush China, 250
Rose, "Brown's Superb Blush", 38
Rose, Cabbage, 36
Rose, Cecile Brunner, 230
Rose, Damask, 32, 37
Rose, Double Yellow Persian, 14
Rose, Fairy, 39
Rose, Lady Banks's, 128
Rose, Major Roulett's, 40
Rose, "Marechal Niel", 250
Rose, Noisette, 250
Rose, Outlandish, 54
Rose, "Paul's Scarlet Climber", 39
Rose, "Persian Yellow", 37

Rose, pink, 35
Rose, Pissart's, 250
Rose, "Queen Mab", 39
Rose, red, 37
Rose, Red, of Lancaster, 31
Rose, Scot, 104
Rose, Standard, 38
Rose, Tea, 213
Rose, Tudor, 32
Rose, White, of Jacobites, 34, 35
Rose, White, of York, 30, 31
Rose, York and Lancaster, 32
Rose gallica versicolor, 33
"Rose of the Indies", 255
Rosemary, 73
Royal Geographic Magazine, 242
Royal Horticultural Society, 19, 26, 129, 136, 137, 142, 179, 182, 187, 206, 210, 212, 213, 222, 229, 238, 254, 258, 260
Rudbeck, Olaus, 75
Rudbeckias, 75
Rue, 14
Russell, George, 258, 259
Ruys, Mr. B., 253, 254

Saffron, 20–23, 54
Salisbury, Lord, 47
Salix babylonica, 113
Satin Bush, South African, 144
Savory, 52
Schizostylis coccinea "Mrs. Blanche Hegarty", 254
Scott of Tushielaw, 28, 29
Selenipedium, 202
Selkirk, Alexander, 73
Senecio, 132, 145
Seringat, 65
Shaddock, Captain, 147
Shaddock tree, 147
Shakespeare, 31, 51, 118, 119, 122
Short, Dr. Charles W., 184
Shortia, 184, 185
Shortia galacifolia, 184

Siebold, Dr. F. P. von, 235, 236
Simmons, D. W., 259
Sion, Vincent, 55
Smith, Sir Thomas, 21
Snapdragon, 77
Snowdrops, 15
Solander, Dr., 126
Solyman the Magnificent, 57
Sophora japonica, 262
"Sops-in-wine", 17
Soulange-Bodin, M., 252
Southernwood, 14
Speedwell, 206
Spencer, W. P., 229
Spicer, Mr., 209
Spiderwort, 46, 47, 79
Spiraea, Blue, 213
Spiraea menziesii, 157
Spruce, Sitka, 157
Stanhope, Sir W., 114
Stanhopea, 202
Stapelia grandiflora, 131
Stilbocarpa polaris, 144
Stoker, Dr., 75
Strabo, Walaford, 24
Strawberry, 196
Strawberry, Common, 48
Strawberry, Plymouth, 48
Streptocarpus dunnii, 166
Streptocarpus kewensis, 167
Streptocarpus parviflorus, 166
Streptocarpus polyanthus, 166
Streptocarpus rexii, 166
Stuart, Dr., 194
Sundew, 155
Sweet Pea, 224
Sweet Pea, "Blanche Ferry", 225
Sweet Pea, "Countess Spencer", 226
Sweet Pea, "The Painted Lady", 225
Sweet Pea, "Grandiflora", 226, 227
Sweet Pea, "Prima Donna", 226
Sweet Pea, Spencer, 259
Sweet Pea, "Waved Spencers", 226

Sweet Potato, 12
Sweet Maudlin, 56
"Sweet-scented Peas", 224–227
Sweet William, 28, 56
Syringa, 65
Syringa chinensis, 64
Syringa persica, 63
Syringa prestopiae, 64
Syringa villosa, 262
Syringa vulgaris, 63, 65
Syrinx, 65

Tagetes erecta, 255
Tagetes patula, 256
T'ao Ming-Yang, 134
Taukata, 13
Tea plant, New Zealand, 144, 145, 155, 227–231
Thatch palm, 142
Theatrum Florae, 223
Thorn tree, 252
Thunberg, Carl, 131, 234
Thyme, 14
Toadflax, Ivy-leaved, 76
Tohunga, 13
Tolmeia menziesii, 157
Tomato, 170
Topf, Herr Kurt, 253
Tournefort, 152
Tradescant, John, 46, 47, 48, 55
Tradescantia virginiana, 46
Treatise on the Cultivation of the Apple and Pear (Knight), 176
Treatise on Fruit Trees (Forsyth), 175, 176
Tree of Heaven, 262
Tricolor, 191
Tudor, Henry, 223
Tulip, 57, 62, 107, 204
Tulip, Breeding or Plain, 59
Tulip, "Semper Augustus", 60, 61
Tulip, "Viceroy", 60
Tulip Tree, 81
Tulipan, 58

Turner, William, 17, 28, 219
Twin-flower, 74

Umberto, Bishop of Pisa, 101
Uvedale, Dr., 225

Vaccinium, 145
Vallota speciosa, 68
Vancouver, Captain George, 96, 154, 156, 251
Vancouveria hexandra, 159
Vanda coerulea, 205
Veitch, J. G., 236, 237
Ventenat, 106
Verbena, 90, 168
Verbena, Moss, 168
Verbena erinoides, 168
Vernon, Mr., 113
Vetch, 224
Viburnum fragrans, 262
Victoria, Queen, 166, 212
Vine, 14
Vine, Cup and Saucer, 262
Viola, 191–195, 198
Viola calcarata, 198
Viola caleyana, 163
Viola commersonii, 92
Viola cornuta, 194, 251
Viola cunninghamii, 172
Viola florairensis, 251
Viola hederacea, 198
Viola Jackanapes, 198
Viola lutea, 192
Viola odorata, 196
Viola pedata, 81
Viola selkirkii, 198
Viola tricolor, 192
Violet, 191, 195–199

Violet, Bird's-foot, 81
Violet, "Car White", 196
Violet, Dog-tooth, 81
Violet, "Double Russian", 196
Violet, "Princess of Wales", 196
Violet, "Rosina", 196
Violet, Rouen, 251
Violet, Sweet, 196
Violet, Yellow, 28
Voiag of Ambassad by Sir Dudlie Digges in the Yeare 1618 (John Tradescant the Elder), 47

Wallflower, 27–30
Walnut, Black Virginian, 261
Ward, Captain Kingdon, 208
Wars of the Roses, 31
Water-lily, 14
Watson, William, 166
Wattle, Australian, 160, 173
Wilks, Rev. W., 188, 189
William the Conqueror, 16
William and Mary, 56
Willow, 113
Willow, Napoleon's, 115
Willow, Pope's, 114
Willow, Weeping, 113, 114, 115
Wilmer, George, 55
Wilson, E. H., 238, 239, 241
Winter, Captain W., 127
Winter's Bark tree, 127, 141
Wisteria sinensis, 213, 214

Yucca, 107

Zauchsneria californica, 156
Zephyranthes candida, 92
Zephyranthes commersonii, 92

A CATALOGUE OF SELECTED DOVER BOOKS
IN ALL FIELDS OF INTEREST

A CATALOGUE OF SELECTED DOVER BOOKS
IN ALL FIELDS OF INTEREST

WHAT IS SCIENCE?, *N. Campbell*
The role of experiment and measurement, the function of mathematics, the nature of scientific laws, the difference between laws and theories, the limitations of science, and many similarly provocative topics are treated clearly and without technicalities by an eminent scientist. "Still an excellent introduction to scientific philosophy," H. Margenau in *Physics Today*. "A first-rate primer . . . deserves a wide audience," *Scientific American*. 192pp. 5⅜ x 8.
Paperbound $1.25

THE NATURE OF LIGHT AND COLOUR IN THE OPEN AIR, *M. Minnaert*
Why are shadows sometimes blue, sometimes green, or other colors depending on the light and surroundings? What causes mirages? Why do multiple suns and moons appear in the sky? Professor Minnaert explains these unusual phenomena and hundreds of others in simple, easy-to-understand terms based on optical laws and the properties of light and color. No mathematics is required but artists, scientists, students, and everyone fascinated by these "tricks" of nature will find thousands of useful and amazing pieces of information. Hundreds of observational experiments are suggested which require no special equipment. 200 illustrations; 42 photos. xvi + 362pp. 5⅜ x 8.
Paperbound $2.00

THE STRANGE STORY OF THE QUANTUM, AN ACCOUNT FOR THE GENERAL READER OF THE GROWTH OF IDEAS UNDERLYING OUR PRESENT ATOMIC KNOWLEDGE, *B. Hoffmann*
Presents lucidly and expertly, with barest amount of mathematics, the problems and theories which led to modern quantum physics. Dr. Hoffmann begins with the closing years of the 19th century, when certain trifling discrepancies were noticed, and with illuminating analogies and examples takes you through the brilliant concepts of Planck, Einstein, Pauli, Broglie, Bohr, Schroedinger, Heisenberg, Dirac, Sommerfeld, Feynman, etc. This edition includes a new, long postscript carrying the story through 1958. "Of the books attempting an account of the history and contents of our modern atomic physics which have come to my attention, this is the best," H. Margenau, Yale University, in *American Journal of Physics*. 32 tables and line illustrations. Index. 275pp. 5⅜ x 8.
Paperbound $1.75

GREAT IDEAS OF MODERN MATHEMATICS: THEIR NATURE AND USE, *Jagjit Singh*
Reader with only high school math will understand main mathematical ideas of modern physics, astronomy, genetics, psychology, evolution, etc. better than many who use them as tools, but comprehend little of their basic structure. Author uses his wide knowledge of non-mathematical fields in brilliant exposition of differential equations, matrices, group theory, logic, statistics, problems of mathematical foundations, imaginary numbers, vectors, etc. Original publication. 2 appendixes. 2 indexes. 65 ills. 322pp. 5⅜ x 8.
Paperbound $2.00

THE MUSIC OF THE SPHERES: THE MATERIAL UNIVERSE — FROM ATOM TO QUASAR, SIMPLY EXPLAINED, *Guy Murchie*
Vast compendium of fact, modern concept and theory, observed and calculated data, historical background guides intelligent layman through the material universe. Brilliant exposition of earth's construction, explanations for moon's craters, atmospheric components of Venus and Mars (with data from recent fly-by's), sun spots, sequences of star birth and death, neighboring galaxies, contributions of Galileo, Tycho Brahe, Kepler, etc.; and (Vol. 2) construction of the atom (describing newly discovered sigma and xi subatomic particles), theories of sound, color and light, space and time, including relativity theory, quantum theory, wave theory, probability theory, work of Newton, Maxwell, Faraday, Einstein, de Broglie, etc. "Best presentation yet offered to the intelligent general reader," *Saturday Review*. Revised (1967). Index. 319 illustrations by the author. Total of xx + 644pp. 5⅜ x 8½.
Vol. 1 Paperbound $2.00, Vol. 2 Paperbound $2.00,
The set $4.00

FOUR LECTURES ON RELATIVITY AND SPACE, *Charles Proteus Steinmetz*
Lecture series, given by great mathematician and electrical engineer, generally considered one of the best popular-level expositions of special and general relativity theories and related questions. Steinmetz translates complex mathematical reasoning into language accessible to laymen through analogy, example and comparison. Among topics covered are relativity of motion, location, time; of mass; acceleration; 4-dimensional time-space; geometry of the gravitational field; curvature and bending of space; non-Euclidean geometry. Index. 40 illustrations. x + 142pp. 5⅜ x 8½.
Paperbound $1.35

HOW TO KNOW THE WILD FLOWERS, *Mrs. William Starr Dana*
Classic nature book that has introduced thousands to wonders of American wild flowers. Color-season principle of organization is easy to use, even by those with no botanical training, and the genial, refreshing discussions of history, folklore, uses of over 1,000 native and escape flowers, foliage plants are informative as well as fun to read. Over 170 full-page plates, collected from several editions, may be colored in to make permanent records of finds. Revised to conform with 1950 edition of Gray's Manual of Botany. xlii + 438pp. 5⅜ x 8½.
Paperbound $2.00

MANUAL OF THE TREES OF NORTH AMERICA, *Charles Sprague Sargent*
Still unsurpassed as most comprehensive, reliable study of North American tree characteristics, precise locations and distribution. By dean of American dendrologists. Every tree native to U.S., Canada, Alaska; 185 genera, 717 species, described in detail—leaves, flowers, fruit, winterbuds, bark, wood, growth habits, etc. plus discussion of varieties and local variants, immaturity variations. Over 100 keys, including unusual 11-page analytical key to genera, aid in identification. 783 clear illustrations of flowers, fruit, leaves. An unmatched permanent reference work for all nature lovers. Second enlarged (1926) edition. Synopsis of families. Analytical key to genera. Glossary of technical terms. Index. 783 illustrations, 1 map. Total of 982pp. 5⅜ x 8.
Vol. 1 Paperbound $2.25, Vol. 2 Paperbound $2.25,
The set $4.50

IT'S FUN TO MAKE THINGS FROM SCRAP MATERIALS,
Evelyn Glantz Hershoff
What use are empty spools, tin cans, bottle tops? What can be made from
rubber bands, clothes pins, paper clips, and buttons? This book provides
simply worded instructions and large diagrams showing you how to make
cookie cutters, toy trucks, paper turkeys, Halloween masks, telephone sets,
aprons, linoleum block- and spatter prints — in all 399 projects! Many are easy
enough for young children to figure out for themselves; some challenging
enough to entertain adults; all are remarkably ingenious ways to make things
from materials that cost pennies or less! Formerly "Scrap Fun for Everyone."
Index. 214 illustrations. 373pp. 5⅜ x 8½. Paperbound $1.50

SYMBOLIC LOGIC and THE GAME OF LOGIC, *Lewis Carroll*
"Symbolic Logic" is not concerned with modern symbolic logic, but is instead
a collection of over 380 problems posed with charm and imagination, using
the syllogism and a fascinating diagrammatic method of drawing conclusions.
In "The Game of Logic" Carroll's whimsical imagination devises a logical game
played with 2 diagrams and counters (included) to manipulate hundreds of
tricky syllogisms. The final section, "Hit or Miss" is a lagniappe of 101 additional puzzles in the delightful Carroll manner. Until this reprint edition,
both of these books were rarities costing up to $15 each. Symbolic Logic:
Index. xxxi + 199pp. The Game of Logic: 96pp. 2 vols. bound as one. 5⅜ x 8.
Paperbound $2.00

MATHEMATICAL PUZZLES OF SAM LOYD, PART I
selected and edited by M. Gardner
Choice puzzles by the greatest American puzzle creator and innovator. Selected
from his famous collection, "Cyclopedia of Puzzles," they retain the unique
style and historical flavor of the originals. There are posers based on arithmetic,
algebra, probability, game theory, route tracing, topology, counter and sliding
block, operations research, geometrical dissection. Includes the famous "14-15"
puzzle which was a national craze, and his "Horse of a Different Color" which
sold millions of copies. 117 of his most ingenious puzzles in all. 120 line
drawings and diagrams. Solutions. Selected references. xx + 167pp. 5⅜ x 8.
Paperbound $1.00

STRING FIGURES AND HOW TO MAKE THEM, *Caroline Furness Jayne*
107 string figures plus variations selected from the best primitive and modern
examples developed by Navajo, Apache, pygmies of Africa, Eskimo, in Europe,
Australia, China, etc. The most readily understandable, easy-to-follow book in
English on perennially popular recreation. Crystal-clear exposition; step-by-
step diagrams. Everyone from kindergarten children to adults looking for
unusual diversion will be endlessly amused. Index. Bibliography. Introduction
by A. C. Haddon. 17 full-page plates, 960 illustrations. xxiii + 401pp. 5⅜ x 8½.
Paperbound $2.00

PAPER FOLDING FOR BEGINNERS, *W. D. Murray and F. J. Rigney*
A delightful introduction to the varied and entertaining Japanese art of
origami (paper folding), with a full, crystal-clear text that anticipates every
difficulty; over 275 clearly labeled diagrams of all important stages in creation.
You get results at each stage, since complex figures are logically developed
from simpler ones. 43 different pieces are explained: sailboats, frogs, roosters,
etc. 6 photographic plates. 279 diagrams. 95pp. 5⅝ x 8⅜. Paperbound $1.00

PRINCIPLES OF ART HISTORY,
H. Wölfflin

Analyzing such terms as "baroque," "classic," "neoclassic," "primitive," "picturesque," and 164 different works by artists like Botticelli, van Cleve, Dürer, Hobbema, Holbein, Hals, Rembrandt, Titian, Brueghel, Vermeer, and many others, the author establishes the classifications of art history and style on a firm, concrete basis. This classic of art criticism shows what really occurred between the 14th-century primitives and the sophistication of the 18th century in terms of basic attitudes and philosophies. "A remarkable lesson in the art of seeing," *Sat. Rev. of Literature.* Translated from the 7th German edition. 150 illustrations. 254pp. 6⅛ x 9¼. Paperbound $2.00

PRIMITIVE ART,
Franz Boas

This authoritative and exhaustive work by a great American anthropologist covers the entire gamut of primitive art. Pottery, leatherwork, metal work, stone work, wood, basketry, are treated in detail. Theories of primitive art, historical depth in art history, technical virtuosity, unconscious levels of patterning, symbolism, styles, literature, music, dance, etc. A must book for the interested layman, the anthropologist, artist, handicrafter (hundreds of unusual motifs), and the historian. Over 900 illustrations (50 ceramic vessels, 12 totem poles, etc.). 376pp. 5⅜ x 8. Paperbound $2.25

THE GENTLEMAN AND CABINET MAKER'S DIRECTOR,
Thomas Chippendale

A reprint of the 1762 catalogue of furniture designs that went on to influence generations of English and Colonial and Early Republic American furniture makers. The 200 plates, most of them full-page sized, show Chippendale's designs for French (Louis XV), Gothic, and Chinese-manner chairs, sofas, canopy and dome beds, cornices, chamber organs, cabinets, shaving tables, commodes, picture frames, frets, candle stands, chimney pieces, decorations, etc. The drawings are all elegant and highly detailed; many include construction diagrams and elevations. A supplement of 24 photographs shows surviving pieces of original and Chippendale-style pieces of furniture. Brief biography of Chippendale by N. I. Bienenstock, editor of *Furniture World.* Reproduced from the 1762 edition. 200 plates, plus 19 photographic plates. vi + 249pp. 9⅛ x 12¼. Paperbound $3.50

AMERICAN ANTIQUE FURNITURE: A BOOK FOR AMATEURS,
Edgar G. Miller, Jr.

Standard introduction and practical guide to identification of valuable American antique furniture. 2115 illustrations, mostly photographs taken by the author in 148 private homes, are arranged in chronological order in extensive chapters on chairs, sofas, chests, desks, bedsteads, mirrors, tables, clocks, and other articles. Focus is on furniture accessible to the collector, including simpler pieces and a larger than usual coverage of Empire style. Introductory chapters identify structural elements, characteristics of various styles, how to avoid fakes, etc. "We are frequently asked to name some book on American furniture that will meet the requirements of the novice collector, the beginning dealer, and . . . the general public. . . . We believe Mr. Miller's two volumes more completely satisfy this specification than any other work," *Antiques.* Appendix. Index. Total of vi + 1106pp. 7⅞ x 10¾.
Two volume set, paperbound $7.50

THE BAD CHILD'S BOOK OF BEASTS, MORE BEASTS FOR WORSE CHILDREN, and A MORAL ALPHABET, *H. Belloc*
Hardly and anthology of humorous verse has appeared in the last 50 years without at least a couple of these famous nonsense verses. But one must see the entire volumes — with all the delightful original illustrations by Sir Basil Blackwood — to appreciate fully Belloc's charming and witty verses that play so subacidly on the platitudes of life and morals that beset his day — and ours. A great humor classic. Three books in one. Total of 157pp. 5⅜ x 8.
Paperbound $1.00

THE DEVIL'S DICTIONARY, *Ambrose Bierce*
Sardonic and irreverent barbs puncturing the pomposities and absurdities of American politics, business, religion, literature, and arts, by the country's greatest satirist in the classic tradition. Epigrammatic as Shaw, piercing as Swift, American as Mark Twain, Will Rogers, and Fred Allen, Bierce will always remain the favorite of a small coterie of enthusiasts, and of writers and speakers whom he supplies with "some of the most gorgeous witticisms of the English language" (H. L. Mencken). Over 1000 entries in alphabetical order. 144pp. 5⅜ x 8.
Paperbound $1.00

THE COMPLETE NONSENSE OF EDWARD LEAR.
This is the only complete edition of this master of gentle madness available at a popular price. *A Book of Nonsense, Nonsense Songs, More Nonsense Songs and Stories* in their entirety with all the old favorites that have delighted children and adults for years. The Dong With A Luminous Nose, The Jumblies, The Owl and the Pussycat, and hundreds of other bits of wonderful nonsense. 214 limericks, 3 sets of Nonsense Botany, 5 Nonsense Alphabets, 546 drawings by Lear himself, and much more. 320pp. 5⅜ x 8.
Paperbound $1.00

THE WIT AND HUMOR OF OSCAR WILDE, ed. by *Alvin Redman*
Wilde at his most brilliant, in 1000 epigrams exposing weaknesses and hypocrisies of "civilized" society. Divided into 49 categories—sin, wealth, women, America, etc.—to aid writers, speakers. Includes excerpts from his trials, books, plays, criticism. Formerly "The Epigrams of Oscar Wilde." Introduction by Vyvyan Holland, Wilde's only living son. Introductory essay by editor. 260pp. 5⅜ x 8.
Paperbound $1.00

A CHILD'S PRIMER OF NATURAL HISTORY, *Oliver Herford*
Scarcely an anthology of whimsy and humor has appeared in the last 50 years without a contribution from Oliver Herford. Yet the works from which these examples are drawn have been almost impossible to obtain! Here at last are Herford's improbable definitions of a menagerie of familiar and weird animals, each verse illustrated by the author's own drawings. 24 drawings in 2 colors; 24 additional drawings. vii + 95pp. 6½ x 6.
Paperbound $1.00

THE BROWNIES: THEIR BOOK, *Palmer Cox*
The book that made the Brownies a household word. Generations of readers have enjoyed the antics, predicaments and adventures of these jovial sprites, who emerge from the forest at night to play or to come to the aid of a deserving human. Delightful illustrations by the author decorate nearly every page. 24 short verse tales with 266 illustrations. 155pp. 6⅝ x 9¼.
Paperbound $1.50

THE PRINCIPLES OF PSYCHOLOGY,
William James
The full long-course, unabridged, of one of the great classics of Western literature and science. Wonderfully lucid descriptions of human mental activity, the stream of thought, consciousness, time perception, memory, imagination, emotions, reason, abnormal phenomena, and similar topics. Original contributions are integrated with the work of such men as Berkeley, Binet, Mills, Darwin, Hume, Kant, Royce, Schopenhauer, Spinoza, Locke, Descartes, Galton, Wundt, Lotze, Herbart, Fechner, and scores of others. All contrasting interpretations of mental phenomena are examined in detail—introspective analysis, philosophical interpretation, and experimental research. "A classic," *Journal of Consulting Psychology.* "The main lines are as valid as ever," *Psychoanalytical Quarterly.* "Standard reading . . . a classic of interpretation," *Psychiatric Quarterly.* 94 illustrations. 1408pp. 5⅜ x 8.

Vol. 1 Paperbound $2.50, Vol. 2 Paperbound $2.50,
The set $5.00

VISUAL ILLUSIONS: THEIR CAUSES, CHARACTERISTICS AND APPLICATIONS,
M. Luckiesh
"Seeing is deceiving," asserts the author of this introduction to virtually every type of optical illusion known. The text both describes and explains the principles involved in color illusions, figure-ground, distance illusions, etc. 100 photographs, drawings and diagrams prove how easy it is to fool the sense: circles that aren't round, parallel lines that seem to bend, stationary figures that seem to move as you stare at them — illustration after illustration strains our credulity at what we see. Fascinating book from many points of view, from applications for artists, in camouflage, etc. to the psychology of vision. New introduction by William Ittleson, Dept. of Psychology, Queens College. Index. Bibliography. xxi + 252pp. 5⅜ x 8½.
Paperbound $1.50

FADS AND FALLACIES IN THE NAME OF SCIENCE,
Martin Gardner
This is the standard account of various cults, quack systems, and delusions which have masqueraded as science: hollow earth fanatics. Reich and orgone sex energy, dianetics, Atlantis, multiple moons, Forteanism, flying saucers, medical fallacies like iridiagnosis, zone therapy, etc. A new chapter has been added on Bridey Murphy, psionics, and other recent manifestations in this field. This is a fair, reasoned appraisal of eccentric theory which provides excellent inoculation against cleverly masked nonsense. "Should be read by everyone, scientist and non-scientist alike," R. T. Birge, Prof. Emeritus of Physics, Univ. of California; Former President, American Physical Society. Index. x + 365pp. 5⅜ x 8.
Paperbound $1.85

ILLUSIONS AND DELUSIONS OF THE SUPERNATURAL AND THE OCCULT,
D. H. Rawcliffe
Holds up to rational examination hundreds of persistent delusions including crystal gazing, automatic writing, table turning, mediumistic trances, mental healing, stigmata, lycanthropy, live burial, the Indian Rope Trick, spiritualism, dowsing, telepathy, clairvoyance, ghosts, ESP, etc. The author explains and exposes the mental and physical deceptions involved, making this not only an exposé of supernatural phenomena, but a valuable exposition of characteristic types of abnormal psychology. Originally titled "The Psychology of the Occult." 14 illustrations. Index. 551pp. 5⅜ x 8.
Paperbound $2.25

FAIRY TALE COLLECTIONS, *edited by Andrew Lang*
Andrew Lang's fairy tale collections make up the richest shelf-full of traditional children's stories anywhere available. Lang supervised the translation of stories from all over the world—familiar European tales collected by Grimm, animal stories from Negro Africa, myths of primitive Australia, stories from Russia, Hungary, Iceland, Japan, and many other countries. Lang's selection of translations are unusually high; many authorities consider that the most familiar tales find their best versions in these volumes. All collections are richly decorated and illustrated by H. J. Ford and other artists.

THE BLUE FAIRY BOOK. 37 stories. 138 illustrations. ix + 390pp. 5⅜ x 8½.
Paperbound $1.50

THE GREEN FAIRY BOOK. 42 stories. 100 illustrations. xiii + 366pp. 5⅜ x 8½. Paperbound $1.50

THE BROWN FAIRY BOOK. 32 stories. 50 illustrations, 8 in color. xii + 350pp. 5⅜ x 8½. Paperbound $1.50

THE BEST TALES OF HOFFMANN, *edited by E. F. Bleiler*
10 stories by E. T. A. Hoffmann, one of the greatest of all writers of fantasy. The tales include "The Golden Flower Pot," "Automata," "A New Year's Eve Adventure," "Nutcracker and the King of Mice," "Sand-Man," and others. Vigorous characterizations of highly eccentric personalities, remarkably imaginative situations, and intensely fast pacing has made these tales popular all over the world for 150 years. Editor's introduction. 7 drawings by Hoffmann. xxxiii + 419pp. 5⅜ x 8½. Paperbound $2.00

GHOST AND HORROR STORIES OF AMBROSE BIERCE,
edited by E. F. Bleiler
Morbid, eerie, horrifying tales of possessed poets, shabby aristocrats, revived corpses, and haunted malefactors. Widely acknowledged as the best of their kind between Poe and the moderns, reflecting their author's inner torment and bitter view of life. Includes "Damned Thing," "The Middle Toe of the Right Foot," "The Eyes of the Panther," "Visions of the Night," "Moxon's Master," and over a dozen others. Editor's introduction. xxii + 199pp. 5⅜ x 8½. Paperbound $1.25

THREE GOTHIC NOVELS, *edited by E. F. Bleiler*
Originators of the still popular Gothic novel form, influential in ushering in early 19th-century Romanticism. Horace Walpole's *Castle of Otranto*, William Beckford's *Vathek*, John Polidori's *The Vampyre*, and a *Fragment* by Lord Byron are enjoyable as exciting reading or as documents in the history of English literature. Editor's introduction. xi + 291pp. 5⅜ x 8½.
Paperbound $2.00

BEST GHOST STORIES OF LEFANU, *edited by E. F. Bleiler*
Though admired by such critics as V. S. Pritchett, Charles Dickens and Henry James, ghost stories by the Irish novelist Joseph Sheridan LeFanu have never become as widely known as his detective fiction. About half of the 16 stories in this collection have never before been available in America. Collection includes "Carmilla" (perhaps the best vampire story ever written), "The Haunted Baronet," "The Fortunes of Sir Robert Ardagh," and the classic "Green Tea." Editor's introduction. 7 contemporary illustrations. Portrait of LeFanu. xii + 467pp. 5⅜ x 8. Paperbound $2.00

EASY-TO-DO ENTERTAINMENTS AND DIVERSIONS WITH COINS, CARDS, STRING, PAPER AND MATCHES, *R. M. Abraham*

Over 300 tricks, games and puzzles will provide young readers with absorbing fun. Sections on card games; paper-folding; tricks with coins, matches and pieces of string; games for the agile; toy-making from common household objects; mathematical recreations; and 50 miscellaneous pastimes. Anyone in charge of groups of youngsters, including hard-pressed parents, and in need of suggestions on how to keep children sensibly amused and quietly content will find this book indispensable. Clear, simple text, copious number of delightful line drawings and illustrative diagrams. Originally titled "Winter Nights' Entertainments." Introduction by Lord Baden Powell. 329 illustrations. v + 186pp. 5⅜ x 8½.   Paperbound $1.00

AN INTRODUCTION TO CHESS MOVES AND TACTICS SIMPLY EXPLAINED, *Leonard Barden*

Beginner's introduction to the royal game. Names, possible moves of the pieces, definitions of essential terms, how games are won, etc. explained in 30-odd pages. With this background you'll be able to sit right down and play. Balance of book teaches strategy — openings, middle game, typical endgame play, and suggestions for improving your game. A sample game is fully analyzed. True middle-level introduction, teaching you all the essentials without oversimplifying or losing you in a maze of detail. 58 figures. 102pp. 5⅜ x 8½.   Paperbound $1.00

LASKER'S MANUAL OF CHESS, *Dr. Emanuel Lasker*

Probably the greatest chess player of modern times, Dr. Emanuel Lasker held the world championship 28 years, independent of passing schools or fashions. This unmatched study of the game, chiefly for intermediate to skilled players, analyzes basic methods, combinations, position play, the aesthetics of chess, dozens of different openings, etc., with constant reference to great modern games. Contains a brilliant exposition of Steinitz's important theories. Introduction by Fred Reinfeld. Tables of Lasker's tournament record. 3 indices. 308 diagrams. 1 photograph. xxx + 349pp. 5⅜ x 8.   Paperbound $2.25

COMBINATIONS: THE HEART OF CHESS, *Irving Chernev*

Step-by-step from simple combinations to complex, this book, by a well-known chess writer, shows you the intricacies of pins, counter-pins, knight forks, and smothered mates. Other chapters show alternate lines of play to those taken in actual championship games; boomerang combinations; classic examples of brilliant combination play by Nimzovich, Rubinstein, Tarrasch, Botvinnik, Alekhine and Capablanca. Index. 356 diagrams. ix + 245pp. 5⅜ x 8½.   Paperbound $1.85

HOW TO SOLVE CHESS PROBLEMS, *K. S. Howard*

Full of practical suggestions for the fan or the beginner — who knows only the moves of the chessmen. Contains preliminary section and 58 two-move, 46 three-move, and 8 four-move problems composed by 27 outstanding American problem creators in the last 30 years. Explanation of all terms and exhaustive index. "Just what is wanted for the student," Brian Harley. 112 problems, solutions. vi + 171pp. 5⅜ x 8.   Paperbound $1.35

SOCIAL THOUGHT FROM LORE TO SCIENCE,
H. E. Barnes and H. Becker

An immense survey of sociological thought and ways of viewing, studying, planning, and reforming society from earliest times to the present. Includes thought on society of preliterate peoples, ancient non-Western cultures, and every great movement in Europe, America, and modern Japan. Analyzes hundreds of great thinkers: Plato, Augustine, Bodin, Vico, Montesquieu, Herder, Comte, Marx, etc. Weighs the contributions of utopians, sophists, fascists and communists; economists, jurists, philosophers, ecclesiastics, and every 19th and 20th century school of scientific sociology, anthropology, and social psychology throughout the world. Combines topical, chronological, and regional approaches, treating the evolution of social thought as a process rather than as a series of mere topics. "Impressive accuracy, competence, and discrimination . . . easily the best single survey," *Nation*. Thoroughly revised, with new material up to 1960. 2 indexes. Over 2200 bibliographical notes. Three volume set. Total of 1586pp. 5⅜ x 8.

Vol. 1 Paperbound $2.75, Vol. 2 Paperbound $2.75, Vol. 3 Paperbound $2.50
The set $8.00

A HISTORY OF HISTORICAL WRITING, *Harry Elmer Barnes*

Virtually the only adequate survey of the whole course of historical writing in a single volume. Surveys developments from the beginnings of historiography in the ancient Near East and the Classical World, up through the Cold War. Covers major historians in detail, shows interrelationship with cultural background, makes clear individual contributions, evaluates and estimates importance; also enormously rich upon minor authors and thinkers who are usually passed over. Packed with scholarship and learning, clear, easily written. Indispensable to every student of history. Revised and enlarged up to 1961. Index and bibliography. xv + 442pp. 5⅜ x 8½. Paperbound $2.50

JOHANN SEBASTIAN BACH, *Philipp Spitta*

The complete and unabridged text of the definitive study of Bach. Written some 70 years ago, it is still unsurpassed for its coverage of nearly all aspects of Bach's life and work. There could hardly be a finer non-technical introduction to Bach's music than the detailed, lucid analyses which Spitta provides for hundreds of individual pieces. 26 solid pages are devoted to the B minor mass, for example, and 30 pages to the glorious St. Matthew Passion. This monumental set also includes a major analysis of the music of the 18th century: Buxtehude, Pachelbel, etc. "Unchallenged as the last word on one of the supreme geniuses of music," John Barkham, *Saturday Review Syndicate*. Total of 1819pp. Heavy cloth binding. 5⅜ x 8.

Two volume set, clothbound $13.50

BEETHOVEN AND HIS NINE SYMPHONIES, *George Grove*

In this modern middle-level classic of musicology Grove not only analyzes all nine of Beethoven's symphonies very thoroughly in terms of their musical structure, but also discusses the circumstances under which they were written, Beethoven's stylistic development, and much other background material. This is an extremely rich book, yet very easily followed; it is highly recommended to anyone seriously interested in music. Over 250 musical passages. Index. viii + 407pp. 5⅜ x 8. Paperbound $2.00

THREE SCIENCE FICTION NOVELS,
John Taine
Acknowledged by many as the best SF writer of the 1920's, Taine (under the name Eric Temple Bell) was also a Professor of Mathematics of considerable renown. Reprinted here are *The Time Stream*, generally considered Taine's best, *The Greatest Game*, a biological-fiction novel, and *The Purple Sapphire*, involving a supercivilization of the past. Taine's stories tie fantastic narratives to frameworks of original and logical scientific concepts. Speculation is often profound on such questions as the nature of time, concept of entropy, cyclical universes, etc. 4 contemporary illustrations. v + 532pp. 5⅜ x 8⅜.
Paperbound $2.00

SEVEN SCIENCE FICTION NOVELS,
H. G. Wells
Full unabridged texts of 7 science-fiction novels of the master. Ranging from biology, physics, chemistry, astronomy, to sociology and other studies, Mr. Wells extrapolates whole worlds of strange and intriguing character. "One will have to go far to match this for entertainment, excitement, and sheer pleasure . . ."*New York Times*. Contents: The Time Machine, The Island of Dr. Moreau, The First Men in the Moon, The Invisible Man, The War of the Worlds, The Food of the Gods, In The Days of the Comet. 1015pp. 5⅜ x 8.
Clothbound $5.00

28 SCIENCE FICTION STORIES OF H. G. WELLS.
Two full, unabridged novels, *Men Like Gods* and *Star Begotten*, plus 26 short stories by the master science-fiction writer of all time! Stories of space, time, invention, exploration, futuristic adventure. Partial contents: *The Country of the Blind, In the Abyss, The Crystal Egg, The Man Who Could Work Miracles, A Story of Days to Come, The Empire of the Ants, The Magic Shop, The Valley of the Spiders, A Story of the Stone Age, Under the Knife, Sea Raiders*, etc. An indispensable collection for the library of anyone interested in science fiction adventure. 928pp. 5⅜ x 8.
Clothbound $4.50

THREE MARTIAN NOVELS,
Edgar Rice Burroughs
Complete, unabridged reprinting, in one volume, of Thuvia, Maid of Mars; Chessmen of Mars; The Master Mind of Mars. Hours of science-fiction adventure by a modern master storyteller. Reset in large clear type for easy reading. 16 illustrations by J. Allen St. John. vi + 490pp. 5⅜ x 8½.
Paperbound $1.85

AN INTELLECTUAL AND CULTURAL HISTORY OF THE WESTERN WORLD,
Harry Elmer Barnes
Monumental 3-volume survey of intellectual development of Europe from primitive cultures to the present day. Every significant product of human intellect traced through history: art, literature, mathematics, physical sciences, medicine, music, technology, social sciences, religions, jurisprudence, education, etc. Presentation is lucid and specific, analyzing in detail specific discoveries, theories, literary works, and so on. Revised (1965) by recognized scholars in specialized fields under the direction of Prof. Barnes. Revised bibliography. Indexes. 24 illustrations. Total of xxix + 1318pp.
Vol. 1 Paperbound $2.00, Vol. 2 Paperbound $2.00, Vol. 3 Paperbound $2.00,
The set $6.00

HEAR ME TALKIN' TO YA, *edited by Nat Shapiro and Nat Hentoff*
In their own words, Louis Armstrong, King Oliver, Fletcher Henderson, Bunk
Johnson, Bix Beiderbecke, Billy Holiday, Fats Waller, Jelly Roll Morton,
Duke Ellington, and many others comment on the origins of jazz in New
Orleans and its growth in Chicago's South Side, Kansas City's jam sessions,
Depression Harlem, and the modernism of the West Coast schools. Taken
from taped conversations, letters, magazine articles, other first-hand sources.
Editors' introduction. xvi + 429pp. 5⅜ x 8½. Paperbound $2.00

THE JOURNAL OF HENRY D. THOREAU
A 25-year record by the great American observer and critic, as complete a
record of a great man's inner life as is anywhere available. Thoreau's Journals
served him as raw material for his formal pieces, as a place where he could
develop his ideas, as an outlet for his interests in wild life and plants, in
writing as an art, in classics of literature, Walt Whitman and other contemporaries, in politics, slavery, individual's relation to the State, etc. The
Journals present a portrait of a remarkable man, and are an observant social
history. Unabridged republication of 1906 edition, Bradford Torrey and
Francis H. Allen, editors. Illustrations. Total of 1888pp. 8⅜ x 12¼.
Two volume set, clothbound $25.00

A SHAKESPEARIAN GRAMMAR, *E. A. Abbott*
Basic reference to Shakespeare and his contemporaries, explaining through
thousands of quotations from Shakespeare, Jonson, Beaumont and Fletcher,
North's *Plutarch* and other sources the grammatical usage differing from the
modern. First published in 1870 and written by a scholar who spent much of
his life isolating principles of Elizabethan language, the book is unlikely ever
to be superseded. Indexes. xxiv + 511pp. 5⅜ x 8½. Paperbound $2.75

FOLK-LORE OF SHAKESPEARE, *T. F. Thistelton Dyer*
Classic study, drawing from Shakespeare a large body of references to supernatural beliefs, terminology of falconry and hunting, games and sports, good
luck charms, marriage customs, folk medicines, superstitions about plants,
animals, birds, argot of the underworld, sexual slang of London, proverbs,
drinking customs, weather lore, and much else. From full compilation comes
a mirror of the 17th-century popular mind. Index. ix + 526pp. 5⅜ x 8½.
Paperbound $2.50

THE NEW VARIORUM SHAKESPEARE, *edited by H. H. Furness*
By far the richest editions of the plays ever produced in any country or
language. Each volume contains complete text (usually First Folio) of the
play, all variants in Quarto and other Folio texts, editorial changes by every
major editor to Furness's own time (1900), footnotes to obscure references or
language, extensive quotes from literature of Shakespearian criticism, essays
on plot sources (often reprinting sources in full), and much more.

HAMLET, *edited by H. H. Furness*
Total of xxvi + 905pp. 5⅜ x 8½. Two volume set, paperbound $4.75

TWELFTH NIGHT, *edited by H. H. Furness*
Index. xxii + 434pp. 5⅜ x 8½. Paperbound $2.25

LA BOHEME BY GIACOMO PUCCINI,
translated and introduced by Ellen H. Bleiler
Complete handbook for the operagoer, with everything needed for full enjoyment except the musical score itself. Complete Italian libretto, with new,
modern English line-by-line translation—the only libretto printing all repeats;
biography of Puccini; the librettists; background to the opera, Murger's La
Boheme, etc.; circumstances of composition and performances; plot summary;
and pictorial section of 73 illustrations showing Puccini, famous singers and
performances, etc. Large clear type for easy reading. 124pp. 5⅜ x 8½.

Paperbound $1.00

ANTONIO STRADIVARI: HIS LIFE AND WORK (1644-1737),
W. Henry Hill, Arthur F. Hill, and Alfred E. Hill
Still the only book that really delves into life and art of the incomparable
Italian craftsman, maker of the finest musical instruments in the world today.
The authors, expert violin-makers themselves, discuss Stradivari's ancestry, his
construction and finishing techniques, distinguished characteristics of many
of his instruments and their locations. Included, too, is story of introduction
of his instruments into France, England, first revelation of their supreme
merit, and information on his labels, number of instruments made, prices,
mystery of ingredients of his varnish, tone of pre-1684 Stradivari violin and
changes between 1684 and 1690. An extremely interesting, informative account
for all music lovers, from craftsman to concert-goer. Republication of original
(1902) edition. New introduction by Sydney Beck, Head of Rare Book and
Manuscript Collections, Music Division, New York Public Library. Analytical
index by Rembert Wurlitzer. Appendixes. 68 illustrations. 30 full-page plates.
4 in color. xxvi + 315pp. 5⅜ x 8½.

Paperbound $2.25

MUSICAL AUTOGRAPHS FROM MONTEVERDI TO HINDEMITH,
Emanuel Winternitz
For beauty, for intrinsic interest, for perspective on the composer's personality,
for subtleties of phrasing, shading, emphasis indicated in the autograph but
suppressed in the printed score, the mss. of musical composition are fascinating
documents which repay close study in many different ways. This 2-volume
work reprints facsimiles of mss. by virtually every major composer, and many
minor figures—196 examples in all. A full text points out what can be learned
from mss., analyzes each sample. Index. Bibliography. 18 figures. 196 plates.
Total of 170pp. of text. 7⅞ x 10¾.

Vol. 1 Paperbound $2.00, Vol. 2 Paperbound $2.00,
The set $4.00

J. S. BACH,
Albert Schweitzer
One of the few great full-length studies of Bach's life and work, and the
study upon which Schweitzer's renown as a musicologist rests. On first appearance (1911), revolutionized Bach performance. The only writer on Bach to
be musicologist, performing musician, and student of history, theology and
philosophy, Schweitzer contributes particularly full sections on history of German Protestant church music, theories on motivic pictorial representations
in vocal music, and practical suggestions for performance. Translated by
Ernest Newman. Indexes. 5 illustrations. 650 musical examples. Total of xix
+ 928pp. 5⅜ x 8½.   Vol. 1 Paperbound $2.00, Vol. 2 Paperbound $2.00,
The set $4.00

THE METHODS OF ETHICS, *Henry Sidgwick*
Propounding no organized system of its own, study subjects every major
methodological approach to ethics to rigorous, objective analysis. Study discusses and relates ethical thought of Plato, Aristotle, Bentham, Clarke, Butler,
Hobbes, Hume, Mill, Spencer, Kant, and dozens of others. Sidgwick retains
conclusions from each system which follow from ethical premises, rejecting
the faulty. Considered by many in the field to be among the most important
treatises on ethical philosophy. Appendix. Index. xlvii + 528pp. 5⅜ x 8½.
Paperbound $2.50

TEUTONIC MYTHOLOGY, *Jakob Grimm*
A milestone in Western culture; the work which established on a modern
basis the study of history of religions and comparative religions. 4-volume
work assembles and interprets everything available on religious and folk-
loristic beliefs of Germanic people (including Scandinavians, Anglo-Saxons,
etc.). Assembling material from such sources as Tacitus, surviving Old Norse
and Icelandic texts, archeological remains, folktales, surviving superstitions,
comparative traditions, linguistic analysis, etc. Grimm explores pagan deities,
heroes, folklore of nature, religious practices, and every other area of pagan
German belief. To this day, the unrivaled, definitive, exhaustive study. Translated by J. S. Stallybrass from 4th (1883) German edition. Indexes. Total of
lxxvii + 1887pp. 5⅜ x 8½. Four volume set, paperbound $10.00

THE I CHING, *translated by James Legge*
Called "The Book of Changes" in English, this is one of the Five Classics
edited by Confucius, basic and central to Chinese thought. Explains perhaps
the most complex system of divination known, founded on the theory that all
things happening at any one time have characteristic features which can be
isolated and related. Significant in Oriental studies, in history of religions and
philosophy, and also to Jungian psychoanalysis and other areas of modern
European thought. Index. Appendixes. 6 plates. xxi + 448pp. 5⅜ x 8½.
Paperbound $2.75

HISTORY OF ANCIENT PHILOSOPHY, *W. Windelband*
One of the clearest, most accurate comprehensive surveys of Greek and Roman
philosophy. Discusses ancient philosophy in general, intellectual life in Greece
in the 7th and 6th centuries B.C., Thales, Anaximander, Anaximenes, Herac-
litus, the Eleatics, Empedocles, Anaxagoras, Leucippus, the Pythagoreans, the
Sophists, Socrates, Democritus (20 pages), Plato (50 pages), Aristotle (70 pages),
the Peripatetics, Stoics, Epicureans, Sceptics, Neo-platonists, Christian Apolo-
gists, etc. 2nd German edition translated by H. E. Cushman. xv + 393pp.
5⅜ x 8. Paperbound $2.25

THE PALACE OF PLEASURE, *William Painter*
Elizabethan versions of Italian and French novels from *The Decameron,*
Cinthio, Straparola, Queen Margaret of Navarre, and other continental sources
— the very work that provided Shakespeare and dozens of his contemporaries
with many of their plots and sub-plots and, therefore, justly considered one of
the most influential books in all English literature. It is also a book that any
reader will still enjoy. Total of cviii + 1,224pp.
Three volume set, Paperbound $6.75

THE WONDERFUL WIZARD OF OZ, *L. F. Baum*
All the original W. W. Denslow illustrations in full color—as much a part of
"The Wizard" as Tenniel's drawings are of "Alice in Wonderland." "The
Wizard" is still America's best-loved fairy tale, in which, as the author expresses
it, "The wonderment and joy are retained and the heartaches and nightmares
left out." Now today's young readers can enjoy every word and wonderful picture of the original book. New introduction by Martin Gardner. A Baum
bibliography. 23 full-page color plates. viii + 268pp. 5⅜ x 8.
Paperbound $1.50

THE MARVELOUS LAND OF OZ, *L. F. Baum*
This is the equally enchanting sequel to the "Wizard," continuing the adventures of the Scarecrow and the Tin Woodman. The hero this time is a little
boy named Tip, and all the delightful Oz magic is still present. This is the
Oz book with the Animated Saw-Horse, the Woggle-Bug, and Jack Pumpkin-
head. All the original John R. Neill illustrations, 10 in full color. 287pp.
5⅜ x 8. Paperbound $1.50

ALICE'S ADVENTURES UNDER GROUND, *Lewis Carroll*
The original *Alice in Wonderland*, hand-lettered and illustrated by Carroll
himself, and originally presented as a Christmas gift to a child-friend. Adults
as well as children will enjoy this charming volume, reproduced faithfully
in this Dover edition. While the story is essentially the same, there are slight
changes, and Carroll's spritely drawings present an intriguing alternative to
the famous Tenniel illustrations. One of the most popular books in Dover's
catalogue. Introduction by Martin Gardner. 38 illustrations. 128pp. 5⅜ x 8½.
Paperbound $1.00

THE NURSERY "ALICE," *Lewis Carroll*
While most of us consider *Alice in Wonderland* a story for children of all
ages, Carroll himself felt it was beyond younger children. He therefore provided this simplified version, illustrated with the famous Tenniel drawings
enlarged and colored in delicate tints, for children aged "from Nought to
Five." Dover's edition of this now rare classic is a faithful copy of the 1889
printing, including 20 illustrations by Tenniel, and front and back covers
reproduced in full color. Introduction by Martin Gardner. xxiii + 67pp.
6⅛ x 9¼. Paperbound $1.50

THE STORY OF KING ARTHUR AND HIS KNIGHTS, *Howard Pyle*
A fast-paced, exciting retelling of the best known Arthurian legends for young
readers by one of America's best story tellers and illustrators. The sword
Excalibur, wooing of Guinevere, Merlin and his downfall, adventures of Sir
Pellias and Gawaine, and others. The pen and ink illustrations are vividly
imagined and wonderfully drawn. 41 illustrations. xviii + 313pp. 6⅛ x 9¼.
Paperbound $1.50

Prices subject to change without notice.

Available at your book dealer or write for free catalogue to Dept. Adsci,
Dover Publications, Inc., 180 Varick St., N.Y., N.Y. 10014. Dover publishes more
than 150 books each year on science, elementary and advanced mathematics,
biology, music, art, literary history, social sciences and other areas.